Progress in Mathematics

3 GENERAL

Natalie Hughes

Gryphon School		
Form	Name	Date
9R	Natalie Hughes	28/11/96

Progress in Mathematics

Pupils' Book 1E
Pupils' Book 2E
Pupils' Book 3E
Pupils' Book 4E
Pupils' Book 5E

Pupils' Book 1G
Pupils' Book 2G
Pupils' Book 3G
Pupils' Book 4G
Pupils' Book 5G

Pupils' Book 1C
Pupils' Book 2C
Pupils' Book 3C
Pupils' Book 4C
Pupils' Book 5C

Progress in Mathematics

3 GENERAL

Les Murray BA
Formerly Senior Teacher and Head of Mathematics,
Garstang County High School

Stanley Thornes (Publishers) Ltd

First published in 1986 by Stanley Thornes (Publishers) Ltd, Old Station Drive, Leckhampton, Cheltenham GL53 0DN, UK.

Reprinted 1987
Reprinted 1988
Reprinted 1990

British Library Cataloguing in Publication Data

Murray, Les
Progress in mathematics.
3G
1. Mathematics – Examinations, questions, etc.
I. Title
510'.76 QA43

ISBN 0-85950-177-9

Typeset by Grafikon Ltd, Oostkamp, Belgium.
Printed and bound in Great Britain at The Bath Press, Avon.

Preface

This book has been written for a teaching/learning situation.

Pupils need to be taught – that is the task of the teacher. Detailed exposition has deliberately been avoided and worked examples have only been included where desirable. Consequently the text does not dictate the teaching method and thus allows a teacher to choose his or her own approach to teaching.

Pupils need to learn – learning by thinking and doing is preferred to the more usual detailed explanation.

The book contains numerous, carefully graded questions. It is not intended to be worked through from cover to cover; the teacher should be selective in the use of exercises and questions.

Throughout the book, revision exercises have been labelled **R**. In addition to this, revision sections have been inserted at intervals, questions being based on preceding chapters.

Photocopy masters are again available to the teacher for exercises where pupils may benefit by their provision. Such exercises have been labelled **M**

The completion of this book has been dependent on the valued help and advice given to me by many people, in particular Mr Roger Wilson, Head of Mathematics at Parklands High School, Chorley, who has carefully and painstakingly worked through the whole text and has provided the answers as well as giving welcome advice; and to Mr J. Britton, Head of Mathematics at Copthall School, London, for his most useful comments. My thanks also go to staff and pupils of Garstang County High School, for their interest and co-operation while writing has been in progress; to Casio Electronics and Texas Instruments for the loan of a selection of calculators thus enabling me to consider the different characteristics of calculators in my writing; to Jodrell Bank, NASA, North West Water and the numerous people who have supplied invaluable information.

Les Murray
1986

To RMB

Acknowledgements

The author and publishers are grateful to the following:
British Railways Board for the timetable on p. 75
Dover Publications for Fibonacci's problem, on p. 30, taken from D.J. Struick, *A Concise History of Mathematics.*
Mathematical Pie Ltd for the idea used in question 2 on p. 127.

We also wish to thank the following who provided photographs:
The Automobile Association 1986, for the section of map on p. 359.
Biofotos for the daisy (*Bellis perennis*) on p. 27 and *Nautilus pompilius* on p. 28.
David Eugene Smith Collection, Rare Book and Manuscript Library, Columbia University for Fibonacci on p. 25.
McGraw-Hill Book Company for Pythagoras on p. 377.
Vallardie Editore Grafiche for the Matterhorn on p. 13.

Contents

1 Sets

Number

Exercise 1

1. Set W shows the set of whole numbers that are less than 13.

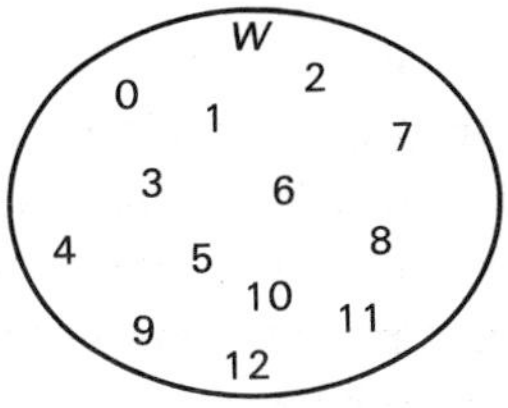

List the set of odd numbers that belong to set W.

2. Here is the set of natural numbers* that are less than 13:
$\{1, 2, 3, 4, 5, 6, 7, 8, 9, 10, 11, 12\}$
List the even numbers that are in the given set of natural numbers.

3. Set R shows a set of numbers.

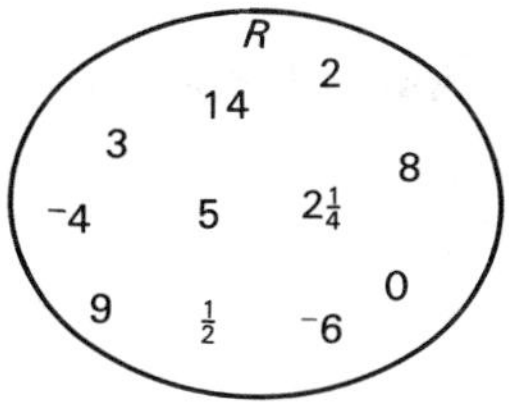

(*a*) List the natural numbers that are in set R.
(*b*) List the whole numbers that are in set R.

* See the glossary, p. 385.

4. From set N below, list:
(*a*) the numbers that are less than 10,
(*b*) the numbers that are greater than 6,
(*c*) the numbers that are less than 12 and bigger than 3,
(*d*) the factors of 20,
(*e*) the numbers that are exactly divisible by 3.

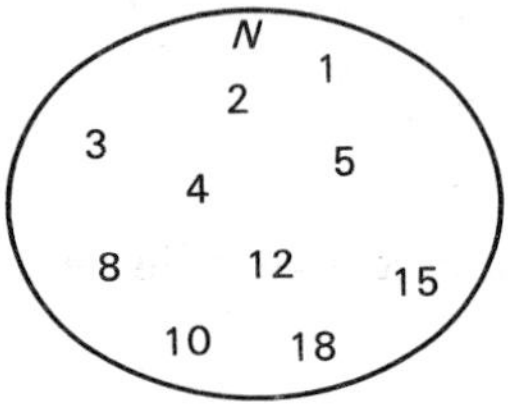

5. (*a*) List the set of factors of 15.
(*b*) List the set of factors of 24.

6. (*a*) List the set of multiples of 6 that are less than 50.
(*b*) List the set of multiples of 9 that lie between 281 and 350.

7. List the set of common factors of:
(*a*) 30 and 18 (*b*) 60 and 90

8. (*a*) List the set of common multiples of 6 and 8 that are less than 75.
(*b*) Which is the least common multiple of 6 and 8?

9. Set Z shows the set of integers that lie between $^-5$ and $^+7$.

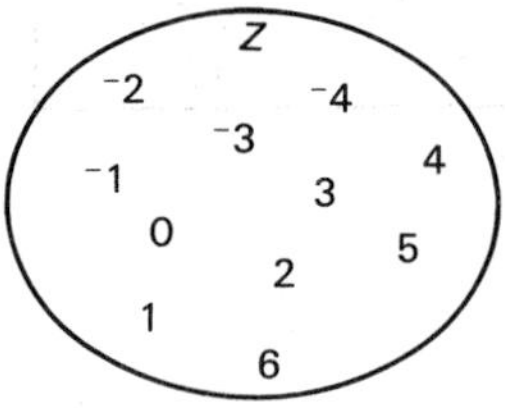

From set Z, list:
(*a*) the set of positive integers,
(*b*) the set of negative integers,
(*c*) the set of whole numbers,
(*d*) the set of natural numbers.

10. (*a*) List the set of integers that lie between $^-6$ and 4.
(*b*) List the set of integers that are bigger than $^-10$ and less than 1.

11. (*a*) From set P below, list the set of prime numbers.
(*b*) Which even number of set P is prime?

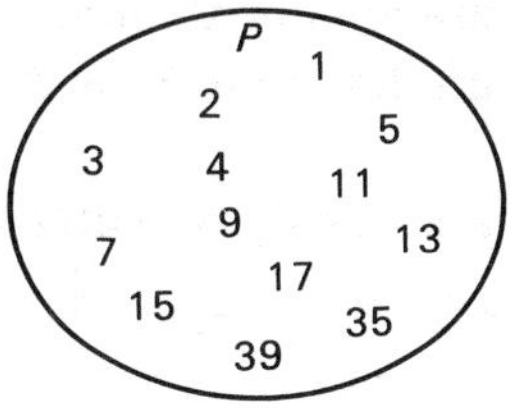

12. List the set of prime numbers that lie between 40 and 60.

Venn Diagrams

Exercise 2

R

1. (*a*) List set A. Use curly brackets.
(*b*) List the numbers that are not in set A.

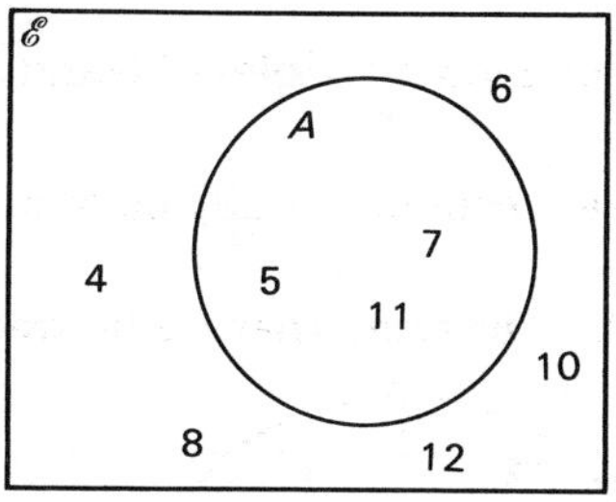

2. (*a*) List set B.
(*b*) List set B'.
(*c*) List set $\mathscr{E}$.

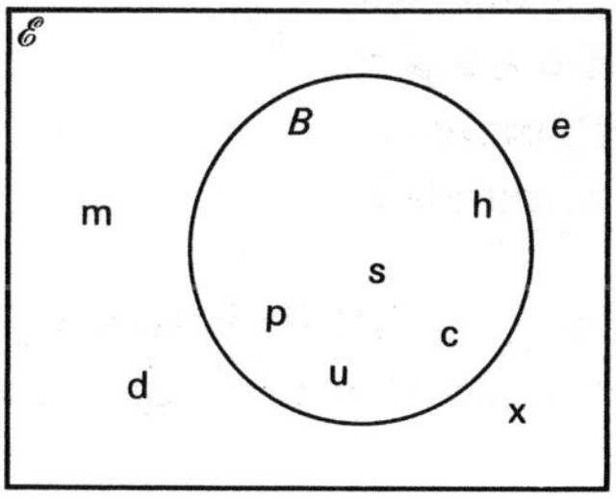

3. Is it true that:

(*a*) $19 \in C$?
(*b*) $8 \in C$?
(*c*) $12 \in \mathscr{E}$?
(*d*) $1 \in C$?
(*e*) $1 \in \mathscr{E}$?
(*f*) $15 \in C$?

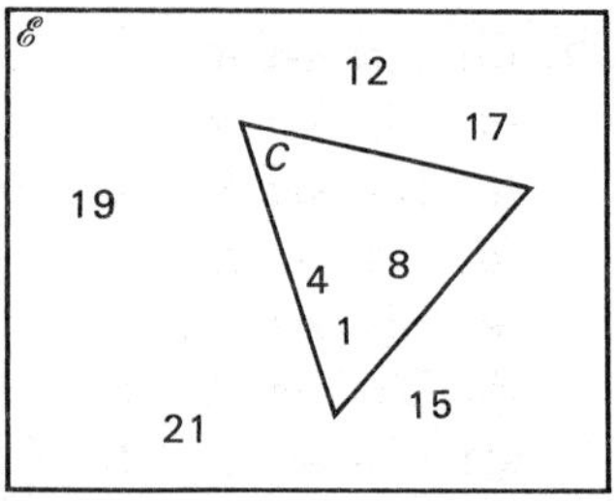

(*Note* Any *simple closed curve** may be used to show a set. Normally, rectangles are used for universal sets and circles are used for other sets.)

4. Copy the Venn diagram.
Note that $4 \in T$, $6 \notin T$ and $9 \in T'$.
Complete your diagram where:
$2 \notin T$, $8 \in T$, $7 \in T$, $10 \notin T$, $5 \in T'$, $12 \in T$, $15 \in T'$, $1 \notin T$, $14 \in T$, $19 \in T'$, $3 \notin T$, $13 \notin T'$.

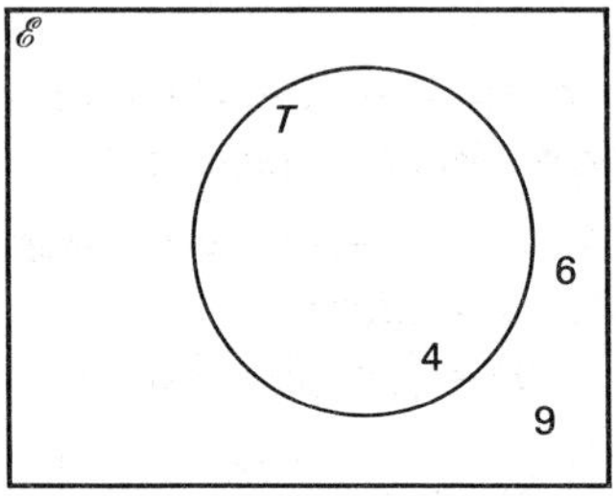

5. (*a*) List set *M*.
(*b*) List set *N*.
(*c*) List the letters that are not in set *M*.
(*d*) List set *N'*.
(*e*) List the letters that are in set *M* but are not in set *N*.

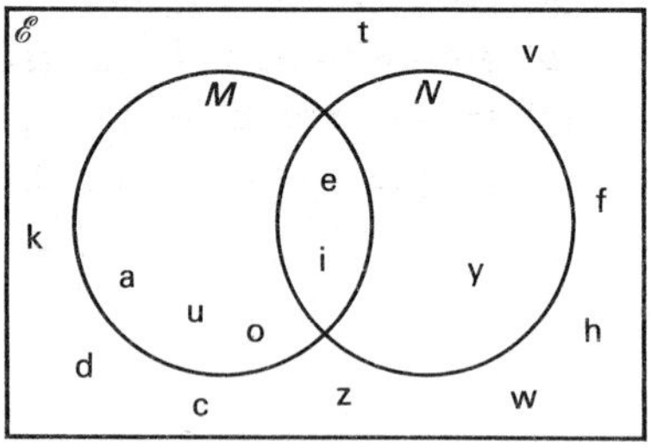

6. (*a*) List the symbols that are in set *P*.
(*b*) List set *Q*.
(*c*) List set *Q'*.
(*d*) List the complement of *P*.
(*e*) List the symbols that are in set *P* or in set *Q* or in both.
(*f*) List the symbols that are in set *P* and set *Q*.

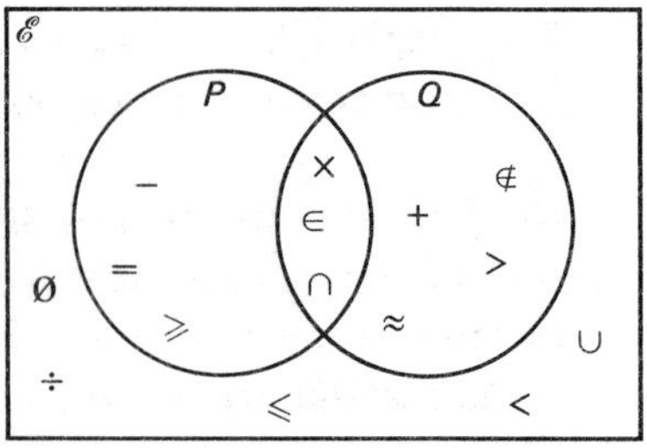

* See the glossary p. 381.

7. (*a*) List set $\mathscr{E}$.
(*b*) List set R.
(*c*) List set S.
(*d*) List set R'.
(*e*) List set S'.
(*f*) List set $R \cap S$.
(*g*) List set $R \cup S$.

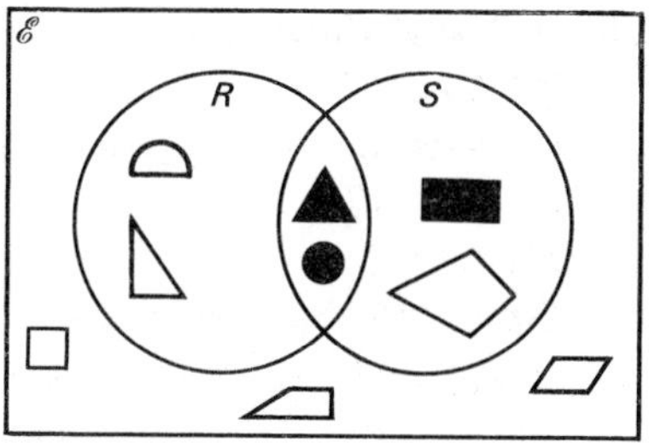

Exercise 3

In this exercise, the numbers given show the number of members (or elements) in each set.

1. $\mathscr{E}$ = {people in a village}
G = {girls}
T = {people who play tennis}

Find the number of:
(*a*) girls who play tennis,
(*b*) girls who do not play tennis,
(*c*) people who play tennis,
(*d*) people who are not girls.

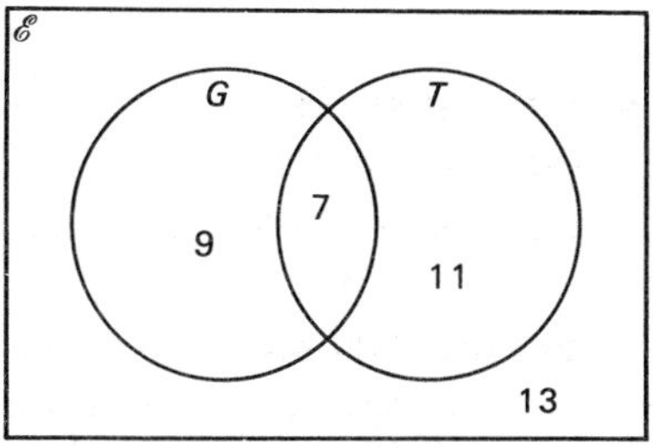

2. $\mathscr{E}$ = {pupils in form 3B}
S = {pupils who like sweets}
C = {pupils who like icecream}

(*a*) How many are there in 3B?
(*b*) How many like sweets?
(*c*) How many like sweets but do not like ice cream?
(*d*) How many like sweets and ice cream?
(*e*) How many like either sweets or ice cream or both?

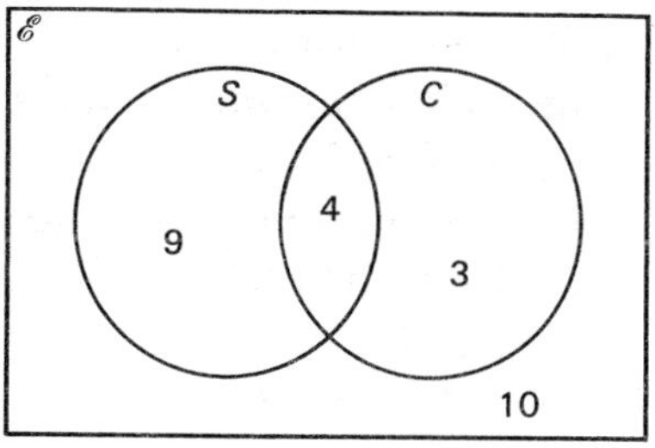

3. $\mathscr{E}$ = {letters in the alphabet}
V = {vowels}
M = {letters in the word MATHEMATICS}
so M = {A, C, E, H, I, M, S, T}

(*Note* Each letter in a set is given only once. For example, there is only one M in the set although the word MATHEMATICS contains two Ms. Note also that $n(M)$ stands for the number of members in set M.)

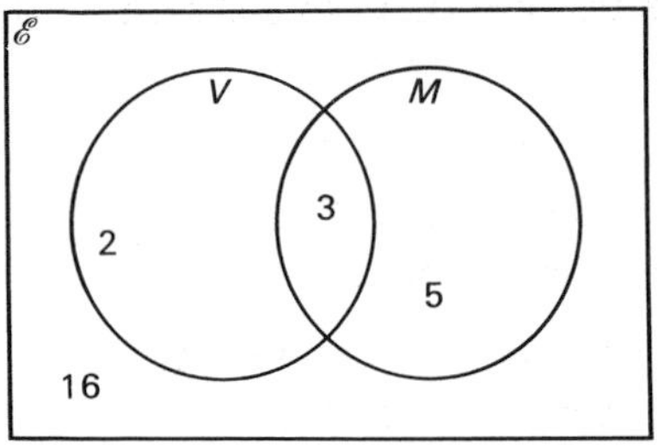

Find:

(*a*) $n(M)$	(*d*) $n(V')$	(*g*) $n(V \cup M)$
(*b*) $n(V)$	(*e*) $n(M')$	(*h*) $n(V \cup M)'$
(*c*) $n(\mathscr{E})$	(*f*) $n(V \cap M)$	(*i*) $n(V \cap M)'$

4. Some people were asked whether they read the *Daily Post* or the *Daily News*.
$\mathscr{E}$ = {people asked}
P = {people who read the *Daily Post*}
N = {people who read the *Daily News*}

The results of the survey are shown in the Venn diagram.
Find:
(*a*) $n(\mathscr{E})$
(*b*) $n(P)$
(*c*) $n(N)$
(*d*) $n(P')$
(*e*) $n(N')$
(*f*) $n(P \cap N)$
(*g*) $n(P \cup N)$
(*h*) $n(P \cup N)'$
(*i*) $n(P \cap N)'$

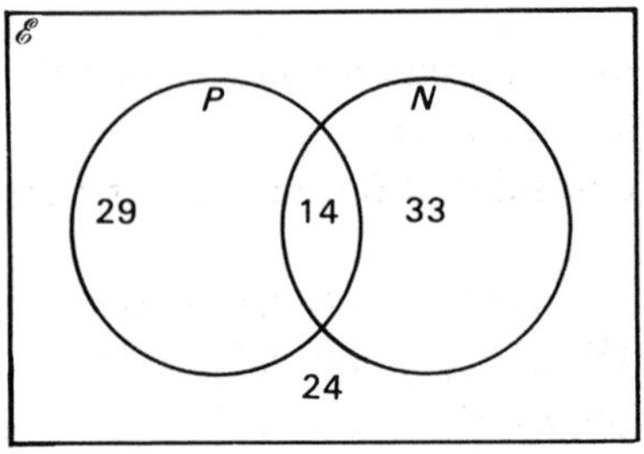

Exercise 4

Draw Venn diagrams for the following, then answer the questions:

1. $\mathscr{E}$ = {the first 13 letters of the alphabet}
A = {a, b, f, k, l}
B = {d, f, g, h, i, k}

(*a*) How many members are there in set A?
(*b*) How many members are not in set B?
(*c*) How many letters are there in both A and B?
(*d*) How many letters are there in either A or B or both?

2. $\mathscr{E}$ = {natural numbers less than 10}
P = {prime numbers less than 10}
V = {even numbers less than 10}

(*a*) How many members are there in set P?
(*b*) How many members are there in set V?
(*c*) How many members are there in set P'?
(*d*) How many members are there in $P \cap V$?
(*e*) How many members are there in $P \cup V$?
(*f*) How many members are there in $(P \cup V)'$?

3. $\mathscr{E}$ = {natural numbers less than 20}
D = {odd numbers less than 20}
M = {multiples of 3 that are less than 20}

(*a*) How many members has set D?
(*b*) How many members has the complement of M?
(*c*) How many members has $D \cap M$?
(*d*) How many members has $D \cup M$?
(*e*) How many members has $(D \cap M)'$?

4. $\mathscr{E}$ = {natural numbers less than 40}
F = {factors of 24}
G = {multiples of 5 that are less than 40}

Find: (*a*) $n(\mathscr{E})$ (*b*) $n(F)$ (*c*) $n(G)$ (*d*) $n(F \cap G)$ (*e*) $n(F \cup G)$ (*f*) $n(F')$ (*g*) $n(G')$ (*h*) $n(F \cap G)'$ (*i*) $n(F \cup G)'$

Exercise 5 Shading Sets

M

A For each question, write which set is shaded:

1. P or Q or $P \cap Q$ or $P \cup Q$?

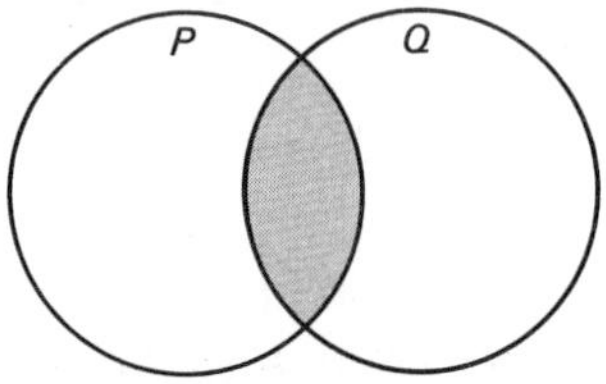

2. X or Y or $X \cap Y$ or $X \cup Y$?

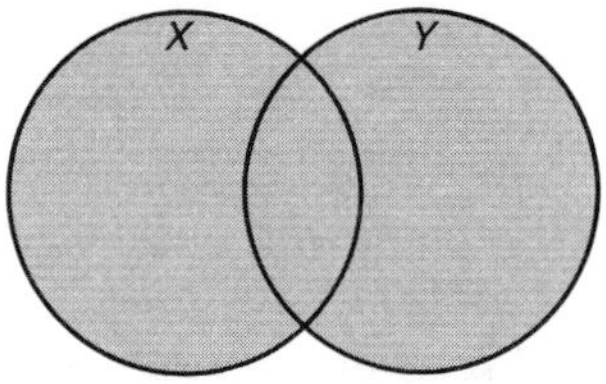

3. M or N or $M \cap N$ or $M \cup N$?

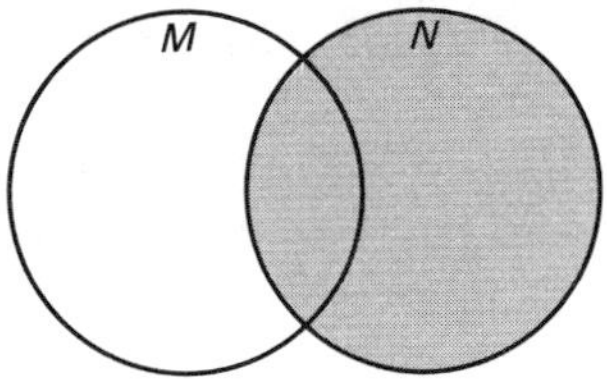

4. C or D or $C \cap D$ or $C \cup D$?

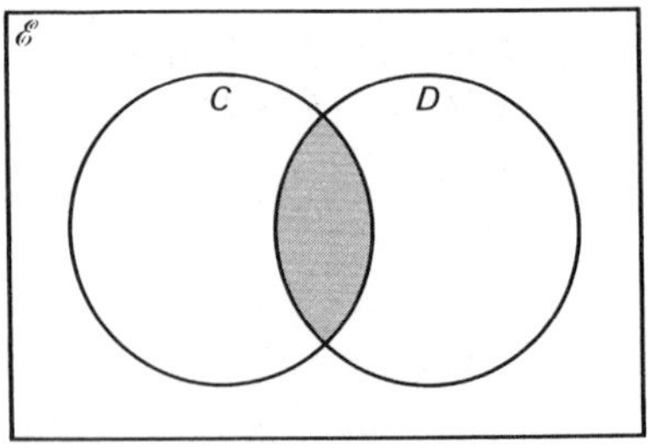

5. K or L or $K \cap L$ or $K \cup L$?

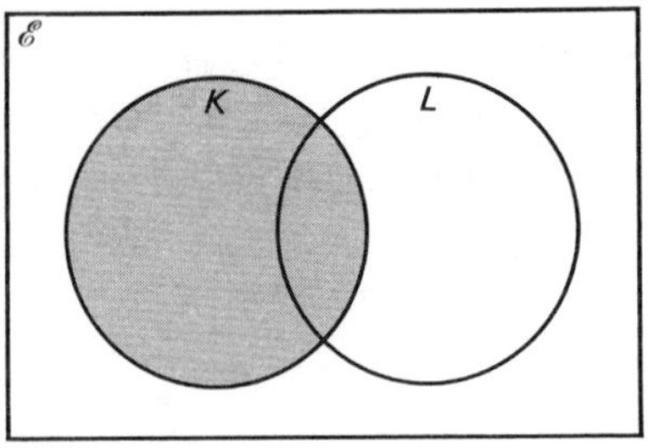

6. V or W or $V \cap W$
or $V \cup W$ or $V \cup W'$?

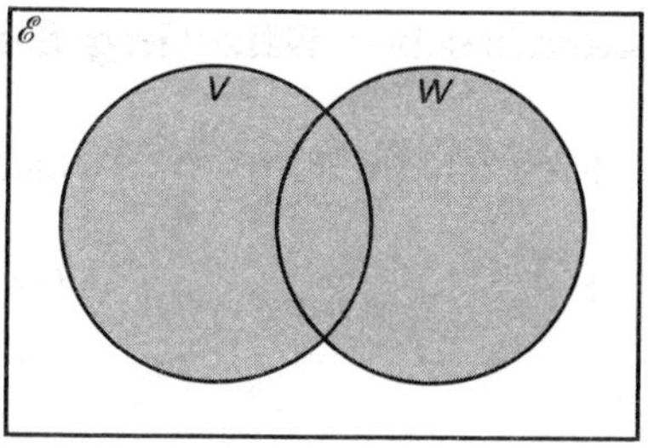

7. $A \cap B$ or $A \cup B$ or A'
or B' or $A \cup B'$?

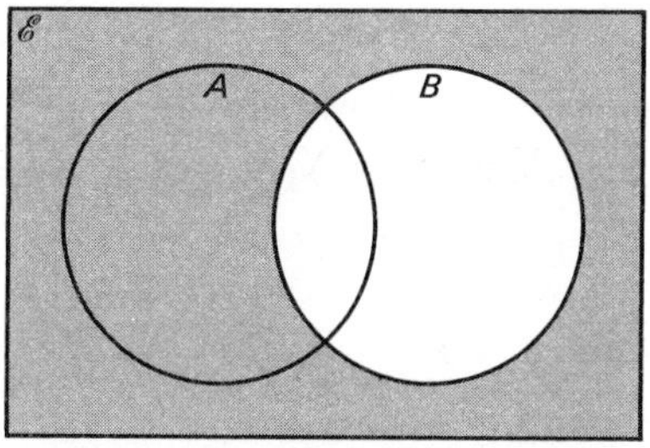

8. $R \cap S$ or $R \cup S$ or $(R \cap S)'$
or $(R \cup S)'$ or $R' \cup S$?

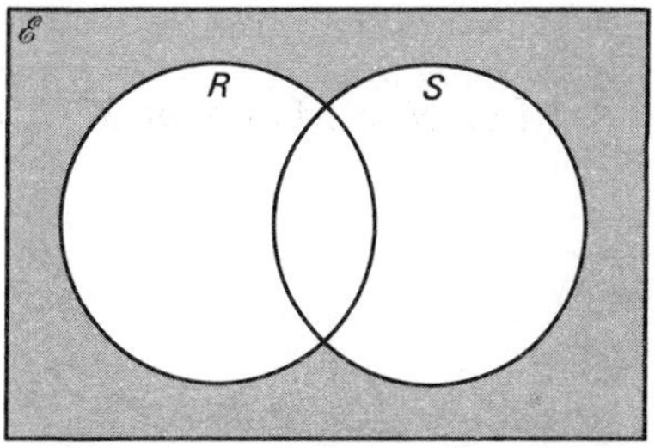

9. $E \cap F$ or $E \cup F$ or E'
or F' or $(E \cap F)'$
or $E' \cap F$?

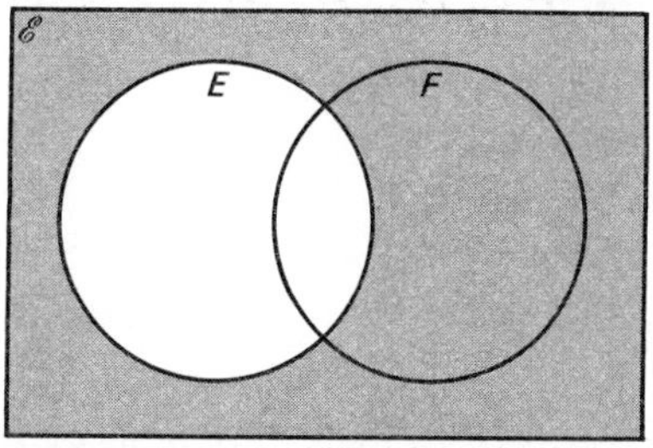

10. $G \cap H$ or $G \cup H$
or $G' \cup H$ or $(G \cap H)'$
or $(G \cup H)'$?

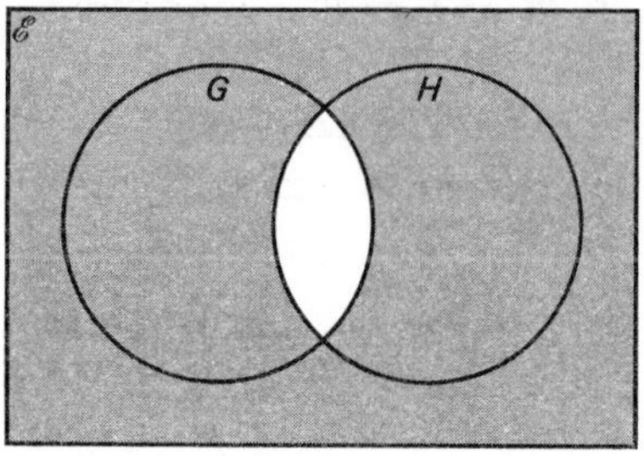

B Make 8 copies of the Venn diagram.

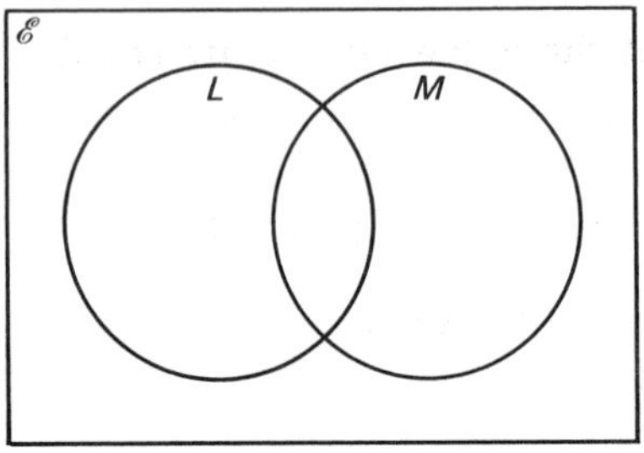

Shade a different diagram for each question. Shade:

1. $L \cup M$
2. L
3. M'
4. L'
5. $(L \cup M)'$
6. $L \cap M$
7. $(L \cap M)'$
8. $L' \cap M$

C Make 8 copies of the Venn diagram.

Shade a different diagram for each question. Shade:

1. X
2. Y'
3. $X \cup Y$
4. $X \cap Y$
5. $(X \cap Y)'$
6. $(X \cup Y)'$
7. $X' \cup Y$
8. $X' \cap Y$

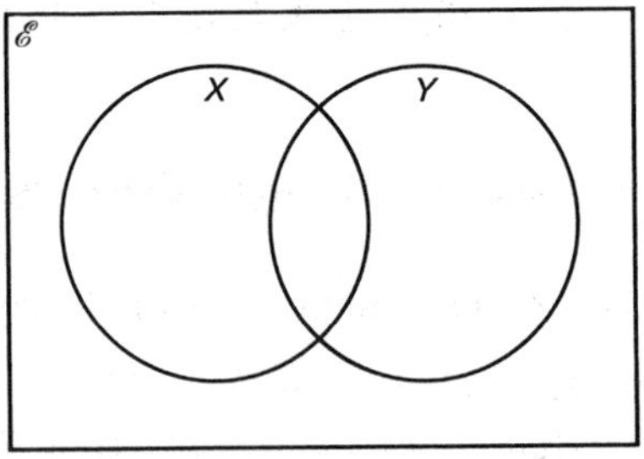

Equal Sets

Two sets are equal if they have the same members.
If $X = \{a, c, d, e\}$ and $Y = \{c, e, d, a\}$
then $X = Y$.
Note that the sets are still equal even though the members are listed in a different order.
If $P = \{\text{even numbers less than } 9\}$ and $Q = \{2, 4, 6, 8\}$
then $P = Q$.
Note that the sets are equal even though they have been described in a different way.

Exercise 6

Write whether or not the following sets are equal:

1. $A = \{x, f, p, y, t\}$ $B = \{f, y, x, t, p\}$
2. $F = \{m, a, g, n, e, t\}$ $G = \{g, a, t, n, i, m\}$
3. $N = \{\text{odd numbers less than } 10\}$
   $P = \{5, 9, 3, 7, 1\}$
4. $V = \{u, e, a, o, i\}$ $W = \{\text{vowels}\}$
5. $S = \{\text{even numbers that lie between 11 and 19}\}$
   $T = \{16, 12, 18, 14\}$
6. $L = \{\text{odd numbers that are bigger than 5 and less than 18}\}$
   $M = \{7, 11, 13, 9, 5, 15, 17\}$
7. $J = \{7, 11, 18, 16, 15, 12, 17, 13\}$
   $C = \{\text{whole numbers that are bigger than 10 and less than 19}\}$
8. $Y = \{\text{natural numbers less than } 10\}$
   $X = \{9, 2, 1, 4, 5, 0, 3, 6, 8, 7\}$

Exercise 7 Logic Problems **R**

Draw Venn diagrams to help you to solve these problems.

1. In a school, the timetables of 83 pupils were checked. It was found that a total of 39 pupils took French, 31 took German, while 14 took both languages.
   (*a*) Copy and complete the given Venn diagram:

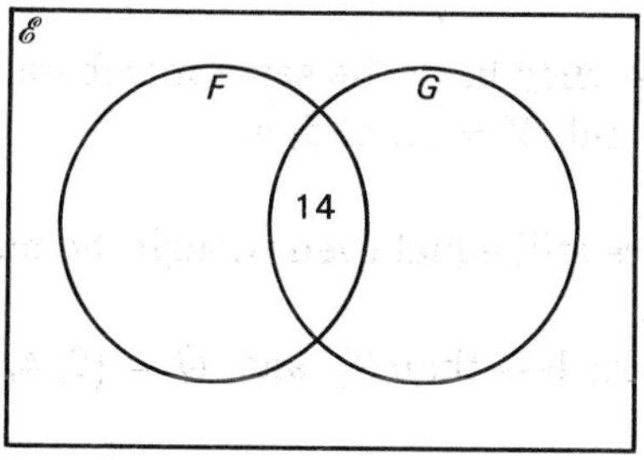

   (*b*) How many took neither French nor German?

2. Out of 94 people, 62 can sew, 34 can both bake and sew while 17 can do neither. Find the total number of people who can bake.

3. In a survey, 115 people were interviewed. A total of 17 people could write with their left hand while 4 people were ambidextrous (that is, they could use both hands).
If everyone could write with one hand or the other or both, find:
(*a*) the total number who could write with their right hand,
(*b*) the number who could use only their right hand.

4. Out of 130 people, 74 were good at history, 48 were good at both history and geography, while 63 were poor at geography.
(*a*) How many were good at geography but poor at history?
(*b*) How many were poor at history?

5. 94 pupils were asked whether they bought crisps or a drink at the school shop. 58 said they bought a packet of crisps. 12 of the 58 also bought a drink.
77 said they either bought a packet of crisps, a drink or both.
(*a*) How many bought a drink?
(*b*) How many bought crisps but did not buy a drink?
(*c*) How many bought a drink but did not buy crisps?
(*d*) How many did not buy crisps or a drink?
(*e*) How many did not buy any crisps?

6. Several people were asked whether they liked apples or oranges or both. 16 liked both while 29 people altogether liked apples. 6 people liked neither apples nor oranges and a total of 14 people did not like apples.
(*a*) How many people were questioned?
(*b*) How many liked oranges?
(*c*) How many liked oranges but not apples?
(*d*) How many liked apples but not oranges?
(*e*) How many liked apples or oranges or both?

2 Approximations and Estimations

Approximations

Exercise 1

1. The Matterhorn (on the border of Switzerland and Italy) is 4477 m high.

Write the height correct to the nearest 100 m.

2. Mr Taylor's house cost £37 800. How much was that to the nearest £1000?

3. The number of pupils at school was 872. Write that number rounded to the nearest hundred.

4. There are 7.3 ℓ of water in a wash-basin. Write that amount correct to the nearest litre.

5. A swimming-pool holds 428 650 ℓ of water. Write that amount correct to the nearest thousand litres.

6. A bar of soap has a mass of 142 g. Write its mass correct to the nearest 10 g.

7. A 5 p piece weighs 5.6552 g. Write its mass correct to the nearest gram.

8. A table is 731 mm high. Write its height correct to the nearest centimetre.

Exercise 2 Decimal Places R

Round each of these decimals to the number of decimal places given in brackets:

1.	8.67	(1 d.p.)	**9.**	0.608	(2 d.p.)
2.	19.812	(2 d.p.)	**10.**	96.35	(1 d.p.)
3.	41.329	(2 d.p.)	**11.**	8.98	(1 d.p.)
4.	9.06	(1 d.p.)	**12.**	24.347	(1 d.p.)
5.	72.653	(2 d.p.)	**13.**	5.639	(1 d.p.)
6.	7.6387	(3 d.p.)	**14.**	8.7615	(1 d.p.)
7.	0.714	(2 d.p.)	**15.**	19.8476	(2 d.p.)
8.	0.0928	(3 d.p.)	**16.**	0.0729	(1 d.p.)

Significant Figures

Exercise 3 R

Write each of the following correct to the number of significant figures shown in the brackets:

1.	3.576	(3 s.f.)	**11.**	4976	(3 s.f.)
2.	52.642	(4 s.f.)	**12.**	9123	(3 s.f.)
3.	79.865	(4 s.f.)	**13.**	47 608	(4 s.f.)
4.	206.75	(4 s.f.)	**14.**	480.315	(5 s.f.)
5.	32.617	(4 s.f.)	**15.**	3.9647	(3 s.f.)
6.	29.34	(3 s.f.)	**16.**	56.2542	(3 s.f.)
7.	5.684	(3 s.f.)	**17.**	4.6819	(1 s.f.)
8.	5.698	(3 s.f.)	**18.**	399.8	(1 s.f.)
9.	24.797	(4 s.f.)	**19.**	399.8	(2 s.f.)
10.	4.89	(2 s.f.)	**20.**	399.8	(3 s.f.)

Exercise 4 **R**

Write each of the following correct to the number of significant figures shown in the brackets:

1. 78.642 (3 s.f.)
2. 0.806 (2 s.f.)
3. 0.003 246 (3 s.f.)
4. 0.187 (2 s.f.)
5. 34.08 (3 s.f.)
6. 0.9165 (3 s.f.)
7. 0.650 72 (4 s.f.)
8. 5.910 52 (4 s.f.)
9. 0.001 607 (3 s.f.)
10. 0.008 476 (2 s.f.)
11. 0.6709 (3 s.f.)
12. 0.9304 (2 s.f.)
13. 0.003 76 (1 s.f.)
14. 547.95 (4 s.f.)
15. 547.95 (3 s.f.)
16. 547.95 (2 s.f.)
17. 0.004 98 (1 s.f.)
18. 0.004 98 (2 s.f.)
19. 2998 (3 s.f.)
20. 2998 (2 s.f.)
21. 2998 (1 s.f.)
22. 0.2998 (3 s.f.)
23. 0.2998 (2 s.f.)
24. 0.2998 (1 s.f.)
25. 0.999 (1 s.f.)

Estimations

Sometimes, mathematics needs to be exact, while at other times, an estimate is good enough.

Exercise 5

A school camp is organised. Coaches are hired to take everyone to the camp site. The journey to the camp begins at school. The camp lasts one week.

To organise such a camp someone needs to carry out some calculations. The calculations may be estimates, or they may need to be exact.

For each of these questions, decide whether the mathematics must be exact or may be estimated.

Write either 'EXACT' or 'ESTIMATED'.

1. How many coaches are needed?

2. What do the coaches cost to hire?

3. How long will the journey to the camp site take?

4. How many tents are needed?

5. How many tins of beans are needed?

6. How many cans of soft drinks are needed?

7. If a 3-hour hike is planned, what distance should the walk be?

8. If a visit to the cinema is arranged, what is the cost of the seats?

When the mathematics needs to be exact, an estimate can be used to check if the answer seems to be correct. In books 1G and 2G, estimating was carried out by rounding the numbers used, correct to one significant figure.

e.g. $52.7 \times 38.4 \approx 50 \times 40$
$= \underline{\underline{2000}}$

This method gives quite a good estimate. (Check the exact answer to the calculation in the example above using a calculator.) However, we may not be able to tell if the estimate is bigger or smaller than the exact answer. Consider the following example:

e.g. $51.6 \times 37.5 \approx 50 \times 40$
$= \underline{\underline{2000}}$

Once again the estimated answer is 2000. (Check the exact answer using a calculator.) This time, the estimated answer is bigger than the exact answer. In the first example, the estimated answer was smaller than the exact answer. We could not tell when estimating.

Sometimes it is useful to find two numbers between which the exact answer lies. Consider again the example 51.6×37.5:

We can write:

$$51.6 \times 37.5 \approx 50 \times 30 = 1500$$

(Both numbers have been rounded *down* to one significant figure.)

or we can write:

$$51.6 \times 37.5 \approx 60 \times 40 = 2400$$

(Both numbers have been rounded *up* to one significant figure.)

We can say the exact answer lies between 1500 and 2400.

Exercise 6

Copy each of the following but replace each question mark with < or > to make the statement true:

1. 6×52	?	6×50	**11.** 81.7×24	?	80×20
2. 17×8	?	20×8	**12.** 693×46	?	700×50
3. 9.6×4	?	9×4	**13.** 693×46	?	600×40
4. 2.7×9	?	3×9	**14.** 45.8×77	?	40×70
5. 7.5×1.9	?	8×2	**15.** 45.8×77	?	50×80
6. 97×41	?	90×40	**16.** 1.27×56.5	?	1×50
7. 5.8×74	?	6×80	**17.** 1.27×56.5	?	2×60
8. 8.6×9.7	?	9×10	**18.** 7.9×341	?	8×400
9. 14.2×6.5	?	10×6	**19.** 86.5×40.2	?	80×40
10. 9.3×68	?	10×70	**20.** 30.6×573	?	30×500

From your answers to Exercise 6, you should have noticed that for multiplication, if both numbers are rounded down, the estimated answer is always less than the exact answer; but if both numbers are rounded up, the estimated answer is always bigger than the exact answer.

Exercise 7

By rounding down and by rounding up, find two numbers between which the exact product lies:

e.g.

$$67.8 \times 2.14 \approx 60 \times 2 = 120 \qquad 67.8 \times 2.14 \approx 70 \times 3 = 210$$

so $120 < 67.8 \times 2.14 < 210$

1. 26.8×7.2
2. 4.9×34.6
3. 51.3×66.7
4. 825×55.8
5. 73×47.1
6. 21.4×589
7. 9.4×39.4
8. 12.7×7.5
9. 6.35×86.7
10. 4.82×971

Exercise 8

A **1.** Write an addition sum. Use two numbers where each number has more than one digit. (Decimals may be used if you wish.)
Round *down* both numbers. Add the rounded values. Is the estimated answer bigger than or less than the exact answer?

Repeat the above for other addition sums. In each case, compare the estimated answer with the exact answer. Write what you notice.

2. Repeat question 1, but this time round *up* both numbers.

B Repeat part A for subtraction instead of addition.

C Repeat part A for division instead of addition.

Exercise 9

A Write two numbers.
By rounding the two numbers to one significant figure (both may be rounded up, both rounded down or one may be rounded up and the other rounded down), investigate subtraction of the two rounded numbers. Try to find which rounding gives the largest possible answer and which rounding gives the smallest possible answer.
Write what you notice.

In subtraction questions, how should you round the two numbers to find two numbers between which the exact answer lies?

B Repeat part A for division.

Exercise 10

Write whether or not each answer is reasonable:

1. A box holds 12 cartons of milk. A shop has 73 boxes. The manager decided that they had almost 700 cartons of milk.

2. Mrs Ray drove 42 km each day in travelling to and from work. She worked a 5-day week. She said she travelled over 200 km per week.

3. Mr Kerai earned £8769 in a year. He said that was almost £180 per week.

4. A car mileometer showed 37 284 miles at the beginning of the year and 46 920 miles at the end of the year. The car travelled over 10 000 miles during the year.

Exercise 11

In this exercise, work with one significant figure.

1. A sales person drove about 240 km each day for 5 days. Estimate the total distance travelled.

2. A box holds 30 tins of soup. Estimate the number of tins in 281 boxes.

3. A box holds 12 bottles of sauce. Estimate the number of bottles in 475 boxes.

4. There are 2780 bottles of shampoo in a warehouse. Estimate the number of boxes needed to store the shampoo if each box holds 18 bottles.

5. Eight people weigh 54 kg, 72 kg, 68 kg, 59 kg, 63 kg, 56 kg, 70 kg and 69 kg. Estimate their total mass.

6. One dining-room suite cost £923 while a cheaper one cost £529.95. Estimate the difference in cost.

7. Helena worked for 18 h at £4.25 an hour. Estimate how much she earned.

8. A jar of jam weighs 678 g including the jar. Estimate the mass of 32 jars of jam. Give your answer in kilograms.

3 Number and Number Patterns

Brackets and Order of Calculations

Exercise 1 R

Write whether each statement is true or false:

1. $7 + 12 = 12 + 7$
2. $49 + 83 = 83 + 49$
3. $14 - 6 = 6 - 14$
4. $184 - 79 = 79 - 184$
5. $6 \times 7 = 7 \times 6$
6. $46 \times 23 = 23 \times 46$
7. $24 \div 6 = 6 \div 24$
8. $368 \div 23 = 23 \div 368$

The use of brackets can change the order in which a calculation is carried out. Calculations inside the brackets must be worked out first. Note that:

$$17 - 9 - 3 = 5 \quad \text{(Check it.)}$$

However,

$$17 - (9 - 3) = 17 - 6 = 11$$

(The calculation inside the brackets must be worked out first.)

Some calculators have brackets (called parentheses) keys on them. When they are used, the calculator automatically works out the calculation inside the brackets first.

Exercise 2

If the calculator you are using has brackets keys on it then answer parts A and B below, otherwise, answer only part B:

A Using a calculator and the parentheses keys on it:

1. Check that $26 - (10 - 7) = 23$.

2. Work out $293 - (165 - 97)$.

B Without using the parentheses keys try to work out:

1. 19 – (12 – 5)
2. 461 – (283 – 108)

To work out 17 – (9 – 3) on a calculator you could have keyed in [9] [–] [3] [=]
(The answer, 6, could have been written on paper.)
Then [AC] [1] [7] [–] [6] [=] would have given the correct answer.

Another method would be to use the memory keys on a calculator. Unfortunately, the memory keys on different calculators may work in different ways.
The usual keys are [Min], [M+], [M–], [MR] and [MC].
(An explanation of these and some other memory keys is given in Appendix 1 on p. 371. If any of the keys do not work as expected then see Appendix 1 and/or your calculator instruction book.

To work out 17 – (9 – 3) try this:

[AC] [9] [–] [3] [=] [Min] [AC] [1] [7] [–] [MR] [=]

Exercise 3

Try to work out the following on a calculator, without using the parentheses keys:

1. (4 + 3) × 2
2. (184 + 349) × 57

[AC] [4] [+] [3] [=] [×] [2] should give the correct answer, 14, to question 1. Note that [=] makes the calculator work out the calculation so far.

Exercise 4

Write whether each statement is true or false:

1. (8 + 7) + 3 = 8 + (7 + 3)
2. (48 + 86) + 75 = 48 + (86 + 75)
3. (15 – 8) – 2 = 15 – (8 – 2)
4. (237 – 91) – 49 = 237 – (91 – 49)
5. (6 × 3) × 4 = 6 × (3 × 4)

6. $(81 \times 16) \times 52 = 81 \times (16 \times 52)$
7. $(24 \div 6) \div 2 = 24 \div (6 \div 2)$
8. $(840 \div 168) \div 14 = 840 \div (168 \div 14)$

Exercise 5

Work out the following:

e.g. Add 4 to 5 then multiply the result by 2.

$$\begin{aligned} & (4 + 5) \times 2 \\ = & \quad 9 \quad \times 2 \\ = & \quad \underline{\underline{18}} \end{aligned}$$

1. Add 6 to 7 then multiply the result by 2.
2. Multiply 8 by 3 then add 6.
3. Take 5 from 9 then multiply the result by 7.
4. Divide 28 by 4 then add 12.
5. Subtract 17 from 38 then divide the result by 3.
6. Multiply 12 by 4 then subtract 19.
7. Divide 50 by 5 then divide the result by 2.
8. Subtract the sum of 18 and 46 from 100.
9. Multiply 23 by 7 and 14 by 18. Add the two results.
10. Find the product of 34 and 57 and the product of 41 and 16. Subtract the second product from the first.

Exercise 6

Write in words how to carry out these calculations, then work them out:

1. $2 \times 6 - 4$
2. $2 \times (6 - 4)$
3. $(9 + 7) \times 3$
4. $9 + 7 \times 3$
5. $18 \div (5 + 4)$
6. $(19 - 7) \div 4$
7. $25 - (19 - 11)$
8. $37 \times (15 \div 3)$
9. $7 \times 9 + 6 \times 8$
10. $19 \times 46 - 14 \times 28$

Exercise 7

Copy each statement. Where necessary, insert brackets to make it correct. (Only use brackets when it is absolutely necessary to do so.)

1. $3 + 6 \times 2 = 18$
2. $4 \times 8 - 9 = 23$
3. $28 - 4 \times 5 = 8$
4. $21 - 12 - 5 = 14$
5. $18 + 8 \div 2 = 13$
6. $40 \div 10 \div 2 = 8$
7. $36 \div 6 \div 3 = 2$
8. $7 + 5 \times 7 = 42$
9. $2 \times 9 - 3 = 12$
10. $20 - 8 \div 4 = 3$
11. $4 \times 9 + 3 \times 8 = 60$
12. $6 \times 10 - 4 \times 6 = 36$

Exercise 8

Work these out. For each question, which two parts have the same answer?

1. (*a*) $6 + 3 \times 5$ (*b*) $(6 + 3) \times 5$ (*c*) $3 \times 5 + 6$
2. (*a*) $4 \times (8 - 2)$ (*b*) $4 \times 8 - 2$ (*c*) $4 \times 8 - 4 \times 2$
3. (*a*) $18 - 9 - 6$ (*b*) $(18 - 9) - 6$ (*c*) $18 - (9 - 6)$
4. (*a*) $54 \div (6 \div 3)$ (*b*) $54 \div 6 \div 3$ (*c*) $(54 \div 6) \div 3$
5. (*a*) $(16 + 8) \div 4$ (*b*) $16 + 8 \div 4$ (*c*) $8 \div 4 + 16$
6. (*a*) $(21 + 12) \div 3$ (*b*) $21 + 12 \div 3$ (*c*) $21 \div 3 + 12 \div 3$

Exercise 9

Without working out the answers, for each question copy out the two parts that have the same answer:

1. (*a*) $23 - (8 + 4)$ (*b*) $23 - 8 + 4$ (*c*) $(23 - 8) + 4$
2. (*a*) $60 \div 6 \div 2$ (*b*) $60 \div (6 \div 2)$ (*c*) $(60 \div 6) \div 2$
3. (*a*) $9 + 12 \div 3$ (*b*) $(9 + 12) \div 3$ (*c*) $12 \div 3 + 9$
4. (*a*) $7 \times (8 + 4)$ (*b*) $7 \times 8 + 7 \times 4$ (*c*) $7 \times 8 + 4$
5. (*a*) $14 + 10 \div 2$ (*b*) $14 \div 2 + 10 \div 2$ (*c*) $(14 + 10) \div 2$
6. (*a*) $27 - 14 - 8$ (*b*) $27 - (14 - 8)$ (*c*) $(27 - 14) - 8$

Exercise 10

It is possible and easy to measure any distance that is a whole number of metres using only two measuring sticks – a 1-metre stick and a 2-metre stick. However, some distances can be measured in different ways. For example, 4 m can be measured in 5 different ways:

$$2 + 2,\ 2 + 1 + 1,\ 1 + 2 + 1,\ 1 + 1 + 2,\ 1 + 1 + 1 + 1$$

where $1 + 2 + 1$ means use the 1-metre stick, then the 2-metre, then the 1-metre again; and $1 + 1 + 2$ means use the 1-metre stick twice then the 2-metre stick last.

Copy and complete the table to show how the lengths were measured:

Length measured	Different ways used	Number of different ways
1 m	1	1
2 m	2, 1 + 1	2
3 m		
4 m	2 + 2, 2 + 1 + 1, 1 + 2 + 1, 1 + 1 + 2,	5
	1 + 1 + 1 + 1	
5 m		
6 m		13

Leonardo of Pisa, better known as Fibonacci (from the Latin *filius Bonacci*, meaning 'son of Bonacci'), lived from about 1175 AD to 1250 AD.

He discovered a sequence that has become one of the most well-known sequences in Mathematics.
The first few terms are:

1, 1, 2, 3, 5, 8, 13, . . .

(Compare these numbers with the numbers in the last column of the table in Exercise 10.)

Exercise 11

Try to write the first 15 terms of the Fibonacci sequence (the first 7 terms are printed above). If you need a clue, here is one:

(1 + 1 = 2. Also, 3 + 5 = 8.)

Exercise 12

A queen bee can lay both fertilised and unfertilised eggs. Male bees, called drones, hatch from the unfertilised eggs, so male bees only have a mother, while female bees, either workers or queens, have both mothers and fathers.

Use the family-tree diagrams for male and female bees given below to help you with the following questions. Compare each answer with the numbers in the Fibonacci sequence.

Five Generations of Bees

(Note that M stands for a male bee and F for a female bee and that each arrow points to a parent.)

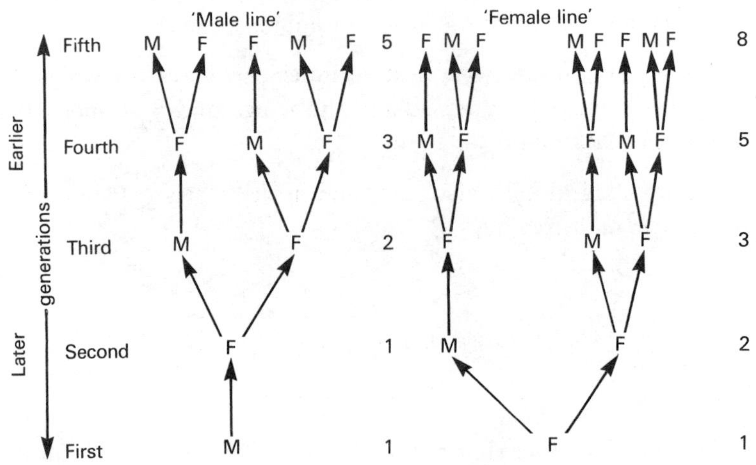

1. Compare the number of bees in each generation with the Fibonacci numbers.
   How many bees will there be in the sixth generation in:
   (*a*) the male line?
   (*b*) the female line?

2. (*a*) In the third generation there are 5 bees altogether (2 from the male line and 3 from the female line). Total the number of bees for each generation. Write what you notice.
   (*b*) For each generation, write the ratio of the number of male bees to the number of female bees.

There are many other instances in nature where the Fibonacci numbers occur, particularly in the growth of flowers and plants*. For instance, the number of petals on some flowers is a Fibonacci number. Here are some examples:

2 petals: enchanter's nightshade
3 petals: some lilies and iris
5 petals: many buttercups and some delphiniums
8 petals: some delphiniums
13 petals: some double delphiniums and corn marigolds
21 petals: some asters
34 'petals' (or ray florets): some daisies
55 'petals': some field daisies and Michaelmas daisies
89 'petals': some Michaelmas daisies

Note that some under-developed (or over-developed) members of the above species may not have the stated number of petals.

The milkwort has flowers with 2 large inner sepals, called wings, 3 smaller sepals, 5 petals hidden inside the wings and 8 stamens (it should have been named after Fibonacci!).

A daisy's florets spiral both clockwise and anticlockwise as shown in the photograph and drawing.

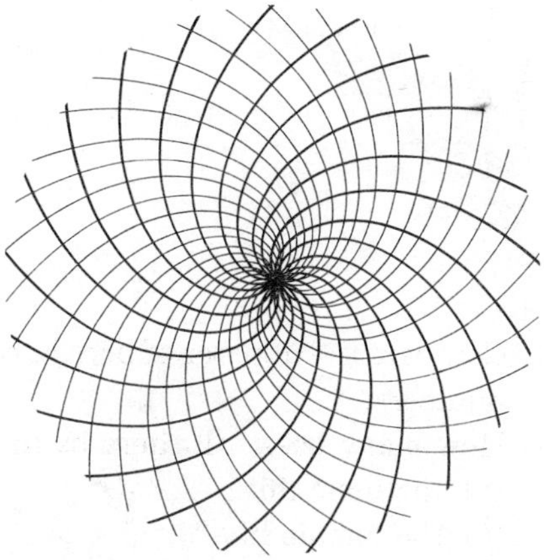

A daisy can have 21 clockwise and 34 anticlockwise spirals as shown above. (Fibonacci numbers again!).

* See the bibliography, p. 387.

Exercise 13

Here is a spiral based on Fibonacci numbers. Try to copy it. (Look carefully at the measurements given.)

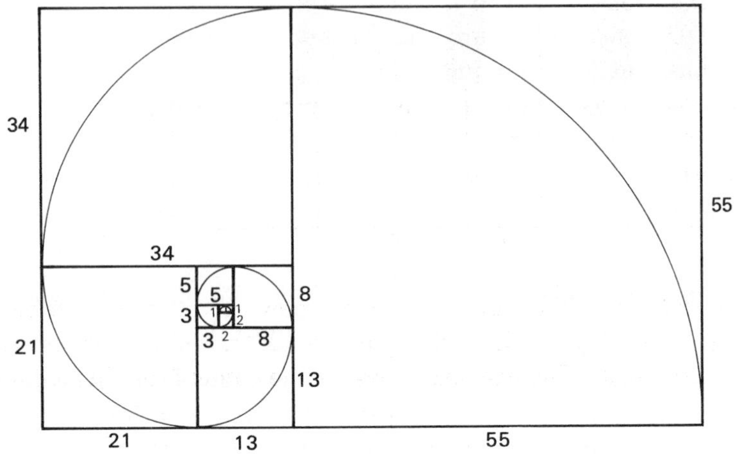

The shell of the chambered nautilus looks quite similar to the spiral above.

Fibonacci numbers also appear in music.
Thirteen piano keyboard or organ keys are shown.

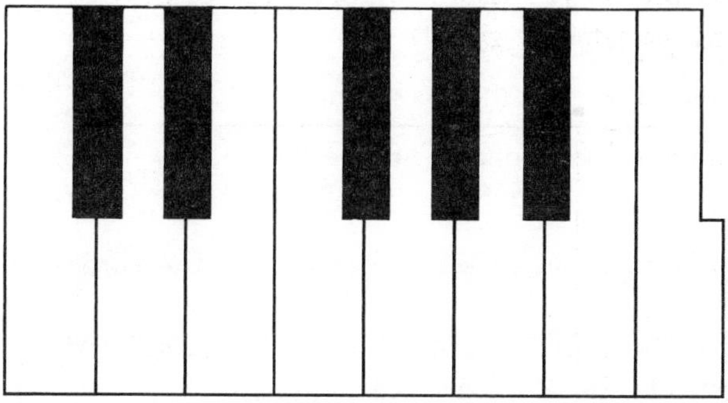

If you play all of them in order you will play one octave of a chromatic scale. If you play the eight white notes in order, you will play an octave of a major scale. The five black keys are the notes of the old pentatonic scale.

Exercise 14

Here are the first 15 Fibonacci numbers:

1, 1, 2, 3, 5, 8, 13, 21, 34, 55, 89, 144, 233, 377, 610

1. What sort of number is every third term?

2. Choose any 3 consecutive Fibonacci numbers. Multiply the first by the third. Square the second. Repeat this for other groups of three. Write what you notice.

3. Choose any 4 consecutive Fibonacci numbers. Multiply the first by the fourth. Multiply the second by the third. Repeat for other groups of four. Write what you notice.

4. Write the squares of the first eight terms:

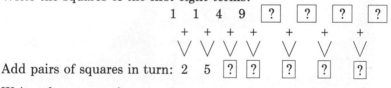

1 1 4 9 [?] [?] [?] [?]

\+ + + + + + +

Add pairs of squares in turn: 2 5 [?] [?] [?] [?] [?]

Write what you notice.

5. Choose 3 consecutive terms and cube each one. Subtract the smallest cube from the sum of the other two cubes.

e.g. $2^3 = 8, \quad 3^3 = 27, \quad 5^3 = 125$

$$5^3 + 3^3 - 2^3 = 125 + 27 - 8$$
$$= 144 \quad \text{(a Fibonacci number)}$$

Will you always obtain a Fibonacci number?

6. If T_1 = the first term, T_2 = the second term, T_3 = the third term and so on:

(*a*) Find the sum of the first 4 terms. Compare the total with T_6.
(*b*) Add the first 5 terms. Compare the total with T_7.
(*c*) Add the first 6 terms. Compare the total with T_8.
(*d*) Without adding, find the sum of the first 12 terms.
(*e*) Show someone how quickly you can 'add'. Ask someone to point to any of the Fibonacci numbers and tell them the total of all the numbers up to and including that one before they can say: 'Maths is great.'

7. Divide each of the first fifteen Fibonacci numbers by 4 and write the remainders. What do you notice?

8. (*a*) Write successive pairs of Fibonacci numbers as ratios:

$\frac{1}{1}, \frac{1}{2}, \frac{2}{3}, \frac{3}{5}, \frac{5}{8}, \boxed{?}, \boxed{?}, \boxed{?}, \boxed{?}, \boxed{?}, \boxed{?}, \boxed{?}, \boxed{?}, \boxed{?}$

(*b*) Add 1 to each of the above. Give the fractions as improper fractions:

$\frac{2}{1}, \frac{3}{2}, \boxed{?}, \frac{8}{5}, \boxed{?}, \boxed{?}, \boxed{?}, \boxed{?}, \boxed{?}, \boxed{?}, \boxed{?}, \boxed{?}, \boxed{?}, \boxed{?}$

$1 + \frac{3}{5} = 1\frac{3}{5} = \frac{8}{5}$

(*c*) Using a calculator to help, write each fraction in part (*a*) as a decimal.
(*d*) Write each fraction in part (*b*) as a decimal.
(*e*) Compare answers to (*c*) and (*d*). Write what you notice.

9. (Fibonacci himself set this problem.) How many pairs of rabbits can be produced from a single pair in a year if (*a*) each pair begets a new pair every month, which from the second month on becomes productive, (*b*) deaths do not occur?

10. Draw a graph to show the first 14 Fibonacci numbers. DO NOT join the crosses.

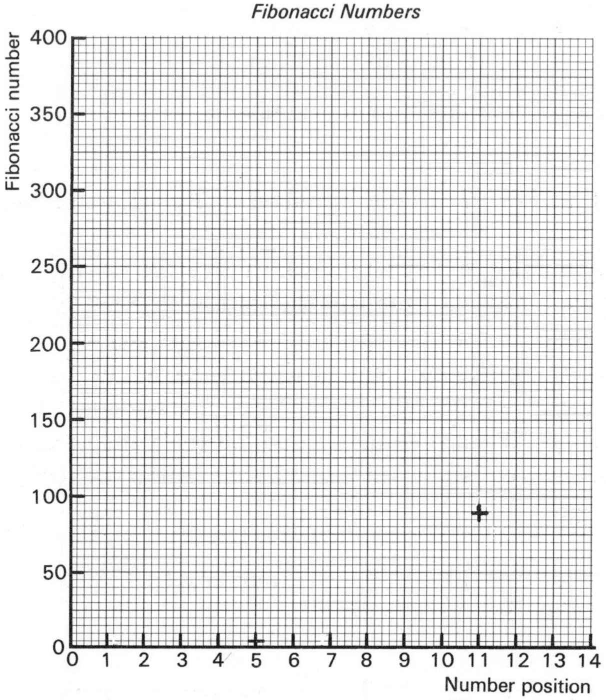

Directed Numbers

Exercise 15

Copy the following sequences and fill in the missing numbers:

1. 1, 5, 9, 13, [?], 21, 25, [?], 33, 37

2. 4, 5, 7, 10, 14, [?], 25, [?], 40, 49

3. 18, 16, 14, [?], 10, 8, [?], 4, 2, 0, $^-2$, $^-4$

4. 11, 9, [?], 5, 3, 1, $^-1$, $^-3$, $^-5$, [?], $^-9$

5. $^-15$, $^-12$, $^-9$, [?], $^-3$, 0, 3, 6, [?], 12

6. 15, 11, 7, 3, $^{-}1$, $^{-}5$, [?], $^{-}13$, [?]

7. 24, 17, 10, 3, [?], $^{-}11$, $^{-}18$, [?], $^{-}32$

8. $^{-}16$, $^{-}15$, $^{-}13$, $^{-}10$, [?], $^{-}1$, [?], 12

Exercise 16

1. What is the difference between the two temperatures shown on the sketch of a thermometer?

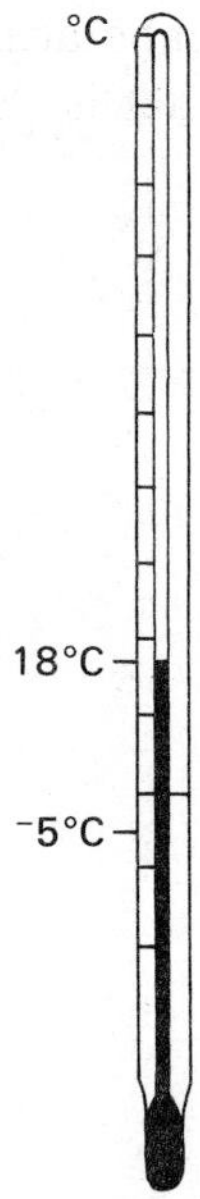

2. If the temperature rises from $^{-}8$ °C to $^{-}2$ °C, by how many degrees has it changed?

3. If the temperature falls from $^{-}4$ °C to $^{-}8$ °C, by how many degrees has it changed?

4. If the temperature falls from $^{-}2$ °C to $^{-}7$ °C, by how many degrees has it changed?

5. If the temperature falls from 2 °C to $^{-}7$ °C, by how many degrees has it changed?

6. The temperature rises by 9 °C from $^{-}4$ °C. What is the new temperature?

7. The temperature falls by 10 °C from 6 °C. What is the new temperature?

8. The temperature falls by 10 °C from $^{-}6$ °C. What is the new temperature?

9. At Tummel Bridge, Tayside, on 9 May 1978 the temperature varied between $^{-}7$ °C and 22 °C. What is the difference between the two temperatures?

10. When Viking 1 landed on Mars on 20 July 1976 it measured the temperature to be $^{-}86$ °C just after dawn and $^{-}31$ °C near noon. What is the difference between these two temperatures?

4 Money

Earning Money

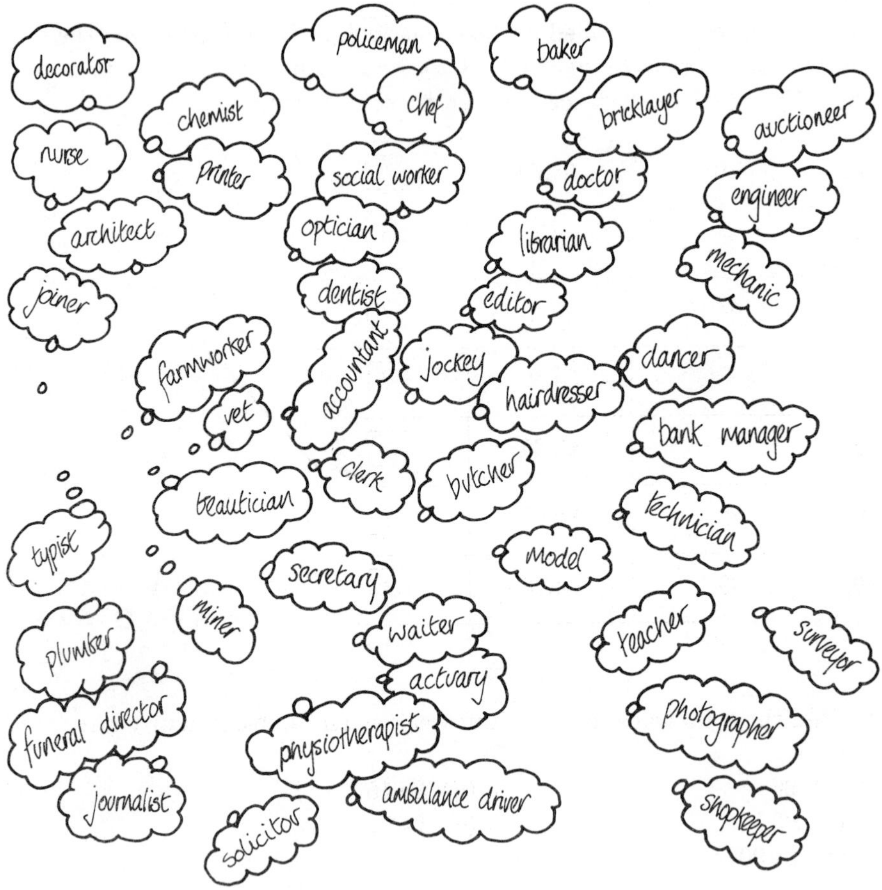

People work to earn money.
Weekly earnings are called *wages*.
Although wages are paid weekly, they are often worked out as an amount paid per hour called the *basic hourly rate* (or *basic rate*).

Wage = hours worked × hourly rate

Exercise 1 **M**

A Copy and complete the table:

	Hours worked	Hourly rate	Wage
1.	20	£4	?
2.	30	£5	?
3.	15	£7	?
4.	10	£4.60	?
5.	30	£3.80	?
6.	34	£6	?
7.	38	£4.50	?
8.	27	£3.25	?
9.	32	£2.80	?
10.	39	£4.76	?

B **1.** Find the total wage for a 40-hour week when the basic hourly rate is:
(*a*) £6
(*b*) £3.50
(*c*) £4.90
(*d*) £6.15
(*e*) £4.72

2. Calculate the total wage for a 35-hour week when the basic hourly rate is:
(*a*) £6
(*b*) £5.50
(*c*) £3.25
(*d*) £3.75
(*e*) £4.29

3. Avril earns £3 an hour. How much does she earn in a week of 40 h?

4. Mr Evans works a 35-hour week. If his basic hourly rate is £4 an hour, calculate his wages for a week.

5. Mr Thakur works a basic 40-hour week earning £3.70 an hour. Calculate his weekly earnings.

6. Mrs Potter works for 37 h at a basic hourly rate of £4.20. Calculate her weekly earnings.

Exercise 2 **M**

A Copy and complete the table:

	Wage	Hours worked	Hourly rate
1.	£100	20	?
2.	£70	10	?
3.	£120	30	?
4.	£220	40	?
5.	£75	25	?
6.	£161	35	?
7.	£122.40	36	?
8.	£185.30	34	?
9.	£136	32	?
10.	£135.42	37	?

B 1. £200 is paid for a basic week of 40 h. Calculate the hourly rate.

2. Calculate the basic hourly rate when the total wage for a 40-hour week is:
(*a*) £160 (*b*) £180 (*c*) £190 (*d*) £172.80 (*e*) £145.20

3. Mr Wright earned £144.30 for a basic week of 37 h. Calculate his basic hourly rate.

4. Calculate the basic hourly rate when the total wage for a basic week of 35 h is:
(*a*) £175 (*b*) £133 (*c*) £154 (*d*) £150.50 (*e*) £166.25

5. A train driver earned £171.60 for a 40-hour week while a bus driver earned £4.07 per hour for a basic week of 39 h. Who earned the most per week?

Exercise 3 M

A ready reckoner can be used to find weekly earnings.

A Copy and complete this ready reckoner:

	Number of hours worked						
Rate	34	35	36	37	38	39	40
£3.30	£112.20	£115.50	£118.80	£122.10	?	£128.70	£132
£3.40	£115.60	£119	£122.40	£125.80	£129.20	£132.60	?
£3.50	£119	£122.50	£126	£129.50	£133	?	£140
£3.60	£122.40	?	£129.60	£133.20	£136.80	£140.40	£144
£3.70	£125.80	£129.50	?	£136.90	£140.60	£144.30	£148
£3.80	£129.20	£133	£136.80	?	£144.40	£148.20	£152
£3.90	?	£136.50	£140.40	£144.30	£148.20	£152.10	£156
£4	£136	£140	?	£148	£152	£156	£160
£4.10	£139.40	£143.50	£147.60	£151.70	£155.80	£159.90	?
£4.20	£142.80	£147	£151.20	?	£159.60	£163.80	£168

B Use the ready reckoner from part A to find the earnings of someone who works:

1. 38 h at £3.80 per hour.
2. 35 h at £3.60 per hour.
3. 40 h at £3.50 per hour.
4. 37 h at £4.20 per hour.
5. 36 h at £3.90 per hour.
6. 34 h at £3.70 per hour.
7. 39 h at £4.10 per hour.
8. 37 h at £3.40 per hour.
9. 34 h at £3.80 per hour.
10. 39 h at £3.30 per hour.

The wages that are earned in a week are called the *gross weekly wages* (or *gross wages* or *gross pay*). Take–home pay is less than the gross pay because of the *deductions* made by an employer. For each employee, an employer must deduct income tax and National Insurance from the gross pay. (Other deductions may also need to be made.) The amount left, the take-home pay, is called the *net weekly wages* (or *net pay*).

Net pay = gross pay – deductions

Exercise 4 M

A Copy and complete:

	Gross pay	Deductions	Net pay
1.	£164	£46	?
2.	£137	£34	?
3.	£152.70	£38.45	?
4.	£114.40	?	£85
5.	£141.80	?	£101.20

	Gross pay	Deductions	Net pay
6.	?	£25.80	£96.70
7.	?	£47.65	£129.75
8.	£245.30	£74.54	?
9.	£191.10	?	£135.45
10.	?	£54.85	£165.50

B Answer these:

1. Mrs Finlay earns £171.90 per week. How much does she receive after deductions of £43.50?
2. Mr Logan's net weekly wage was £128. If deductions totalled £36.70, find his gross weekly wage.
3. Mr Man earned £180.80 gross per week. If he paid £16.27 National Insurance and £34.20 income tax, find his net weekly wage.
4. Mrs Simpson earned £4.25 per hour for a 35-hour week. Calculate her gross weekly wage.
5. Mrs Bryant earned £5.12 per hour for a 30-hour week. Her income tax came to £32.56 while her National Insurance payment was £13.82. Calculate her net weekly earnings.

In some jobs, the workers may work more than the basic number of hours. Such work is called *overtime*. Extra money is paid for the extra work and this extra money is also usually referred to as *overtime*.

Gross wage = basic wage + overtime

Exercise 5 M

A Copy and complete the table:

	Basic wage	Overtime	Gross wage
1.	£160	£30	?
2.	£175	£37.50	?
3.	£122.40	£20.40	?
4.	£199.50	£42.75	?
5.	£170.20	£17.25	?
6.	£243	?	£279.45
7.	?	£28.80	£201.60
8.	£183.06	£40.68	?
9.	£218.92	?	£256.81
10.	?	£36.05	£192.61

B **1.** Mrs Regan's basic wage was £108.80. Find her gross wage if she earned £20.40 overtime.

2. Find Mr Walton's gross wage if his basic wage is £153.36 and he earned £31.95 overtime.

3. Mr Man earned £26.80 overtime. If his basic wage was £144.72 per week find his gross weekly wage.

4. Mrs Aspinall's basic wage was £216.32. If her gross wage was £247.52, how much overtime did she earn?

5. Mr Clayton's gross wage was £215.14 while his basic wage was £159.62. How much overtime did he earn?

Overtime is usually paid at a higher rate of pay, for example, *double time* or *time and a half.*
Double time means that for every 1 h worked, a worker receives 2 h pay.
Time and a half means that for every 1 h worked, a worker receives $1\frac{1}{2}$ h pay.
If, for instance, Mr Newton's basic rate of pay is £4 an hour and he does 3 h overtime at double-time rate, here are three different methods of calculating his overtime. (You need not learn all three methods.)

Method 1

Basic rate of pay = £4
Number of hours overtime = 3
Number of hours for pay = 6 (double the time of 3 h)
∴ Overtime = 6 × £4
= £24

Method 2

Number of hours overtime = 3
Basic rate of pay = £4
Overtime rate of pay = £8 (double the basic rate)
∴ Overtime = 3 × £8
= £24

Method 3

Basic rate of pay = £4
Number of extra hours worked = 3
Extra earned at basic rate = 3 × £4 = £12
∴ Overtime = 2 × £12 (twice as much)
= £24

Here are the same three methods used to calculate Mrs Cooper's overtime if she did 4 h overtime at time and a half when her basic rate was £5 an hour.

Method 1

Basic rate of pay = £5
Number of hours overtime = 4
Number of hours for pay = 6 ($1\frac{1}{2} \times 4$ h)
$\therefore$ Overtime = 6 × £5
= £30

Method 2

Number of hours overtime = 4
Basic rate of pay = £5
Overtime rate of pay = £7.50 ($1\frac{1}{2} \times$ £5)
$\therefore$ Overtime = 4 × £7.50
= £30

Method 3

Basic rate of pay = £5
Number of extra hours worked = 4
Extra earned at basic rate = 4 × £5 = £20
$\therefore$ Overtime = $1\frac{1}{2} \times$ £20 ($1\frac{1}{2}$ times as much)
= £30

Exercise 6 M

A Copy and complete the table:

	Overtime hours worked	Basic hourly rate	Type of overtime		Overtime earnings
e.g. 1	3	£4	double time	(×2)	£24
e.g. 2	4	£5	time and a half	($\times 1\frac{1}{2}$)	£30
1.	8	£7	double time	(×2)	?
2.	5	£4.50	double time	(×2)	?

	Overtime hours worked	Basic hourly rate	Type of overtime	Overtime earnings
3.	2	£6	time and a half $(\times 1\frac{1}{2})$	?
4.	7	£3	time and a half $(\times 1\frac{1}{2})$	?
5.	6	£6.25	double time $(\times 2)$	?
6.	4	£9	time and a half $(\times 1\frac{1}{2})$	?
7.	9	£6	time and a third $(\times 1\frac{1}{3})$	?
8.	10	£8	time and a quarter $(\times 1\frac{1}{4})$	?

B **1.** Calculate the overtime pay at double-time rate for:
(*a*) 2 h overtime at £5 basic rate.
(*b*) 5 h overtime at £4 basic rate.
(*c*) 6 h overtime at £7.50 basic rate.
(*d*) 3 h overtime at £5.25 basic rate.
(*e*) 7 h overtime at £3.82 basic rate.

2. Calculate the overtime pay at time and a half for:
(*a*) 4 h overtime at £6 basic rate.
(*b*) 3 h overtime at £10 basic rate.
(*c*) 8 h overtime at £5 basic rate.
(*d*) 2 h overtime at £7.50 basic rate.
(*e*) 5 h overtime at £4.64 basic rate.

3. Mrs Thomas does 6 h overtime at time and a half. If her basic rate is £3 an hour, calculate her overtime pay.

4. Mrs Burns normally earns £5.20 an hour. If she does 5 h overtime at double-time rate, how much overtime pay does she earn?

5. Mr Todd earns £4.90 an hour for a basic week of 35 h. Overtime is at time and a half. Calculate his weekly earnings when he works:
(*a*) 40 h (*b*) 38 h (*c*) 45 h

Exercise 7 **M**

Here is a *wage slip* (*pay slip*) showing one week's earnings and deductions:
Copy and complete the pay slip:

Pay ref. no.	Nat. Ins. no.			Net pay
OE216072	ZX442931C	**Herrick Brothers**		£
Name			*Address*	

	Pay and allowances			*Deductions*
	Units	*Rate*	*Amount*	
Basic week	40	£3.50	£140	
Hours of overtime (at time and a half)	6	£5.25	£	*Tax* £38.90 *N.I.* £17.96
Hours of overtime (at double time)	4	£7	£	*Total* £
		Gross pay	£	

1. Enter your own name and address.

2. Work out and enter the pay including the gross pay.

3. Work out and enter the total deductions.

4. Work out and enter the net pay.

Exercise 8

A How much per annum is:

1. £120 per week?
2. £150 per week?
3. £141.50 per week?
4. £176.80 per week?
5. £167.20 per week?

B How much per week is:

1. £9360 p.a.?
2. £7540 p.a.?
3. £8476 p.a.?
4. £6037.20 p.a.?
5. £8938.80 p.a.?

Some people are paid monthly instead of weekly. Their monthly earnings is called a *salary* (not a wage). Usually the salary is stated to be so much per annum. Often when people are paid a salary, they are expected to work extra hours as necessary without being paid overtime.

Net salary = gross salary − deductions

Exercise 9 M

A Copy and complete:

	Gross salary	Deductions	Net salary
1.	£8000	£2265	?
2.	£6500	£1436	?
3.	£9750	£2984	?
4.	£12 480	£4207	?
5.	£10 275	£3159	?
6.	£16 920	?	£11 390
7.	£14 370	?	£9672
8.	?	£6470	£12 170
9.	?	£5387	£10 338
10.	£7142	£2064	?

B

1. A quantity surveyor earns £877.50 per month. How much is that per annum?

2. A police inspector earns £16 026 p.a. How much is that per month?

3. A laboratory technician's gross salary is £8397. Calculate the monthly income before deductions.

4. A fireman's monthly salary before deductions is £759.50. Calculate his gross annual salary.

5. A teacher earns £6732 p.a. Deductions total £2539.38. Calculate the teacher's net annual salary.

6. An engineer's net annual salary was £9043.67. If deductions totalled £3712.33 find the engineer's gross annual salary.

7. A nurse earned £591.93 per month. Deductions totalled £187.44. Calculate the nurse's net monthly earnings.

8. Mrs Edwards earned £155.20 per week. Is that more than £672 per month?

9. Is £184.60 per week, greater than, less than or equal to £738.40 per month?

10. Is £227.70 per week, greater than, less than or equal to £986.70 per month?

Spending Money

Exercise 10

For each advert, calculate the missing sum of money:

1.

2.

3.

TUMBLE DRIER

9 lb load, reverse action

~~£159.90~~ SAVE £ [?]

£134.99

4.

LOW PRICE
HI-FI RACK SYSTEM
Complete with cabinet. 60 watts RMS per channel.
Direct Drive Turntable. Digital Tuner.
Dolby Twin Cassette Deck. 3-Way Speakers
~~£549.90~~ SAVE £ [?] £399.99

5.

6. Find the sale price.

VACUUM CLEANER

including tools

~~£89.90~~ SAVE £9.91

£ [?]

7. Find the sale price.

8. What was the price before discount?

Cash price

The cash price is the price paid for goods at the time of buying. Note that the payment need not be cash. The cash price may be paid by cheque or by credit card*.

Buying on credit (easy terms)

This is a way of buying goods over a period of time (payments are usually made weekly or monthly).

Hire-purchase (HP)

HP is one way of buying on credit. Goods do not belong to you (and are only on hire) until the last payment has been made.

Credit sales

This is another way of buying on credit. The goods belong to you as soon as the first payment is made.

* See the glossary, p. 382.

Deposit
The amount that is paid straight away when agreement is made to buy on credit is called the deposit.

Balance (amount outstanding)
The balance is the amount that is owed at a particular time.

Instalments
These are the payments that are made at regular intervals when buying on credit.

Interest charges (interest or credit charge)
The extra charge made for buying on credit.

HP price = deposit + balance
HP price − cash price = credit charge

Exercise 11

1. A lawn mower costs £109.99. Find the balance payable after a deposit of £29.99 has been paid.

2. A greenhouse costs £179.99 on HP. After a deposit of £37.49, find the balance.

3. A food processor costs £74.50 on HP. If a deposit of £7.45 is paid, find the balance.

4. If the HP price of an exercise bike is £61.50 while the cash price is £49, find the credit charge.

5. The cash price of a frame tent is £199.99. If the HP price is £258.50, find the credit charge.

6. The HP price of £415 for dining-room furniture includes a credit charge of £85.50. Find the cash price.

7. A television costs £259.50 cash. There is an extra credit charge of £75.25 when buying on HP. Find the HP price.

8. A sewing machine costs £144.95 cash. It costs £42.76 extra on HP. Find the HP price.

When money is borrowed from a finance company, the company charges interest (the credit charge).

Loan + interest = HP price

Exercise 12 M

Here is a table giving a finance company's interest charges. Copy and complete it.

Loan	Interest	HP price
£5	£1.50	£6.50
£10	£3	£13
£20	£6	£26
£25	£7.50	£32.50
£30	£9	?
£40	?	£52
£50	£15	?
£60	?	£78
?	£21	£91
£75	?	£97.50
£80	£24	?
?	£27	£117
£100	£30	?
£150	?	£195

Loan	Interest	HP price
£200	£60	?
£250	£75	?
£300	?	£390
?	£120	£520
£500	£150	?

Exercise 13

1. A tennis racket can be bought from a mail-order catalogue for 20 payments of £1.30. How much does the tennis racket cost?
2. A bed can be bought on HP for a down-payment (deposit) of £28.99 followed by 20 payments of £5.85. Calculate the HP price of the bed.
3. A cassette recorder can be bought for a deposit of £17.95 followed by 12 monthly payments of £6. Find the total HP cost.
4. A 3-piece suite can be bought on mail order for 38 weekly payments of £13.20. Find its total cost.
5. A motor bike can be bought for a deposit of £23.79 followed by 52 weekly payments of £18.50. Calculate the total HP cost of the motor bike.
6. Mrs Cross pays a deposit followed by 20 payments of £1.85 for a nest of tables. If the HP price was £49.99, find the deposit paid.
7. A video cost Mr Newton £499.95 on HP. Find the deposit paid if he paid 36 instalments of £11.11.
8. A rowing exerciser costs £47 by mail order. If it can be paid for in 20 equal instalments, calculate each instalment.
9. A music centre cost £239.95 on HP. If the deposit was £48.19 and the balance was paid in 24 equal instalments, find each instalment.

10. The cash price of a garden shed is £299.99. It can be bought for a deposit of £148.03 followed by 36 instalments of £8.22. Calculate the extra paid on HP (the credit charge).

11. A fridge-freezer costs £259.99 cash. On HP the credit charge is £80.60. It can be bought for a deposit of £113.55 followed by 12 equal monthly instalments. Calculate each instalment.

12. A washing machine can be bought for a deposit of £167.80 followed by 36 monthly payments of £9.30. If its cash price is £329.95, how much extra does it cost on HP?

5 Units of Measurement

Time

Exercise 1 R

1. How many seconds are there in 4 min?

2. How many minutes are there in 3 h?

3. A timer needs to be set for 1 h 35 min. How many minutes is that?

4. A film starts at 19.45 and finishes at 21.30; give the length of the film in minutes.

5. Write these times using the 24-hour clock notation:
(*a*) Twenty past three in the morning.
(*b*) Quarter past two in the afternoon.
(*c*) Quarter to eight in the evening.

6. Write these times in words:
(*a*) 18.30
(*b*) 09.40
(*c*) 4.10 a.m.
(*d*) 4.50 p.m.

7. Write these times using the 24-hour clock:
(*a*) 7.00 p.m.
(*b*) 6.05 a.m.
(*c*) 10.23 a.m.
(*d*) 11.56 p.m.

8. Write these times using the 12-hour clock:
(*a*) 15.35
(*b*) 10.18
(*c*) 22.54
(*d*) 12.21

9. How many hours are there from 04.15 on Friday to 02.15 of the next day?

10. Mr Turner's coach journey started at 08.45. He got off the coach at 15.35. How long was the journey?

Exercise 2

R

1. Which month is the fifth month of the year?

2. Which of the following years were leap years?
   1930, 1941, 1948, 1958, 1964, 1968, 1975, 1984

3. How many days are there in June?

4. (*a*) How many days are there from 19.30 on 24 September to 19.30 on 6 October of the same year?
   (*b*) A play was shown on successive nights. Its first night was 24 September and it finished on 6 October of the same year. For how many nights did it run?

5. If 4 January was a Tuesday, what was the date of the last Tuesday in the same month?

6. If 27 July was a Friday, what was the date of the last Friday in August of the same year?

7. Ian Grant was 17 years old on 16 March 1986. In which year was he born?

8. How many days were there from midnight on 12 February 1986 to midnight on 12 March 1986?

Length

Exercise 3

A Estimate the lengths of the given lines:

1.
2.
3.
4.

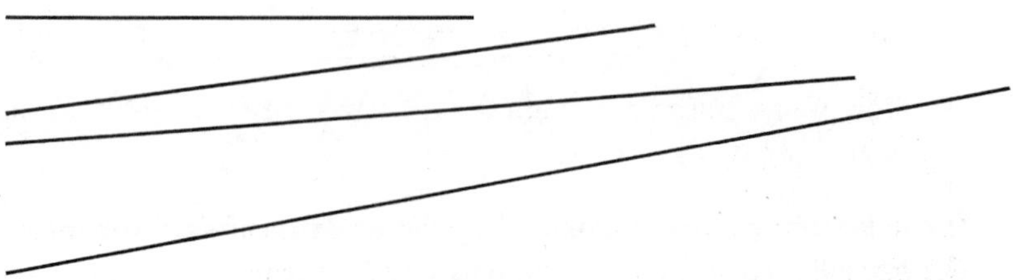

5.

6.

7.

8.

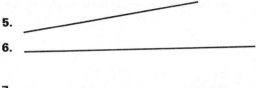

B Check your estimates by measuring.

Exercise 4

A A plan of a semi-detached bungalow is given.

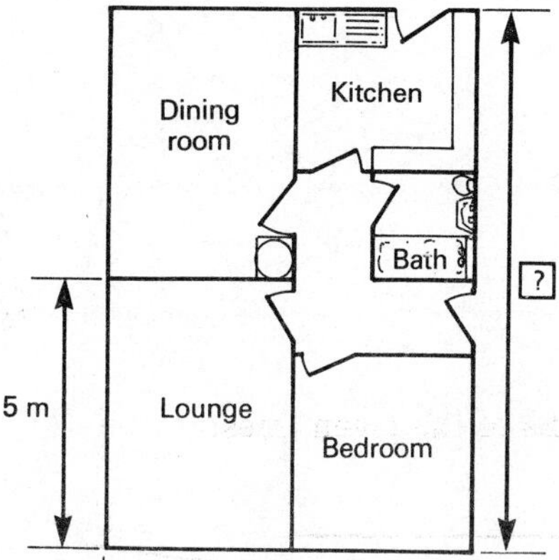

If the length of the lounge is 5 m, *estimate* the outside dimensions of the bungalow. Check your answers by measuring.

B The direct distance between London and Liverpool is 338 km. *Estimate* the direct distances between the given places. Use the map to help you.

1. Liverpool and Newcastle
2. Glasgow and Aberdeen
3. London and Dover
4. London and Penzance
5. Cardiff and Liverpool
6. Edinburgh and Glasgow
7. Newcastle and Edinburgh
8. Liverpool and Edinburgh
9. Dover and Penzance
10. Aberdeen and Cardiff

Exercise 5

Choose the best answer:

1. The length of a small car is about:
   A. 2.5 m B. 3.5 m C. 5 m D. 7 m

2. The length of a tennis court is about:
   A. 12 m B. 24 m C. 42 m D. 60 m

3. The length of a teaspoon is about:
   A. 12 cm B. 15 cm C. 18 cm D. 21 cm

4. The diameter of a 10 p piece is about:
   A. 15 mm B. 1 cm C. 2 cm D. 3 cm

5. The length of a large suitcase is about:
   A. 6 m B. 1.5 m C. 75 cm D. 75 mm

Exercise 6

1. The perimeter of a square field is 1.2 km. Write the length of each side in metres.

2. (*a*) Write 3.5 km in metres. (*b*) Write 0.75 km in metres.

3. After walking 4.75 km I have a further 500 m to go. How far, in kilometres, is that altogether?

4. After walking 3.125 km, how many metres further must I walk to walk a total distance of 4.5 km?

5. A piece of rope, 8.5 m long, is cut into two pieces one of which is 2.5 m longer than the other. How long is each piece?

6. A knitting pattern usually gives the tension at which you must knit. The tension is the number of stitches in a given length (normally 5 cm or 10 cm).
   (*a*) To knit a sweater for a chest size of 86 cm a pattern gives a tension of 10 sts to 5 cm (that is, 10 stitches to 5 cm). If the back of the sweater needs 100 sts, how wide is it?
   (*b*) The same pattern states that 12 rows should be knitted in a length of 5 cm. How many rows should be knitted for a sweater 65 cm in length?

7. A waistcoat needs a tension of 12 sts and 16 rows to 5 cm.
   (*a*) How many stitches are needed to knit one row of the back if the width of the back is 45 cm?
   (*b*) How long is the waistcoat if there are 176 rows?

Exercise 7

1. A piece of material is folded to make four 10 cm pleats with 4 cm overlaps.

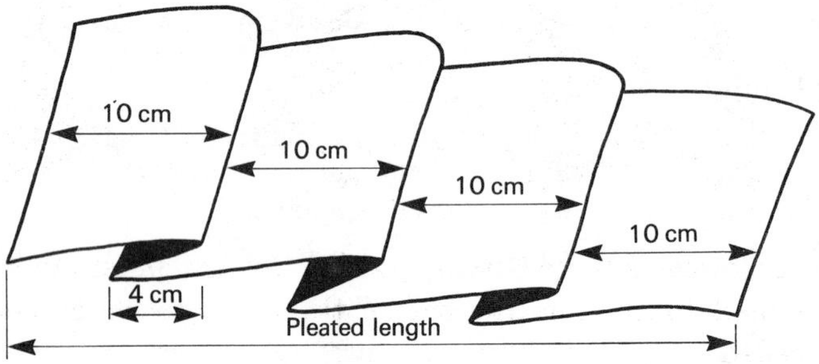

   (*a*) Calculate the pleated length.
   (*b*) Calculate the total length of the material.

2. A ladder is 4.5 m long. Find the distance between the centres of the rungs if there are 17 rungs and if there is 35 cm space at the foot of the ladder and 15 cm space at the top.

3. A piece of paper measures 296 mm by 210 mm.

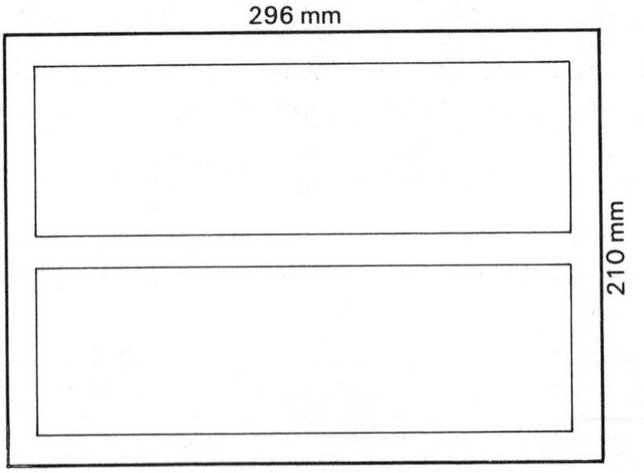

If it is divided as shown so that the borders are all 20 mm wide, find the dimensions of the rectangles if they are both the same size.

4. Potatoes are to be planted 30 cm apart in 5 rows with 60 cm space between each row.

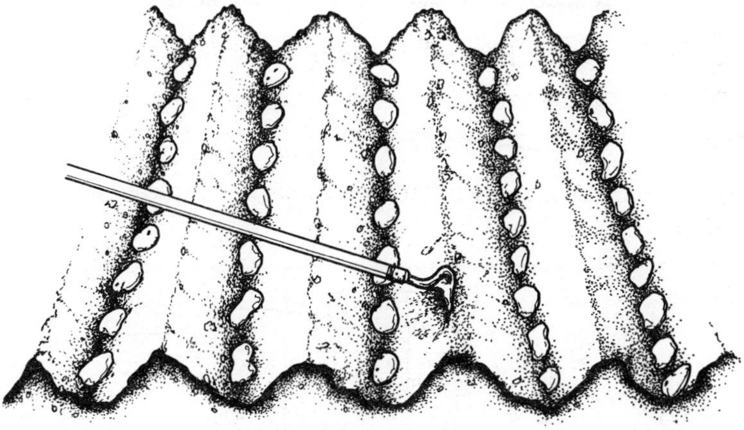

If each row is to be 6 m long and if the first potato in each row is planted 15 cm from the end of the row, how many potatoes are needed?

Exercise 8

1. A kerbstone is 3 ft long.

(*a*) What length of pavement will 20 kerbstones make? (Give the answer in yards where 3 ft = 1 yd.)

(*b*) How many kerbstones are needed for a distance of 80 yd?

2. Onion sets are to be planted 9 in apart in three rows in a strip of garden 5 yd long. The distance between each row is 12 in. How many onion sets are needed if the first in each row is planted $4\frac{1}{2}$ in from the end of the row? (36 in = 1 yd.)

3. A batten is 2 ft 2 in long. It is fixed to a wall using five equally spaced screws.

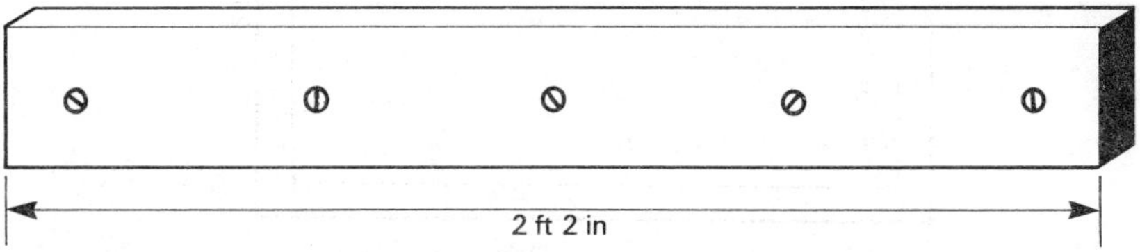

Each end screw is 1 in from its nearest end. Calculate the distance between the centre of one hole and the next. (12 in = 1 ft.)

4. A gas fire of length 29 in is fixed against a straight wall. If the fire is in a central position on the wall and if the wall is 12 ft 7 in long, what length of space is there on each side of the fire?

5. A cardigan is being knitted. It has to have five buttonholes all equally spaced.

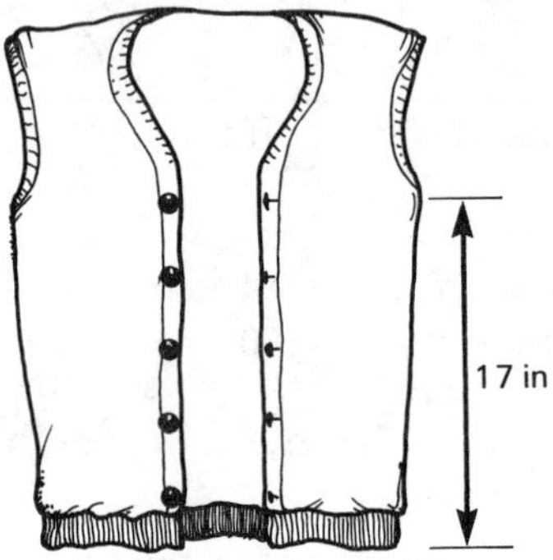

The distance from the bottom of the cardigan to the top buttonhole must be 17 in. Calculate the distance between each buttonhole if there is a 1 in space at the bottom.

Mass

Exercise 9

Choose the best answer:

1. A bag of flour has a mass of about:
   A. 1.5 g B. 150 mg C. 1.5 kg D. 15 kg

2. A bar of soap has a mass of about:
   A. 14 mg B. 140 mg C. 140 g D. 1.4 kg

3. A bicycle weighs about:
   A. 5 kg B. 15 kg C. 50 kg D. 450 g

4. A teabag has a mass of about:
   A. 300 mg B. 3 g C. 30 mg D. 30 g

5. A car has a mass of about:
   A. 1 t B. 4 t C. 500 kg D. 200 kg

Exercise 10

1. Which is heavier, $1\frac{1}{2}$ kg or 1600 g?

2. A packet of tea weighs 125 g. What is the total mass of 10 packets?

3. A tennis racquet weighs 370 g. Find the total mass, in kilograms, of 4 racquets.

4. A jar of jam has a mass of 680 g. If the jam weighs 454 g, how heavy is the jar?

5. Find the total mass of 3 jars of coffee, each weighing 142 g, a container of talcum powder at 160 g and a box of teabags weighing 750 g.

6. A box contains the masses:

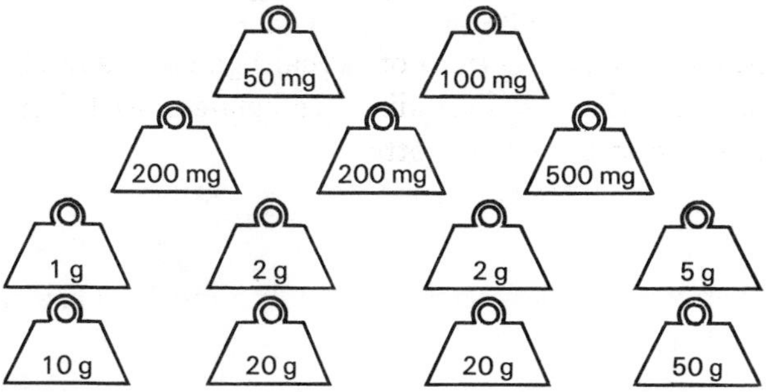

   Which masses would you use to weigh the following?
   (*a*) 27 g (*b*) 46.5 g (*c*) 71.3 g (*d*) 82.45 g

7. The ingredients for a coffee and walnut cake are:
   225 g butter, 225 g caster sugar, 3 eggs, 225 g self-raising flour, 30 ml coffee essence, 75 g chopped walnuts and some coffee buttercream. Assuming each egg weighs 56 g and ignoring the coffee essence and buttercream find:
   (*a*) the total mass of the ingredients,
   (*b*) the mass of the cake after baking if the cake mix loses one-ninth of its mass in baking.

8. The luggage allowance on an aeroplane is 20 kg per person. A family of three use three suitcases where each one weighs 3 kg. The contents of the suitcases weigh 16.4 kg, 17.9 kg and 15.7 kg. How many kilograms of the total allowance is left?

9. A box weighs 3.5 kg when only half full. It weighs 5 kg when three-quarters full.
   Find (*a*) the mass of the box when full,
   (*b*) the mass of the empty box.

10. A small lorry with a tare weight (the mass of the unladen lorry) of 5 t is carrying 3000 bricks each weighing 2.58 kg. Find the total mass of the lorry and bricks.

11. An empty box has a mass of 0.8 kg. When it contains 125 g packets of tea the total mass is 13.3 kg. How many packets of tea are in the box?

12. A coach of mass 7 t is carrying 41 passengers plus the driver. It reaches a bridge that will carry a maximum load of 10 t. If the average mass of the driver and passengers is 65 kg:
    (*a*) Is it safe for the coach to cross the bridge?
    (*b*) What is the maximum number of passengers the coach can safely carry across the bridge?

Exercise 11

1. A thirteen-year-old boy weighs 6 st 4 lb. Find his mass in pounds (14 lb = 1 st).

2. A nine-year-old girl weighs 4 st 6 lb. Find her mass in pounds.

3. A 'welterweight' boxer must weigh less than 148 lb. How heavy is that in stones and pounds?

4. A 'flyweight' boxer must weigh less than 112 lb. How many stones is that?

5. Anna works in a factory. She must work out how many packets are on a pallet.
   (*Note* 16 oz = 1 lb.)
   (*a*) How many 1 oz packets should she find on a pallet containing 130 lb?
   (*b*) How many 2 oz packets should she find on a pallet containing 108 lb 4 oz?
   (*c*) How many $\frac{1}{2}$ oz packets should she find on a pallet containing 92 lb 12 oz?

Capacity

Exercise 12

Choose the best answer:

1. A mug holds about:

A. 25 mℓ
B. 75 mℓ
C. 125 mℓ
D. 250 mℓ

2. A washing-up bowl holds about:

A. 950 ℓ
B. 3 ℓ
C. 6 ℓ
D. 20 ℓ

3. A watering-can holds about:

A. 1000 mℓ
B. 9 ℓ
C. 24 ℓ
D. 600 mℓ

4. A wine glass holds about:

A. 15 mℓ
B. 150 mℓ
C. 75 mℓ
D. 250 mℓ

5. A tablespoon holds about:

A. 15 mℓ
B. 150 mℓ
C. 5 mℓ
D. 50 mℓ

Exercise 13

1. A medicine bottle holds 150 mℓ. How many 5 mℓ doses can be taken from one bottle?

2. How many litres of milk are needed to fill 8 glasses if each glass holds 300 mℓ?

3. Mr Cooper uses 15 mℓ of milk in a cup of tea. How much milk does he use in a day if he makes 16 cups of tea?

4. A coffee pot holds 1.1 ℓ and a small coffee cup holds 120 mℓ. How many full cups of coffee can be poured?

5. A bottle contains 1 ℓ of concentrated orange juice. How much water must be added to fill twenty 300 mℓ glasses?

Exercise 14

(Use 1 gal = $4\frac{1}{2}$ *l* and 1 gal = 8 pt.)

1. How many 2-pint cans can be filled from a 5-gallon drum?

2. How many litres will a 5-gallon drum hold?

3. My family uses $1\frac{1}{2}$ pt of milk per day. In how many days do we use 1 gal?

4. From a 5-gallon drum of creosote, 20 pt are used. How many pints are left?

5. I normally buy 6 gal of petrol for my car. How many litres is that?

6. Change to litres:
   (*a*) 2 gal
   (*b*) 7 gal
   (*c*) 8 gal
   (*d*) 13 gal

7. Change to gallons:
   (*a*) 18 *l*
   (*b*) 45 *l*
   (*c*) 13.5 *l*
   (*d*) 63 *l*

8. My car does 36 miles to the gallon.
   (*a*) How many miles will it travel on 1 *l*?
   (*b*) Given that 1 mile = 1.6 km, how many kilometres will it travel on 1 *l*?

Change of Units

Exercise 15

1. Emma ran 4600 m. Write the distance in kilometres.

2. My pencil is 14.3 cm long. Write its length in millimetres.

3. A sheet of paper is 210 mm wide. How many centimetres is that?

4. A sheet of A4 paper is almost 300 mm long. Write its length in metres.

5. A brick has a mass of 2.58 kg. How many grams is that?

6. A box of oranges weighs 3400 g. Write its mass in kilograms.

7. A kettle holds 1.7 ℓ of water. How many millilitres is that?

8. 4900 mℓ of water is poured into a washing-up bowl. Write the amount of water in litres.

9. A wine bottle contains 70 cℓ of wine. Write that amount in litres.

10. A small bottle holds 0.25 ℓ. Write its capacity in millilitres.

Capacity and Volume

A container that has a volume of 1000 cm^3 will hold 1 litre of liquid, that is, its capacity is 1 ℓ.
Since 1 ℓ = 1000 mℓ:

a container with a volume of 1000 cm^3 holds 1000 mℓ
so a volume of 1 cm^3 holds 1 mℓ

Units of volume	Units of capacity
1 cm^3	1 mℓ
1000 cm^3	1000 mℓ
1000 cm^3	1 ℓ
1 m^3	1000 ℓ

It is often written that: 1 cm^3 = 1 mℓ

and 1000 cm^3 = 1 ℓ

Exercise 16

1. What is the volume of a carton that holds 500 mℓ?

2. A 1-pint milk bottle has a capacity of 568 mℓ. What is its volume?

3. A medicine bottle holds 150 mℓ. What is its volume?

4. A car's petrol tank has a volume of 55 000 cm^3. How many litres does it hold?

5. Another car's petrol tank has a volume of 40 000 cm^3. What is its capacity?

6. A bath has a volume of 257 000 cm^3. How many litres does it hold?

7. What is the capacity of a cistern that has a volume of 1.319 m^3?

8. A certain reservoir has a volume of 15 000 000 m^3. How many litres of water does it hold?

6 Use of Tables and Charts

Exercise 1

Great Rivers in North America

River	Length (km)
Missouri (USA)	4342
Mackenzie (Canada)	4022
Mississippi (USA)	3760
St Lawrence (Canada – USA)	3760
Yukon (Canada – USA)	3166
Rio Grande (USA – Mexico)	2880
Arkansas (USA)	2320
Colorado (USA – Mexico)	2240
Ohio (USA)	2090
Red (USA)	2080
Saskatchewan (Canada)	1928
Columbia (USA)	1920
Peace (Canada)	1686
Snake (USA)	1661

1. How long are the following rivers?
(*a*) the Mississippi,
(*b*) the Colorado,
(*c*) the Mackenzie.

2. How many kilometres longer than the Yukon is the Missouri?

3. By how many kilometres is the St Lawrence longer than the Snake?

4. (*a*) Which is the sixth longest river given in the table?
(*b*) How long is it?

Exercise 2

Distances of Planets from the Sun

Planet	Maximum distance from the Sun (km)	Minimum distance from the Sun (km)
Mercury	69 700 000	45 900 000
Venus	109 000 000	107 400 000
Earth	152 100 000	147 100 000
Mars	249 100 000	206 700 000
Jupiter	815 700 000	740 900 000
Saturn	1 507 000 000	1 347 000 000
Uranus	3 004 000 000	2 735 000 000
Neptune	4 537 000 000	4 456 000 000
Pluto	7 375 000 000	4 425 000 000

1. The *maximum* distance of Saturn from the Sun is one thousand, five hundred and seven million kilometres. Write in words the *minimum* distance of Uranus from the Sun.
2. Write in words the maximum distance of Neptune from the Sun.
3. Find the difference between the maximum and minimum distances of Jupiter from the Sun.
4. Find the difference between the maximum and minimum distances of Mars from the Sun.
5. Which is greater: the difference between the maximum distances of Pluto and Mercury from the Sun, or the difference between their minimum distances from the Sun?

Exercise 3

Average Mass and Height of Young People

Girls			Boys	
Mass (kg)	Height (cm)	Age (years)	Mass (kg)	Height (cm)
35.7	145	11	35.2	144
39.7	152	12	38.3	147
45	157	13	42.2	155
49.2	160	14	48.8	163
51.5	161	15	54.5	168
53.1	162	16	58.8	172
54	163	17	61.8	173
54.4	163	18	63.1	175

1. What is the average height of a boy aged 13 years?
2. What is the average mass of a girl aged 15 years?
3. What age group of girls has an average height of 157 cm?
4. Give the average height of 17-year-old boys in metres.
5. Find the difference in the masses of 18-year-old boys and girls.
6. How much heavier is a 17-year-old girl when compared with a 12-year-old girl?
7. How much heavier is a 17-year-old boy when compared with a 12-year-old boy?

Exercise 4

Tides for October

Date	Morning		Evening	
	Time	Height (m)	Time	Height (m)
1 Thur	00 40	9.3	12 58	9.2
2 Fri	01 08	9.1	13 27	9.0
3 Sat	01 38	8.7	13 57	8.6
4 Sun	02 09	8.3	14 32	8.2
5 Mon	02 49	7.9	15 17	7.8
6 Tue	03 41	7.4	16 16	7.5
7 Wed	04 53	7.1	17 32	7.3
8 Thur	06 19	7.1	18 55	7.5
9 Fri	07 42	7.5	20 05	8.0
10 Sat	08 43	8.1	20 58	8.6
11 Sun	09 28	8.8	21 43	9.3
12 Mon	10 09	9.3	22 24	9.8
13 Tue	10 49	9.7	23 05	10.1
14 Wed	11 31	10.0	23 49	10.3
15 Thur	–	–	12 14	10.1
16 Fri	00 32	10.2	12 56	10.0
17 Sat	01 16	10.0	13 39	9.6
18 Sun	02 02	9.5	14 26	9.2
19 Mon	02 55	8.9	15 20	8.6
20 Tue	03 57	8.2	16 27	8.1
21 Wed	05 15	7.8	17 49	7.8
22 Thur	06 44	7.7	19 17	7.9
23 Fri	08 03	8.1	20 29	8.4
24 Sat	09 01	8.5	21 21	8.8
25 Sun	09 45	8.9	22 01	9.1
26 Mon	10 22	9.2	22 36	9.3
27 Tue	10 56	9.3	23 09	9.3
28 Wed	11 27	9.4	23 41	9.3
29 Thur	11 59	9.3	–	–
30 Fri	00 12	9.2	12 28	9.2
31 Sat	00 41	9.0	12 57	9.1

1. (*a*) Find the height of the morning tide on 21 October.
   (*b*) At what time was that tide?

2. (*a*) Find the height of the evening tide on 10 October.
   (*b*) What was the time of that tide?

3. On which date was there no morning tide?

4. On which date was there no evening tide?

5. Give the date and time of the highest tide.

6. (*a*) Give the times of both tides on 26 October.
   (*b*) How many hours and minutes are there between those two tides?

7. (*a*) Give the times of both tides on 9 October.
   (*b*) How many hours and minutes are there between those two tides?

8. Give the difference in the heights of the morning tides on 5 October and 16 October.

9. Give the difference in the heights between the evening tides on 6 October and 18 October.

10. Ignoring the dates 15 October and 29 October, on how many days was the evening tide higher than the morning tide?

Exercise 5

The following table shows the average sizes of boys from the age of 4 years to 16 years:

Boyswear

Approx. age (years)		4	5	6	7	8	9	10
Collar size	(in)	11	11	11½	11½	12	12	13
	(cm)	28	28	29	29	30/31	30/31	33
To fit chest	(in)	22/23	22/23	24/25	24/25	26/27	26/27	28/30
	(cm)	56/58	56/58	61/63	61/63	66/69	66/69	71/76
To fit waist	(in)	22	22½	23	23½	24	24½	25
	(cm)	56	57	58	60	61	62	63
Inside leg trs	(in)	18	19	22	23	25	26	27
	(cm)	46	48	56	58	63	66	69

Approx. age (years)		11	12	13	14	15	16
Collar size	(in)	13	13	13½	13½	14½	14½
	(cm)	33	33	34/35	34/35	37	37
To fit chest	(in)	28/30	28/30	31/33	31/33	34/36	34/36
	(cm)	71/76	71/76	79/84	79/84	86/91	86/91
To fit waist	(in)	26	27	28	29	30	31
	(cm)	66	69	71	74	76	79
Inside leg trs	(in)	28	29	30	31	32	33
	(cm)	71	74	76	79	81	84

1. What is the chest size, in centimetres, of a 15-year-old boy?

2. Find, in inches, the inside-leg measurement of a 9-year-old boy.

3. Find the collar size of 14-year-old boys. Give your answer in:
(*a*) inches, (*b*) centimetres.

4. What is the waist size, in centimetres, of 12-year-old boys?

5. Using the inside-leg measurements of 8-year-olds, calculate how many centimetres there are in 1 in.

Exercise 6

Monthly Savings Plan 9.25% net = 13.21% gross
Regular deposits from £1 to £250 bring high interest security.
One withdrawal a year is allowed without loss of interest on the remaining sum (maximum monthly investment: £500 in a joint account).

Monthly Savings Accumulation Table

Monthly savings	Value of investment, assuming the continuance of the current rate of interest, at the end of a period of:		
	1 year	3 year	5 year
£	£	£	£
5	63.04	207.59	380.80
10	126.09	415.19	761.60
20	252.17	830.38	1523.20
50	630.44	2075.95	3808.01
100	1260.87	4151.90	7616.02
200	2521.75	6303.80	15 232.05
500	6304.37	20 759.49	38 080.12

1. If you save £20 per month, what is the value of your investment after 3 years?

2. How much needs to be invested for 5 years to reach a value of £7616.02?

3. How much interest do you get from saving £50 per month for 1 year?

4. How much interest do you get from saving £500 per month for 3 years?

Exercise 7

KITCHEN MEASURES	
1 teaspoon	= 5 mℓ
1 tablespoon	= 3 teaspoons
1 cup	= 16 tablespoons
4 cups	≈ 1 ℓ

1. How many millilitres does 1 tablespoon hold?
2. How many teaspoons will fill a cup?
3. In a recipe, $\frac{1}{4}$ of a cup is used. How many millilitres is that?
4. The table gives 4 cups ≈ 1 ℓ. If the other three entries in the table are accurate:
   (*a*) How many millilitres do 4 cups actually hold?
   (*b*) By how many millilitres is the entry in the table for 4 cups wrong?

Timetables

Exercise 8

Answer these using the timetable given:

1. If I leave Newark Castle at 17.13, at what time will I arrive in Nottingham?
2. At what time does the train that leaves Lowdham at 13.49 arrive at Newark Castle?
3. A train was due to leave Carlton at 18.36 on a Sunday. At what time did it leave Newark Castle?
4. A train was due to leave Burton Joyce at 16.32. At what time did it leave Rolleston?
5. Give the time in minutes of the journey from Nottingham to Newark Castle on (*a*) the 07.21 train, (*b*) the 10.36 train.
6. If I travelled from Bleasby to Carlton leaving Bleasby at 07.07, on which day did I travel?

7. I travelled from Thurgarton to Rolleston leaving Thurgarton after six o'clock in the evening. At what time did I leave Thurgarton?

8. Which train can I catch from Fiskerton if I want to travel on a Sunday to arrive in Nottingham as soon after half past five in the evening as possible?

Newark → Nottingham

Mondays to Saturdays

	SX	SO	SX								
Newark Castle	0637	0655	0726	0802	0903	0959	1058	1152	1301	1359	1502
Rolleston	0643	0701	0732	0808	——	1005	——	1158	——	——	1508
Fiskerton	0645	0703	0735	0810	0910	1008	1105	1200	1308	1406	1510
Bleasby	0649	0707	0739	0814	0914	1012	1109	1204	1312	1410	1514
Thurgarton	0652	0710	0742	0817	0917	1015	1112	1208	1315	1413	——
Lowdham	0657	0715	0746	0822	0921	1019	1116	1212	1319	1418	1520
Burton Joyce	0702	0720	0751	0827	0926	1024	1121	1217	1324	1423	1525
Carlton	0706	0724	0756	0831	0931	1029	1126	1222	1329	1427	1529
Nottingham	0715	0731	0802	0840	0937	1035	1134	1232	1335	1434	1536

	Mondays to Saturdays					Sundays					
Newark Castle	1607	1713	1812	1912	2059	——	1500	1657	1808	1904	2039
Rolleston	1613	1719	1818	——	2105	——	——	——	——	——	——
Fiskerton	1615	1721	1820	1919	2107	——	1507	1704	1815	1911	2046
Bleasby	1619	1725	1824	1923	2111	——	1511	1708	1819	1915	2050
Thurgarton	1622	1728	1827	1926	2114	——	1514	1711	1822	1918	2053
Lowdham	1627	1733	1832	1930	2119	——	1519	1715	1827	1922	2057
Burton Joyce	1632	1738	1837	1935	2124	——	1524	1720	1832	1927	2102
Carlton	1636	1742	1841	1940	2128	——	1528	1725	1836	1932	2107
Nottingham	1643	1749	1848	1946	2135	——	1535	1731	1843	1938	2113

Nottingham → Newark

Mondays to Saturdays

Nottingham	0721	0812	0922	1036	1142	1242	1334	1445	1537	1632	1719
Carlton	0727	0818	0928	1042	1148	1248	1340	1451	1543	1638	1725
Burton Joyce	0731	0822	0932	1046	1152	1252	1344	1455	1547	1642	1729
Lowdham	0736	0827	0937	1051	1157	1257	1349	1500	1552	1647	1734
Thurgarton	0740	0831	0942	——	1201	1301	1353	1504	1556	1652	1738
Bleasby	0743	0835	0945	1056	1204	1305	1356	1508	1559	1655	1741
Fiskerton	0747	0839	0949	——	1208	1309	1400	1512	1603	1659	1745
Rolleston	0750	0841	0951	——	1211	——	——	——	1606	1701	——
Newark Castle	0757	0848	0958	1107	1218	1316	1407	1519	1613	1708	1751

	Mondays to Saturdays				Sundays						
Nottingham	1756	1843	2035	2141	——	1524	1819	1934	2048	2154	2215
Carlton	1802	1849	2041	2147	——	1530	1825	1940	2054	2200	2230s
Burton Joyce	1806	1853	2045	2151	——	1534	1829	1944	2058	2204	2235s
Lowdham	1811	1858	2050	2156	——	1539	1834	1949	2103	2209	2245s
Thurgarton	1815	1902	2054	2200	——	1543	1839	1953	2107	2214	2255s
Bleasby	1819	1905	2057	2203	——	1546	1842	1956	2110	2217	2300s
Fiskerton	1823	1909	2101	2207	——	1550	1846	2000	2114	2221	2305s
Rolleston	1825	——	——	——	——	——	——	——	——	——	——
Newark Castle	1832	1916	2108	2214	——	1557	1852	2007	2122	2228	2320

S Saturdays, plus the letter O for only X for excepted

s stops to set down only

Exercise 9 A Conversion Graph

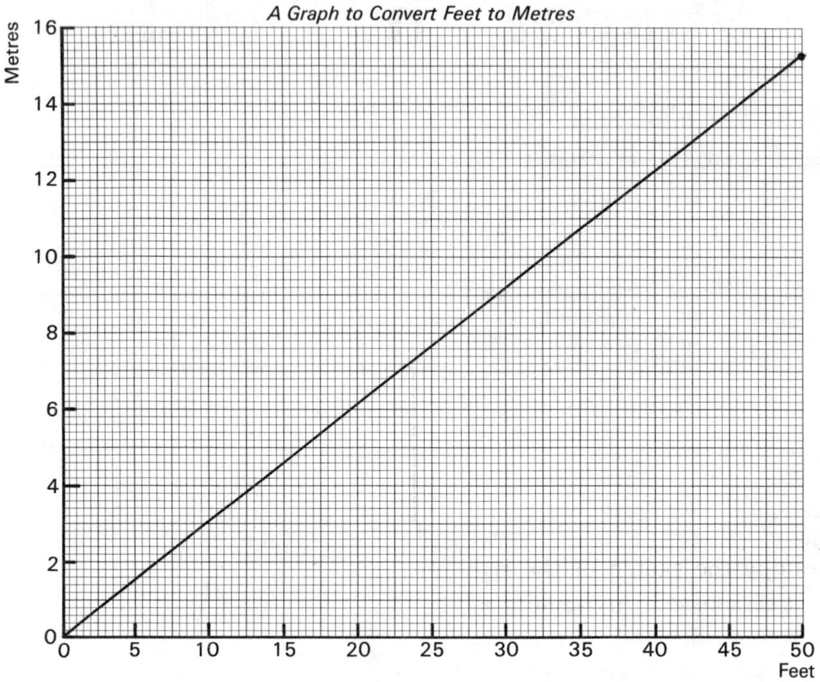

Use the graph to help with these questions:

A Change to metres (to the nearest tenth of a metre):

1. 23 ft	**3.** 13 ft	**5.** 33 ft	**7.** 41 ft	**9.** 49 ft
2. 36 ft	**4.** 46 ft	**6.** 10 ft	**8.** 18 ft	**10.** 28 ft

B Change to feet (to the nearest 0.5 ft):

1. 11 m **2.** 14 m **3.** 9 m **4.** 7 m **5.** 12.5 m

7 Shapes and Solids

Solids and their Nets

Exercise 1

1. Copy the sketch of the cuboid. (The broken lines show the hidden edges.)

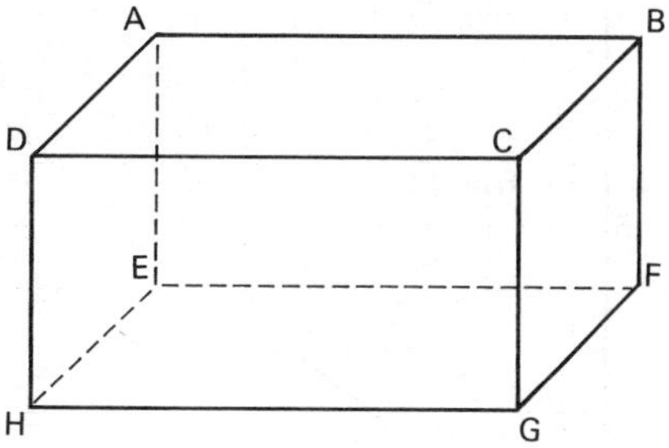

2. Copy the sketch of the right*, square-based pyramid. (The dotted lines are not normally drawn. They have only been drawn here to help you. You may put them in your sketch if you wish.)

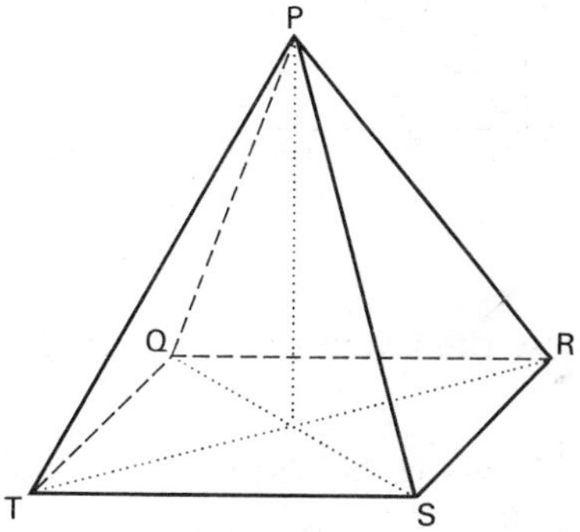

Exercise 2

These questions refer to the sketches in Exercise 1.

A In the cuboid:

1. Which edges are the same length as AB?

2. Which lengths equal distance DE?

3. Which lengths equal diagonal AG?

* See the glossary, p. 385

B In the right, square-based pyramid:

1. Which edges are the same length as PQ?

2. Which length equals distance RT?

3. Which triangles are congruent to (that is, identical to) triangle PRS?

In the sketch of the square-based pyramid in Exercise 1, QRST can be recognised as a square. ∠QTS would be 90° in a square, but it has been drawn as 45°. This type of drawing is called an *oblique projection.*

There are three main directions used*: across (labelled OX in the diagram), up and down (labelled OZ) and an oblique direction at 45° to the across direction (labelled OY). In drawing a solid, angle XOY stands for 90°.

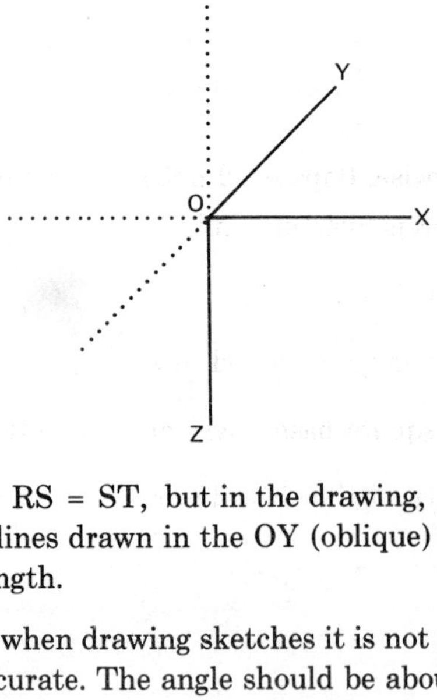

In square QRST, RS = ST, but in the drawing, RS = $\frac{1}{2}$ ST. In this type of drawing, lines drawn in the OY (oblique) direction should be half their true length.

Note However, when drawing sketches it is not necessary for everything to be so accurate. The angle should be about 45° and the lines drawn in the OY (oblique) direction should be *about half* their true length.

Exercise 3

Draw a sketch of a cube. You may draw it to any size you wish.

* See appendix 2, p. 375.

Exercise 4 R

1. How many edges has a cube?

2. How many faces has a square-based pyramid?

3. How many vertices has a cuboid?

4. How many edges has a triangular-based prism?

5. How many vertices has a triangular-based pyramid?

6. How many faces has a triangular-based pyramid?

7. How many faces has a cylinder?

8. How many faces has a cone?

Exercise 5

Unless stated otherwise, flaps need not be drawn on the given nets:

1. Draw three different nets of a cube.

2. Draw a net of a cuboid.

3. Draw a net of a triangular-based prism.

4. Draw a net of a square-based pyramid. (Give flaps.)

5. Draw a net of a triangular-based pyramid.

Angles

Exercise 6 R

Calculate the angles labelled with letters:

1.

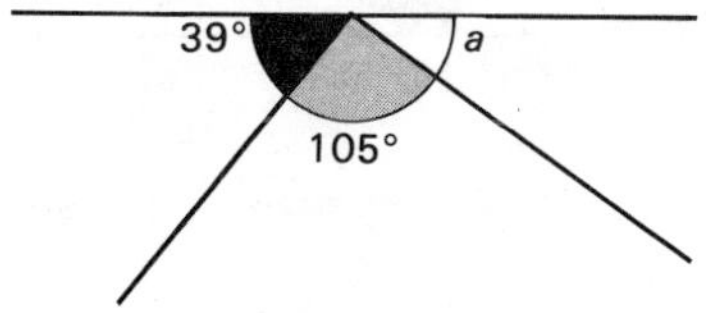

2.

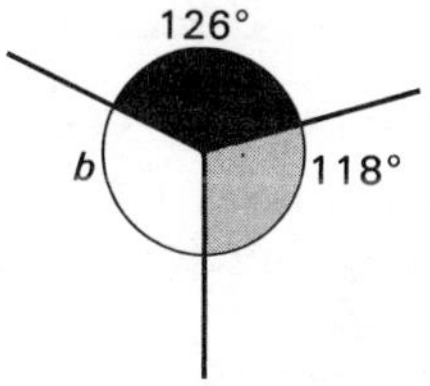

3.

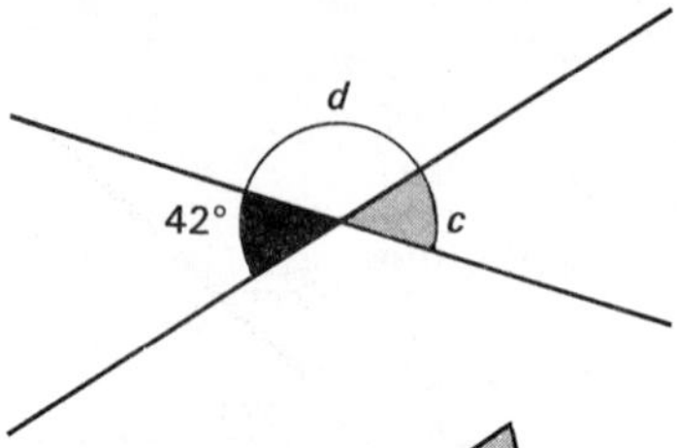

4.

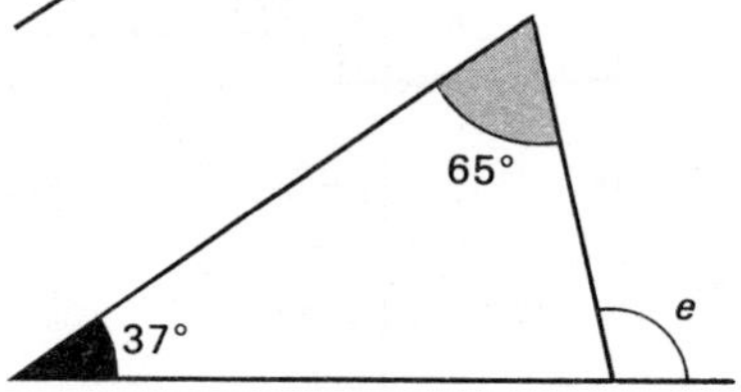

5.

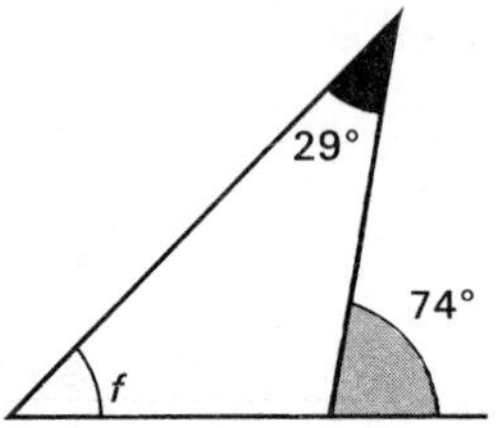

6.

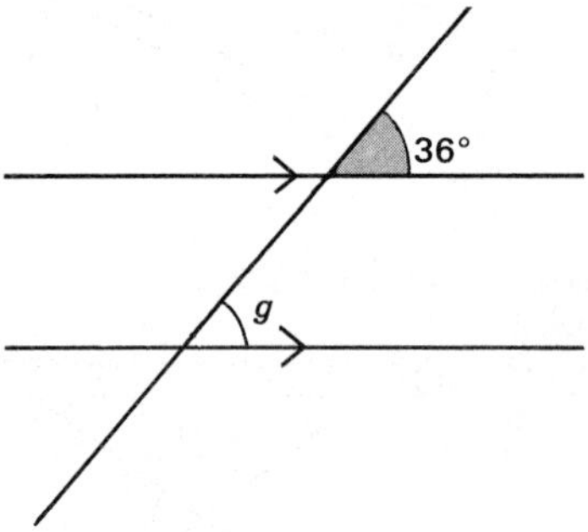

7.

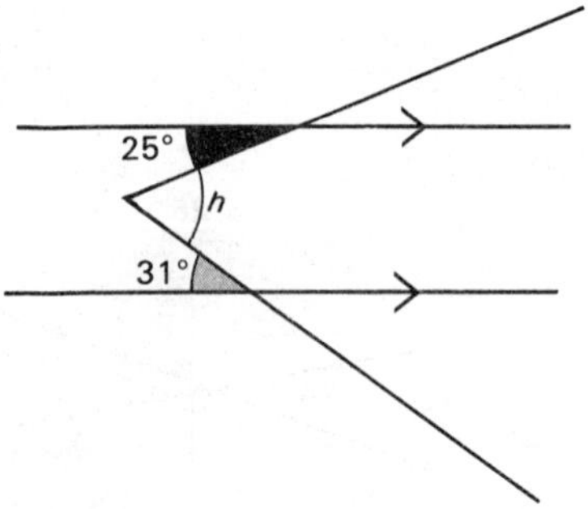

8.

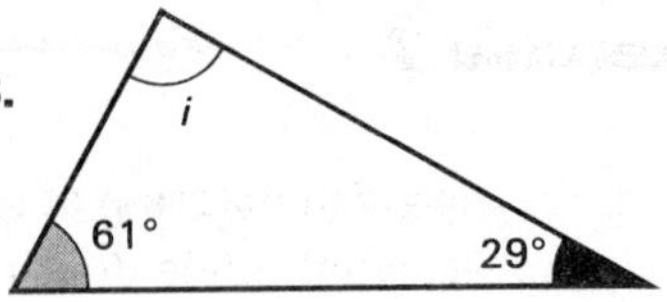

9.

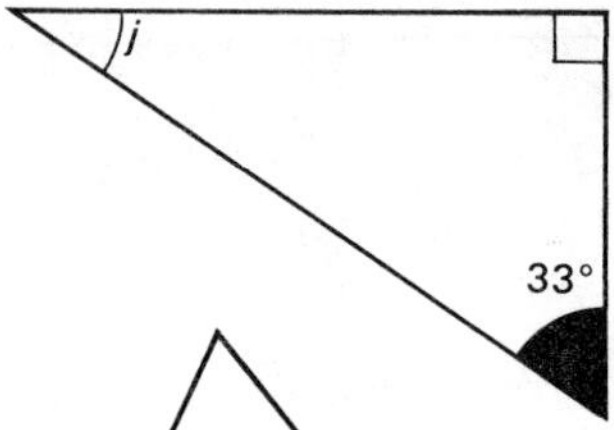

10.

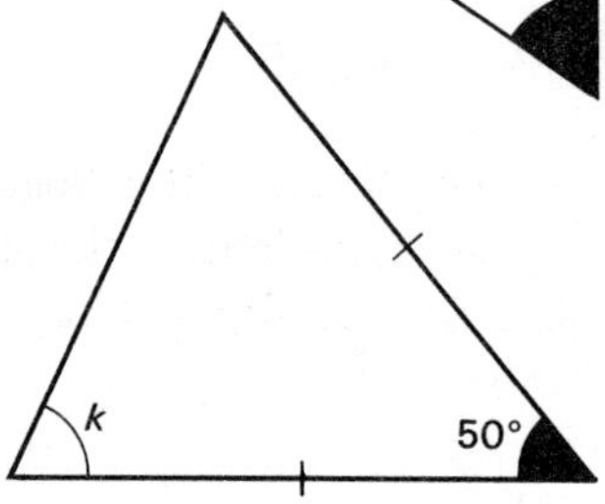

11.

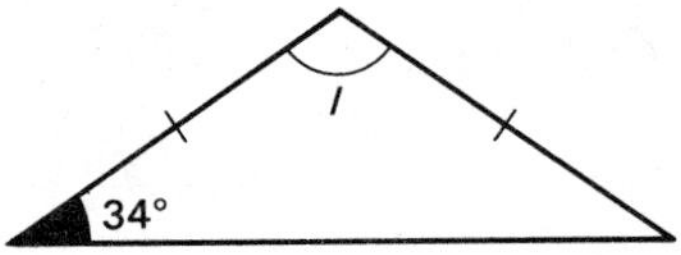

12.

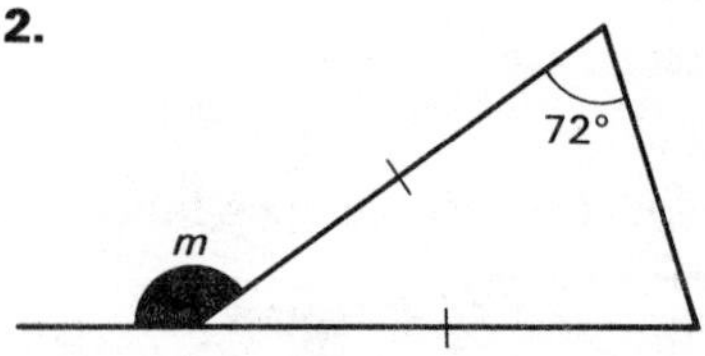

Exercise 7

1. In the given diagram of part of a house, what angle does the roof make with the wall?

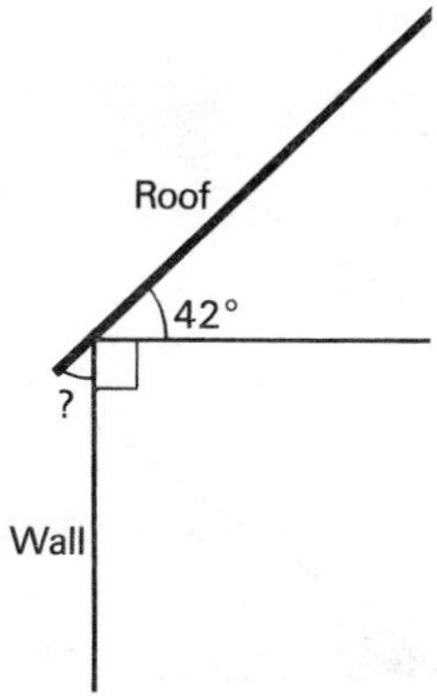

2. Scaffolding fits together as shown. Calculate the size of the angle marked x.

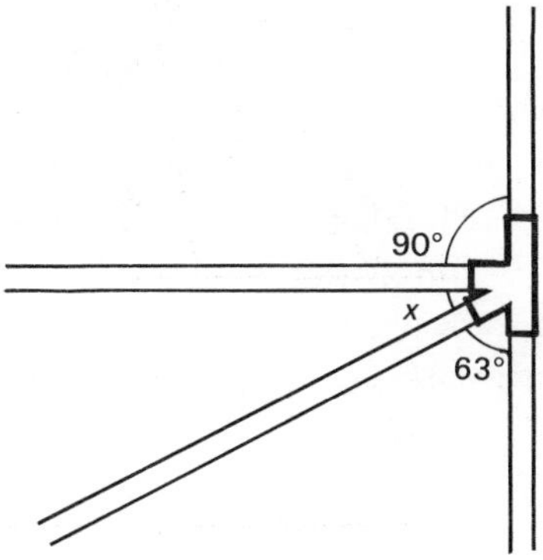

3. The legs of an ironing board cross as shown.
Calculate the angles marked a, b and c.

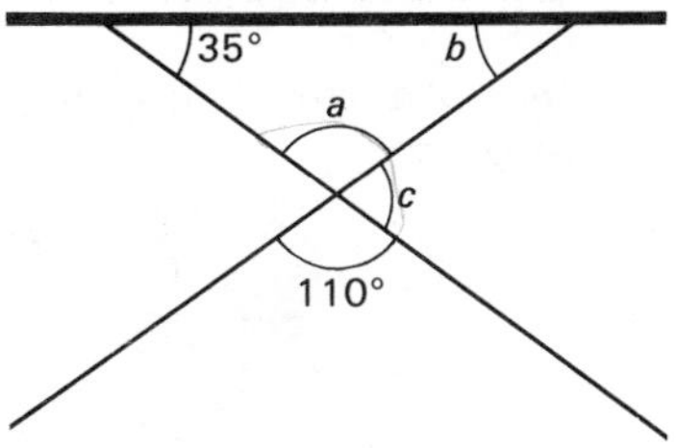

4. The spokes on a bicycle cross at 29° as shown.
Calculate the angles marked d and e.

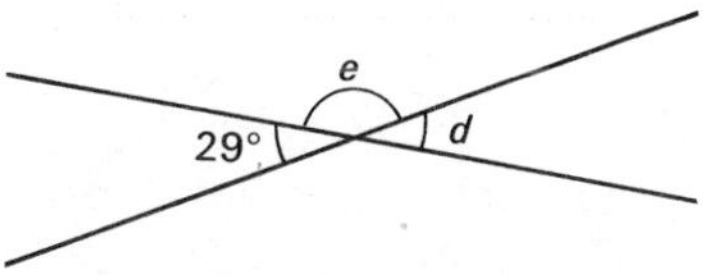

5. The handles on a mower form an angle of 83° with the stays as shown.
Calculate the angle labelled f.

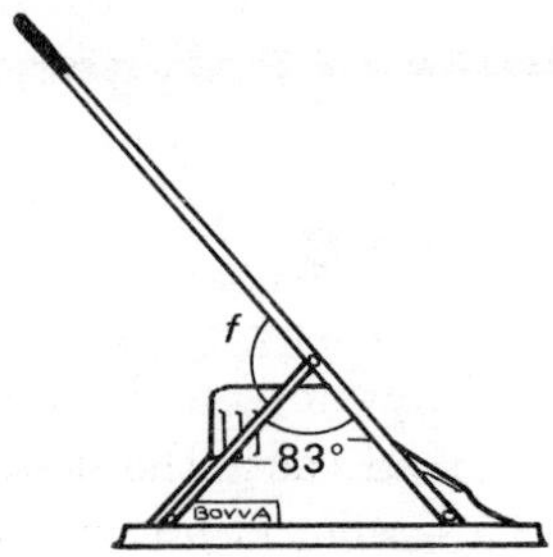

6. Part of the frame of an exercise bike is shown.
Angle $g = 57°$, angle $h = 75°$.
Calculate angle i.

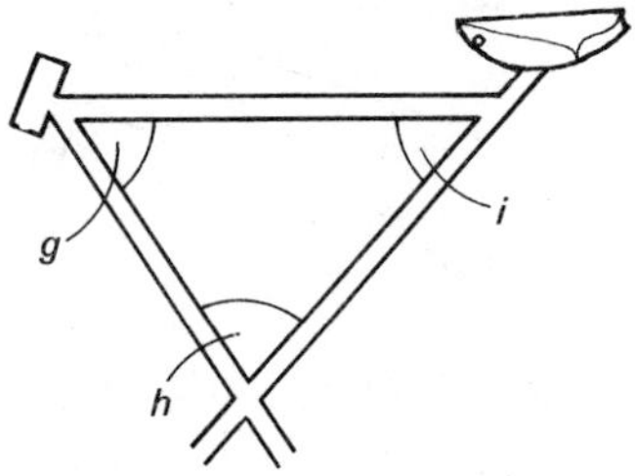

7. The sketch shows a banister rail and a staircase.
Use the given angle of 35° to help you to calculate angles j and k.

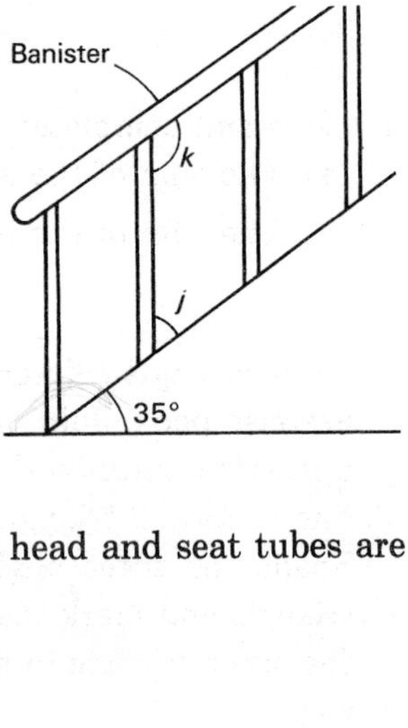

8. Here is a sketch of a bicycle frame. The head and seat tubes are parallel.

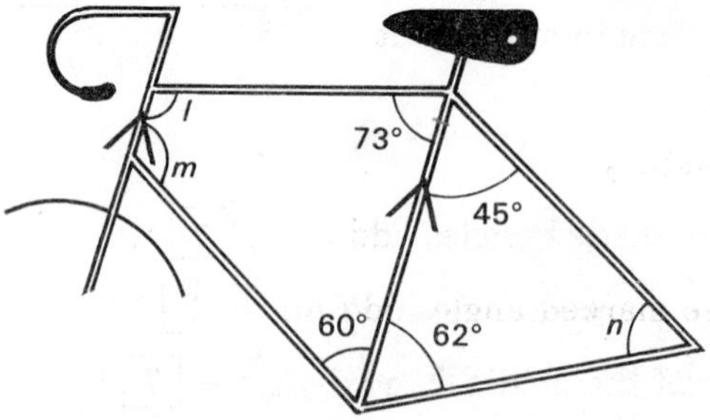

Various angles have been given in the sketch.
Calculate angles l, m and n.

Angles of Polygons

Exercise 8

A **1.** Draw any quadrilateral on a piece of paper. Label the angles p, q, r and s as in the sketch below. *Tear* off the corners then place them together at a common point.

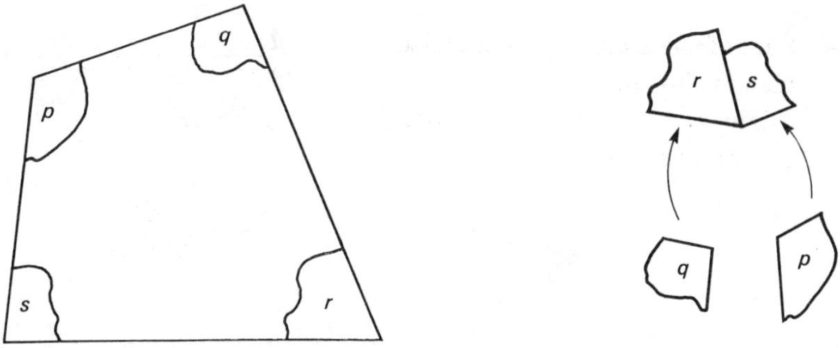

2. Copy and complete:

(*a*) The sum of the angles at a point = ? °.

(*b*) The sum of the interior angles of a quadrilateral = ? °.

B **1.** Draw any quadrilateral in your exercise book. Join any pair of opposite vertices with a straight line to form 2 triangles. Shade the three angles of one triangle and mark the angles of the other triangle in a different way.

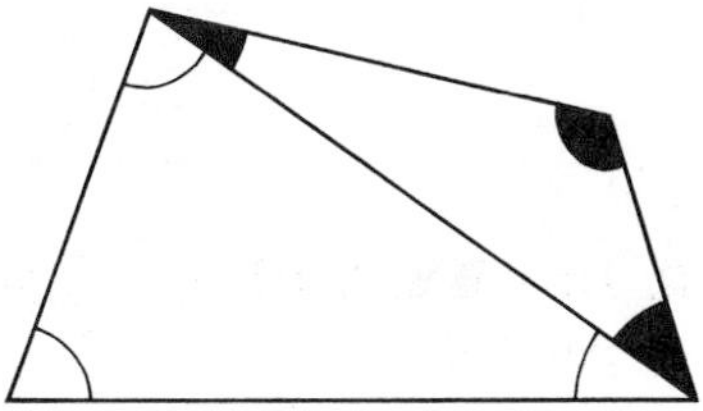

2. Copy and complete:

(*a*) The three shaded angles add up to ? °.

(*b*) The three marked angles add up to ? °.

(*c*) The sum of the angles of a triangle = ? °.

(*d*) The sum of the angles of two triangles = ? °.

(*e*) The sum of the angles of a quadrilateral = ? °.

C Calculate the missing angles:

1.

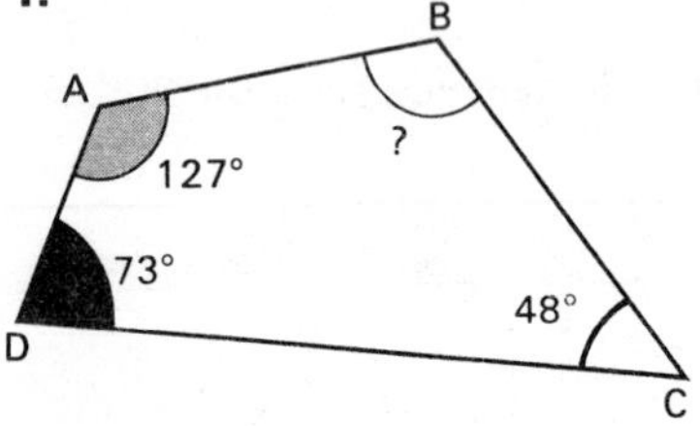

2.

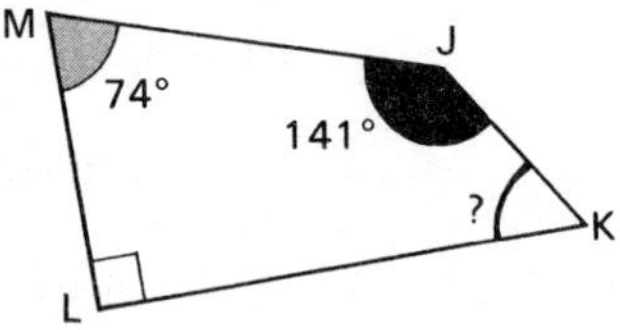

3.

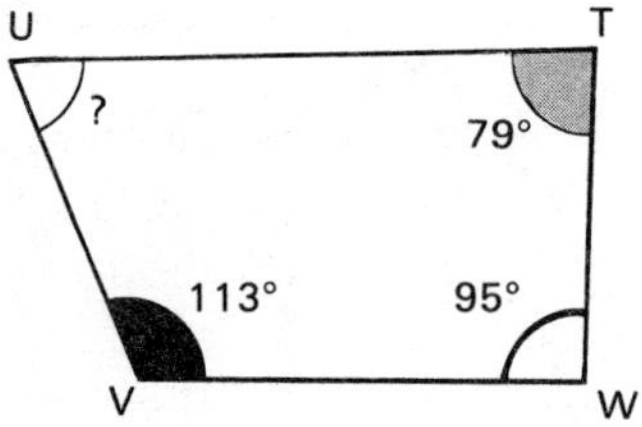

4.

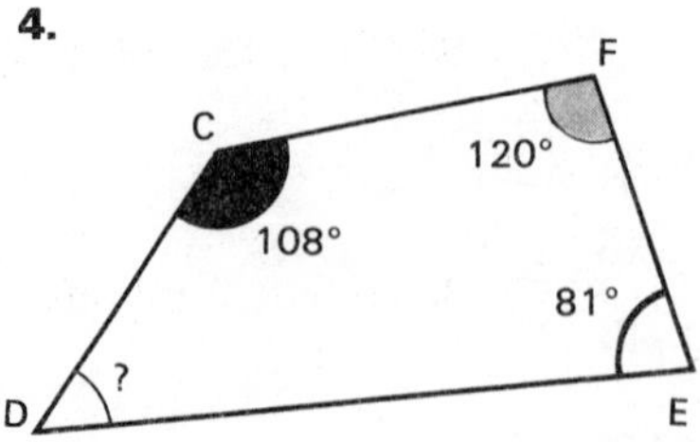

5.

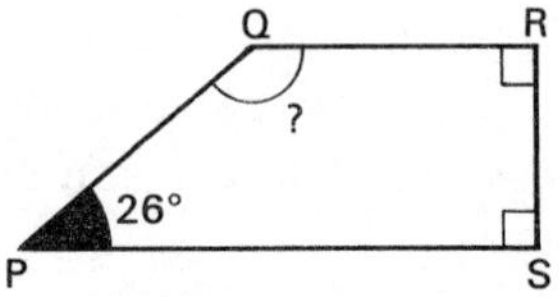

6.

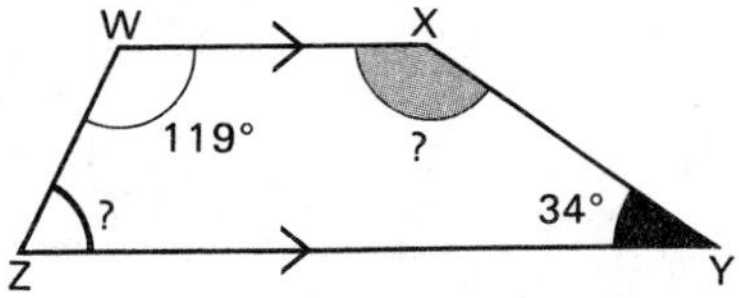

7.

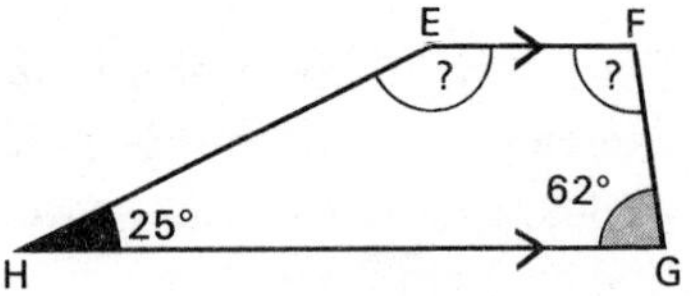

8.

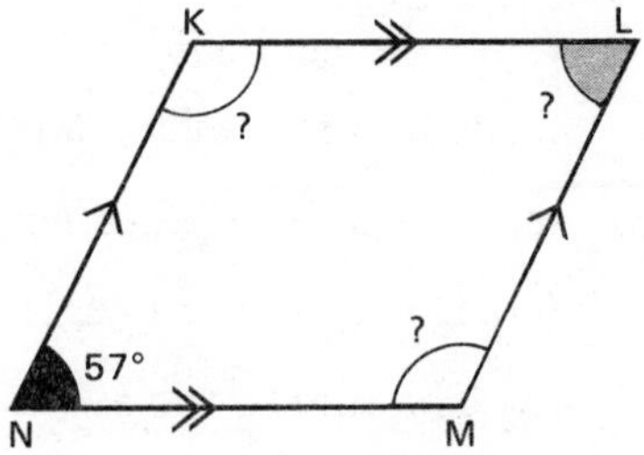

Exercise 9

A By joining vertices of a pentagon, the smallest number of triangles it can be divided into is three.

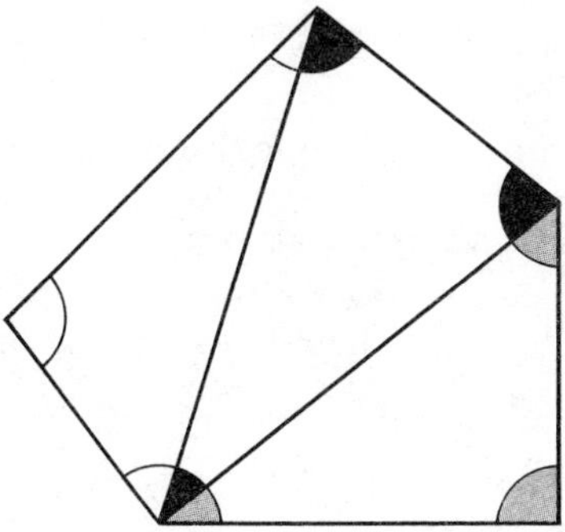

Copy and complete:

1. The sum of the angles of a triangle = ? °.

2. The sum of the angles of three triangles = ? °.

3. The sum of the interior angles of a pentagon = ? °.

B **1.** Draw any hexagon.

2. By joining the vertices, divide your hexagon into the smallest possible number of triangles.

3. How many triangles did you obtain in question 2?

4. What is the sum of the interior angles of a hexagon?

C Find the sum of the interior angles of the following polygons (you need not draw a polygon for each question):

1. an octagon,

2. a decagon,

3. a 12-sided polygon,

4. a 20-sided polygon.

Exercise 10 **M**

To obtain a formula for the sum of the interior angles of a polygon:

A *Method 1*

1. Copy and complete this table. Your answers to Exercise 9 may help.

Number of sides	Smallest number of triangles	Sum of the interior angles
3	1	180°
4	2	360°
5	3	
6		
7		
8		
9		
10		
11		
12		
n		

2. An n-sided polygon can be divided into $(n - 2)$ triangles.

∴ The sum of the interior angles of a polygon, $S = (n - 2) \times 180°$

Test this formula.

B *Method 2*

1. Draw any convex* polygon. Mark any point inside.
Join the point to every vertex. Note the number of triangles formed.

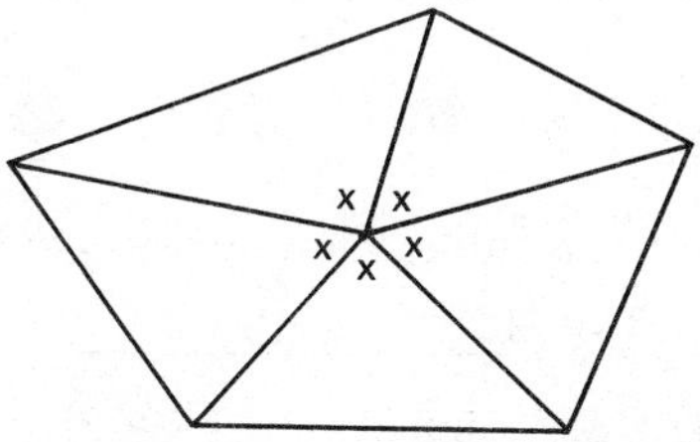

2. Repeat question 1 for a different polygon. Write what you notice about the number of sides of a polygon and the number of triangles formed.

3. n triangles can be formed from an n-sided polygon.

The sum of the angles of a triangle $= 180°$

So the sum of the angles of n triangles $= n$ lots of $180°$

$$= n \times 180°$$
$$= n \times 2 \times 90°$$
$$= 2n \times 90°$$
$$= 2n \text{ right-angles}$$

However the angles of the n triangles include the angles at the point inside the polygon (marked with crosses in the diagram). These angles total 360°. (The sum of the angles at a point = 360°.)
If the sum of the interior angles of an n-sided polygon = S, then

$$S = \begin{pmatrix}\text{the sum of the angles} \\ \text{of } n \text{ triangles}\end{pmatrix} - \begin{pmatrix}\text{the sum of the angles at the} \\ \text{point inside the polygon}\end{pmatrix}$$

$\therefore \quad S = 2n$ right-angles $- 360°$

$S = 2n$ right-angles $- 4$ right-angles $(360° = 4$ right-angles$)$

$S = (2n - 4)$ right-angles

So the sum of the interior angles of a polygon,

$S = (2n - 4)$ right-angles

Test this formula.

* See the glossary, p. 382.

C In part A, the formula obtained for the sum of the interior angles of a polygon was:

$$S = (n - 2) \times 180°$$

Since $180° = 2 \times 90°$

the formula becomes

$$S = (n - 2) \times 2 \times 90°$$

so $\quad S = 2 \times (n - 2) \times 90°$

$\therefore \quad S = (2n - 4) \times 90° \quad$ since $\quad 2 \times (n - 2) = (2n - 4)$

so $\quad S = (2n - 4)$ lots of $90°$

or $\quad S = (2n - 4)$ right-angles

which is the formula obtained in part B.

Hence the formulae obtained in parts A and B are really the same.

A polygon that has all its sides and all its angles equal is called a *regular polygon*. The polygon shown here is a regular pentagon.

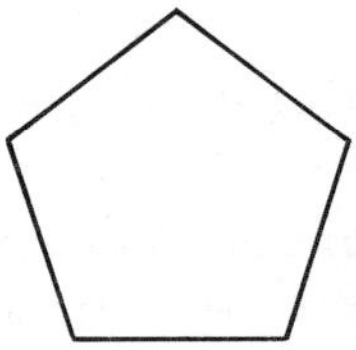

Exercise 11

A **1.** Find each interior angle of a regular pentagon if the sum of the interior angles is 540°.

2. The sum of the interior angles of a 10-sided polygon is 1440°. Calculate each interior angle if the polygon is regular.

B Calculate each interior angle of the following regular polygons:

1. an octagon,
2. a 9-sided polygon,
3. a 15-sided polygon,
4. an 18-sided polygon.

Exercise 12

A **1.** Draw any polygon. Produce its sides to form the exterior angles.

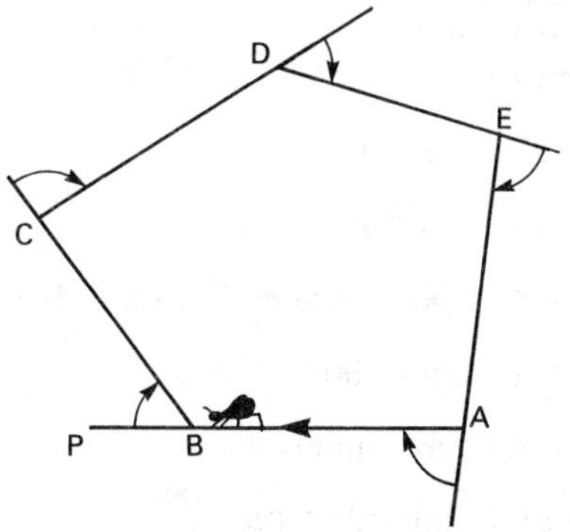

Measure all the exterior angles and find their sum.

2. Repeat question 1 for several different polygons. Write what you notice.

B In the given pentagon ABCDE, the exterior angles have been marked. If a little flea crawled along side AB in the direction of the arrow until it reached B and it then turned to face C, it would have turned through exterior angle PBC. If it crawled completely around the pentagon along each side turning through the exterior angle when it reached a vertex, through how many degrees would it have turned altogether?

C

The sum of the exterior angles of a polygon = 360°

In a regular polygon, all the exterior angles are equal. Calculate each exterior angle of the following polygons:

1. a square,
2. an equilateral triangle,
3. a regular hexagon,
4. a regular octagon,
5. a regular pentagon,
6. a regular 12-sided polygon,
7. a regular 20-sided polygon,
8. a regular 15-sided polygon.

8 Constructions and Circles

Constructions

Exercise 1

Throughout this exercise, all construction lines must be shown. Unless told otherwise, you may use a protractor.

1. Construct $\triangle ABC$ where $BC = 70$ mm, $AB = 40$ mm and $AC = 80$ mm. Measure $\angle ACB$.

2. Construct $\triangle DEF$ where $DE = 65$ mm, $\angle EDF = 50°$ and $DF = 50$ mm. Measure EF.

3. The *angle of elevation* of the top of a bungalow from a point 6 m away is 40° (as shown in the sketch).

   Using a scale drawing find the height of the bungalow. Use a scale of 1 cm to 1 m.

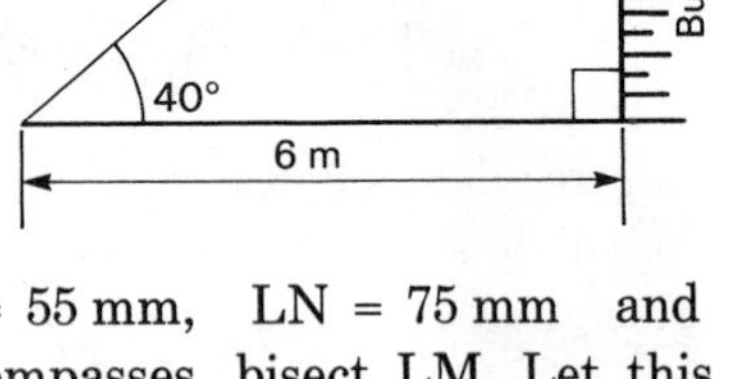

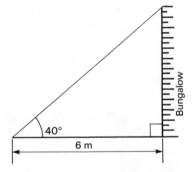

4. Construct $\triangle LMN$ where $LM = 55$ mm, $LN = 75$ mm and $MN = 64$ mm. Using a pair of compasses, bisect LM. Let this bisector meet LN at P.
   How long is LP?

5. Construct $\triangle XYZ$ where $YZ = 70$ mm, $XY = 94$ mm and $XZ = 54$ mm. Using a pair of compasses, bisect angle XYZ.
   Let this bisector meet XZ at point Q.
   Measure ZQ.

6. Draw a straight line PQ, 80 mm in length. Using pencil, ruler and set square draw QR perpendicular to PQ making QR 35 mm long then draw RS parallel to QP making RS 31 mm in length. Measure SP.

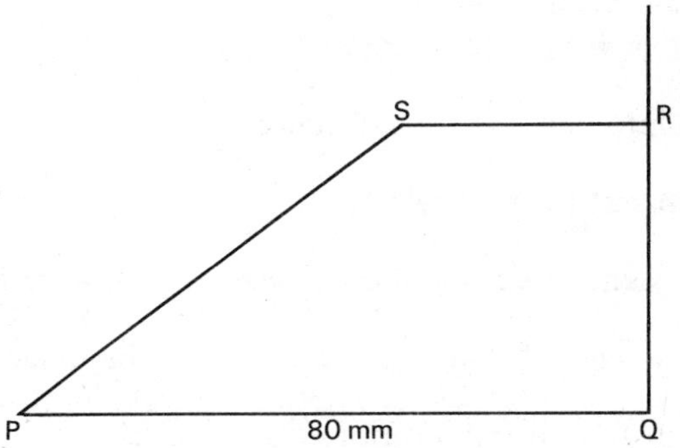

7. Without using a protractor, construct a square with side 41 mm. Measure a diagonal.

8. Construct parallelogram TUVW where TU = 35 mm, UV = 56 mm and $\angle TUV = 70°$. Measure the short diagonal.

9. Draw a straight line FG 68 mm in length. At F, construct angle GFH equal to 60° using a pair of compasses, where FH = 40 mm. Measure GH.

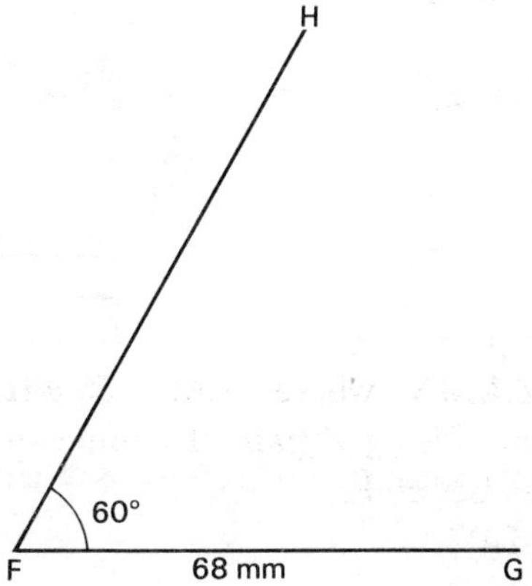

10. Without using a protractor, construct $\triangle HIJ$ where HI = 75 mm, angle HIJ = 45° and IJ = 50 mm. Measure HJ.

Circle Theorems

Exercise 2

A 1. Draw a circle with a diameter of 60 mm.

2. Mark a point T on its circumference.

3. Draw a tangent to the circle at T.

4. Draw a straight line from T to the centre of the circle (a radius).

5. Measure the angle between the radius and the tangent at T.

6. Repeat the above using a different-sized circle.

B 1. Draw a circle with a radius of 35 mm.

2. Draw any diameter and label it AB.

3. Mark a point P anywhere on the circumference of the circle.

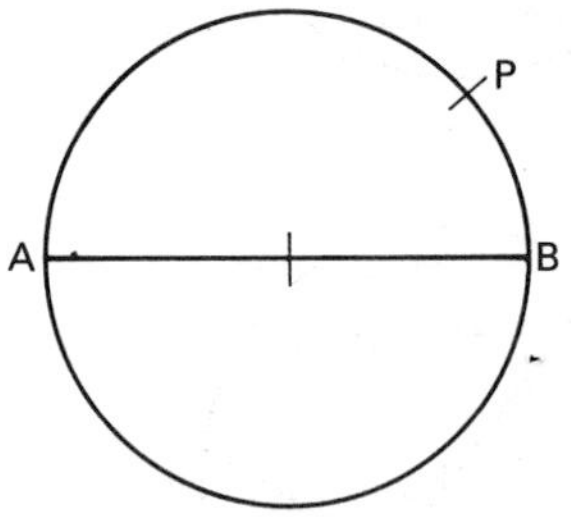

4. Join AP and BP.

5. Measure ∠APB.

6. What do you notice?

7. Mark another point somewhere else on the circumference of the circle. Label it Q. Now repeat steps 4 to 6 using Q in place of P.

8. Is your answer to question 6 true for any circle?

C Copy and learn the following:

1. The angle between a tangent and a radius is 90°.

2. Angles in a semi-circle equal 90°.

Exercise 3

Calculate the angles labelled with letters:

1.

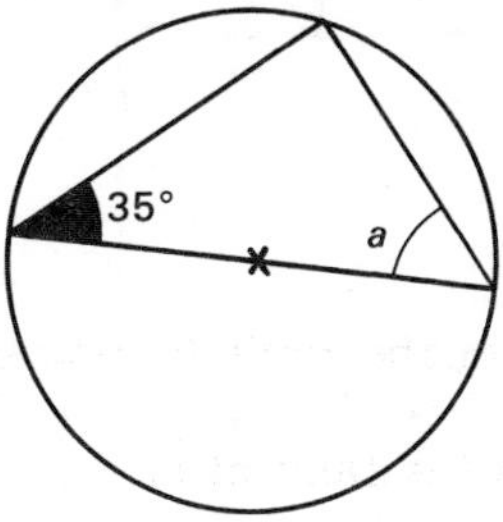

2.

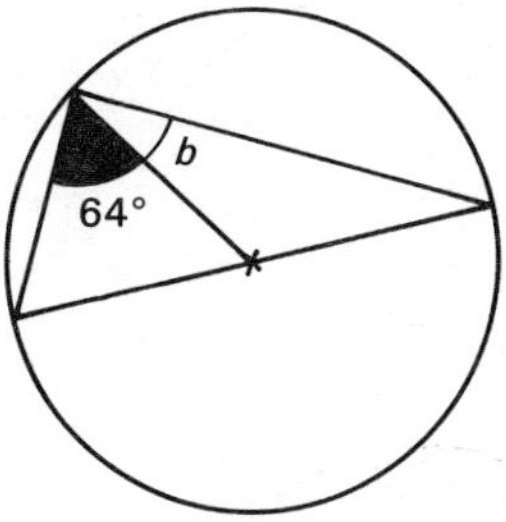

3.

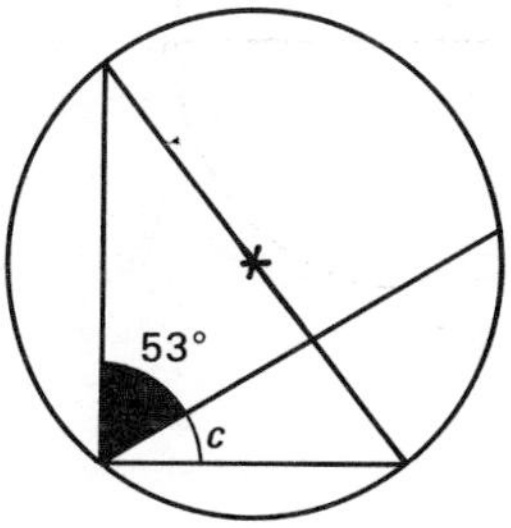

4.

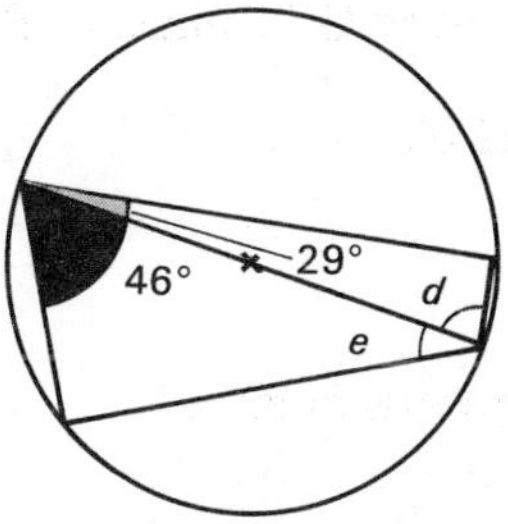

5.

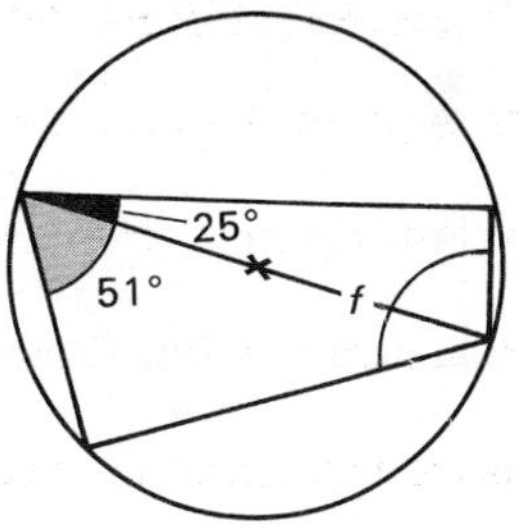

6.

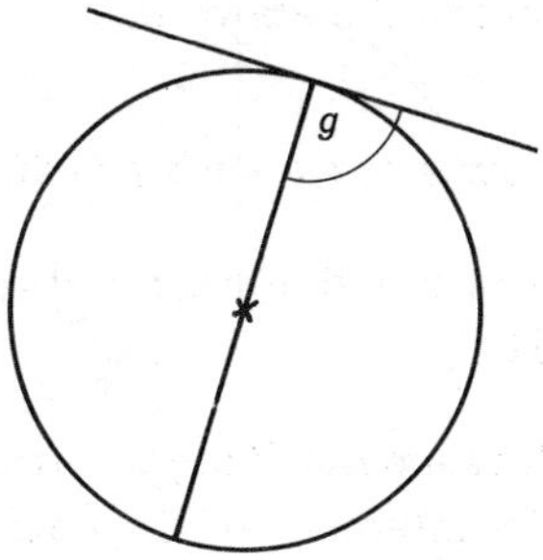

7.

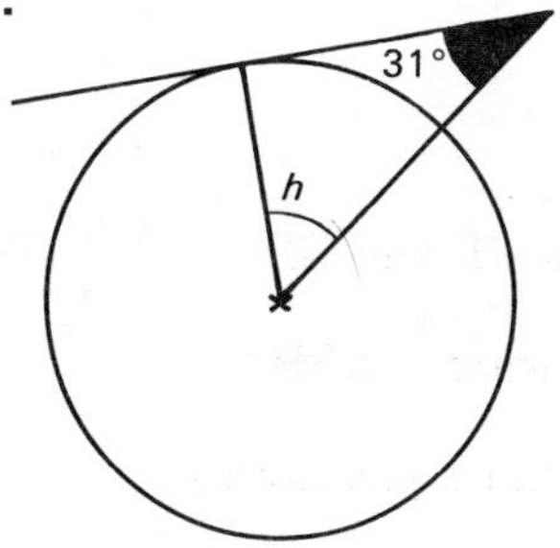

8.

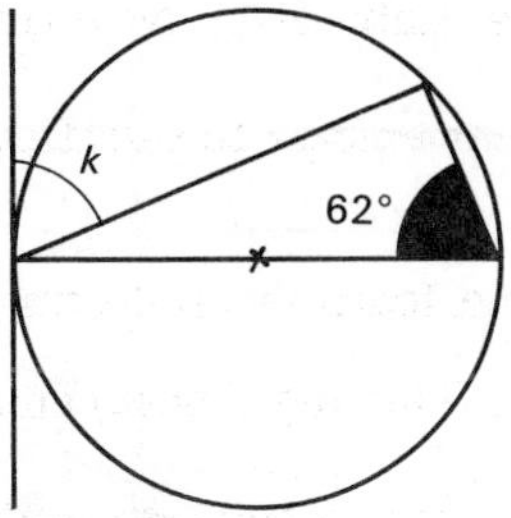

9.

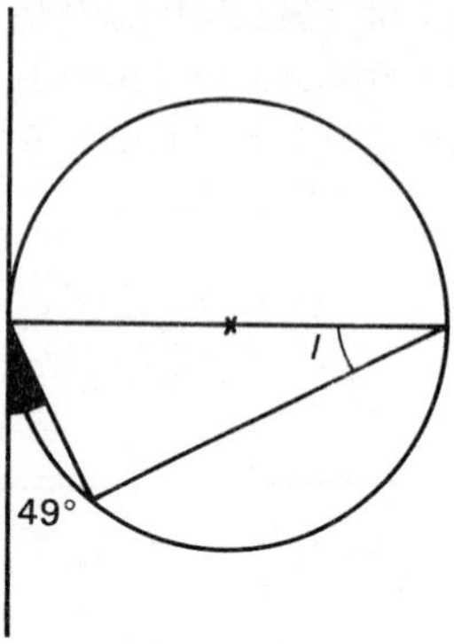

11.

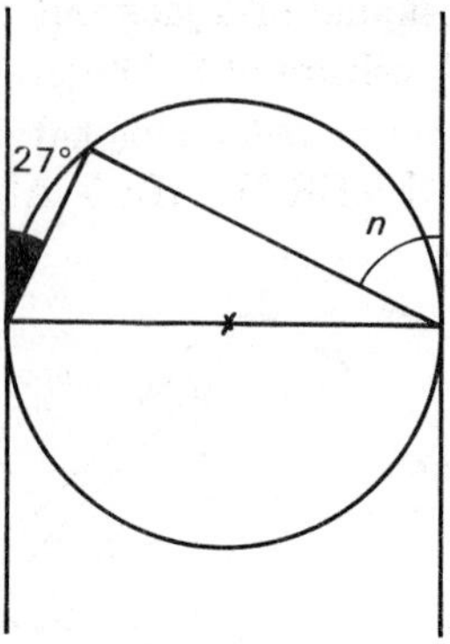

10.

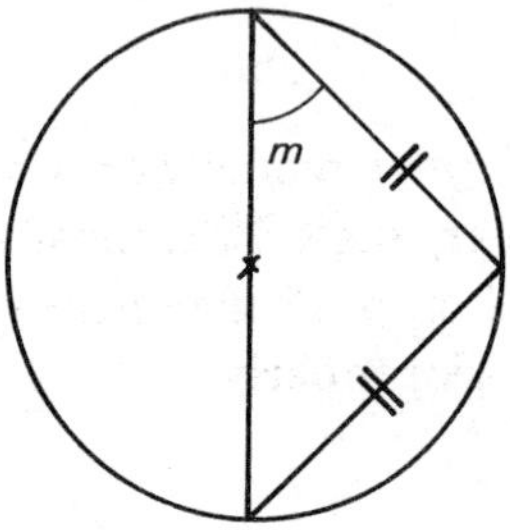

12.

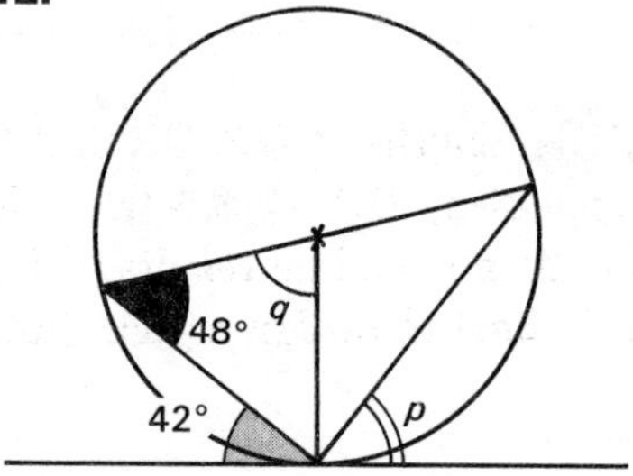

Exercise 4

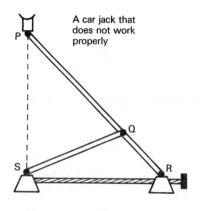

This is meant to be a car jack. It has been badly designed. It does not work properly.

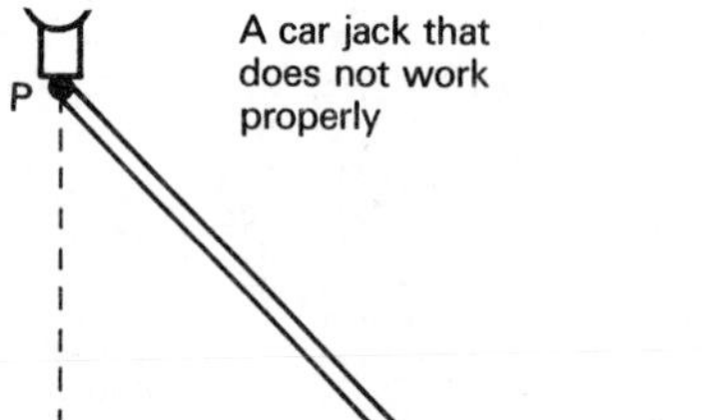

Make a model of a jack out of geo-strips or strips of card to try it. Fix the position of S. When R is moved outwards or inwards (always level with S) the strips pivot at Q, and point P MUST ALWAYS REMAIN VERTICALLY ABOVE S.

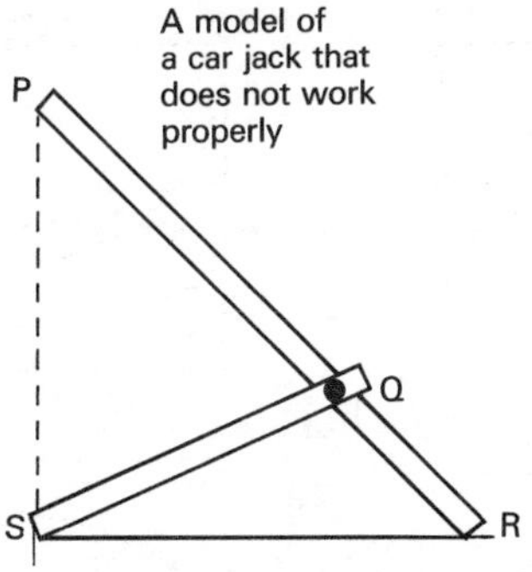

Vary the lengths of QP, QR and QS until your model works. (In the model shown, QP > QS > QR.) Remember, angle PSR must always be a right-angle. The results of Exercise 2 on p. 92 may help you. Explain how to design a jack that will work properly.

9 Indices and Square Roots

Indices

This straight line is 3 cm long.
A *square* can be drawn on this line.
Its area is 9 cm^2 (3 *squared*).

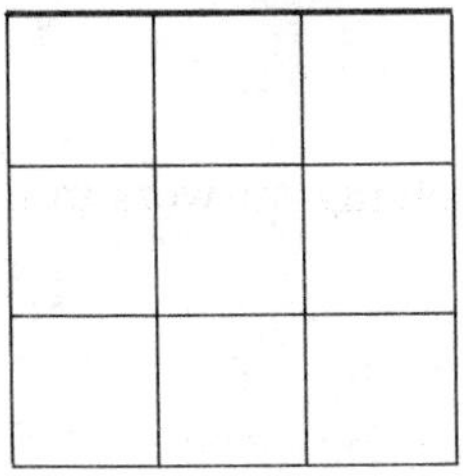

3 squared is normally written as 3^2. There are 3 rows of 3 squares (3 × 3), so $3^2 = 3 \times 3$

A *cube* can also be drawn using the 3 centimetre line.
Its volume is 27 cm^3 (3 *cubed*).
3 cubed is normally written as 3^3.
There are 3 layers and in each layer there are 3 rows of 3 cubes.
So there are 3 × 3 × 3 cubes,
so $3^3 = 3 \times 3 \times 3$

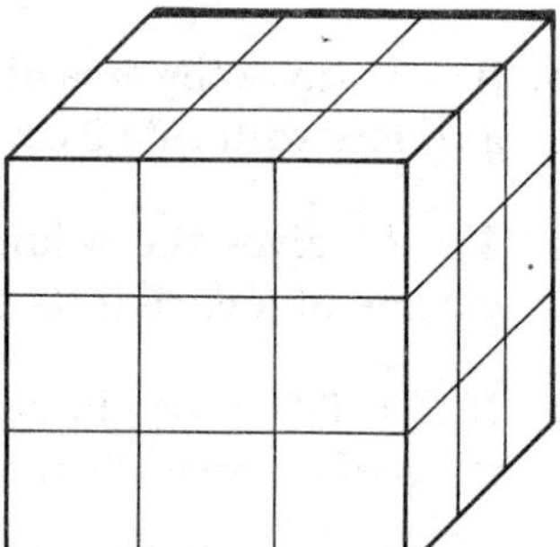

Exercise 1

R

A Find the value of:

1. 7^2	**3.** 8^2	**5.** 2^3	**7.** 6^3	**9.** 2^4
2. 4^2	**4.** 10^2	**6.** 4^3	**8.** 10^3	**10.** 3^4

B Copy these but write the correct sign (<, > or =) in place of each question mark:

1. 2^5 [?] 5^2	**3.** 6^2 [?] 2^6	**5.** 4^5 [?] 5^4
2. 5^3 [?] 3^5	**4.** 2^{10} [?] 10^2	**6.** 7^3 [?] 3^7

C Simplify, leaving answers in index form:

1. $t^5 \times t^4$	**3.** $2^9 \times 2^7$	**5.** $u^3 \times u^2 \times u^7$
2. $6^4 \times 6^3$	**4.** $g^4 \times g^{10}$	**6.** $m^2 \times m^5 \times m$

D Simplify, leaving answers in index form:

1. $\dfrac{a^6}{a^2}$ **2.** $\dfrac{n^9}{n^5}$ **3.** $\dfrac{x^{11}}{x^4}$ **4.** $w^7 \div w^5$ **5.** $h^{12} \div h^8$

E Simplify, leaving answers in index form:

1. $2x \times 3x$	**7.** $9d^2 \times 2d^2$
2. $4a \times 2a$	**8.** $6l^3 \times 3l^4$
3. $3k \times 5k$	**9.** $8b^6 \times 4b$
4. $4t^2 \times t^3$	**10.** $7z^5 \times 4z^6$
5. $3u^3 \times 2u^2$	**11.** $7p^7 \times 7p^7$
6. $5v \times 2v^2$	**12.** $5e^2 \times 5e^2$

Exercise 2

1. $A = l^2$ gives the area of a square with side l units. Find the area of a square with side 9 cm.

2. $V = l^3$ gives the volume of a cube with edge l units. Find the volume of a cube if its edge measures 5 cm.

3. If $S = 6\,l^2$ gives the surface area of a cube with edge l units, find the surface area when the edge measures 2 m.

4. If $s = 5t^2$ gives the distance fallen by a stone in a time t seconds, the distance being in metres, find the height of a cliff if when a stone is dropped it takes 3 s to hit the ground.

5. $V = l^2h$ gives the volume of a square-based prism with perpendicular height h units and with a base edge of l units. Find the volume of such a prism with a base edge of 4 cm and perpendicular height 3 cm.

6. $V = \frac{1}{3}l^2h$ gives the volume of a square-based pyramid with base edge l units and perpendicular height h units. Find the volume of a square-based pyramid with base edge 5 cm and perpendicular height 9 cm.

7. The formula $A = \pi r^2$ gives the area of a circle with radius r units. Find the area of a circle with radius 3 cm. Use $\pi = 3.14$.

8. $A = 4\pi r^2$ gives the surface area of a sphere with radius r units. Find the surface area for a radius of 5 cm taking π to be 3.14.

Exercise 3

Find the value of:

1. (*a*) 6^2	(*b*) 60^2	(*c*) 0.6^2	(*d*) 0.06^2
2. (*a*) 9^2	(*b*) 90^2	(*c*) 0.9^2	(*d*) 0.09^2
3. (*a*) 4^2	(*b*) 40^2	(*c*) 0.4^2	(*d*) 0.04^2
4. (*a*) 3^2	(*b*) 30^2	(*c*) 0.3^2	(*d*) 0.03^2

To find squares or cubes on a calculator you can use the multiplication key repeatedly. However there are other methods. For example, to cube a number, the calculator key [x^y] or [y^x] can be used (see book 2G, p. 298).

[AC] [5] [x^y] [3] [=] should give 125.

Try it. (*Note* You may need to use a function key [F] or an inverse key [INV] before using [x^y] – check how to use [x^y] on your calculator.)

To square a number, the [x^y] key can be used but there are easier ways. You can use [x^2] or [×] [=] (see book 2G, p. 156).

If [AC] [7] [×] [=] gives 49 on the display then [×] [=] will square numbers on the calculator you are using. If at any time you are not sure whether something works on your calculator then try it out using *simple* numbers.

Exercise 4

Work these out on a calculator. Give each answer correct to 4 significant figures.

1. 3.8^2	**4.** 12.9^2	**7.** 8.07^2	**10.** 6.9^3	**13.** 8.7^3
2. 51^2	**5.** 7.96^2	**8.** 0.18^2	**11.** 15^3	**14.** 1.47^3
3. 27.2^2	**6.** 41.9^2	**9.** 0.983^2	**12.** 34^3	**15.** 0.92^3

Exercise 5

If [AC] [7] [×] [=] gives 49 then the calculator is suitable for this exercise. In this exercise you are not allowed to use the power key ([x^y] or [y^x] or similar). Also, clear the display before starting each new question.

Find correct to 4 significant figures:

1. 6^4 (Do not depress the keys more than 5 times.)

2. 1.4^4 (Do not depress the keys more than 7 times.)

3. 3^8 (Do not depress the keys more than 7 times.)

4. 2.8^8 (Do not depress the keys more than 9 times.)

5. 2^{16} (Do not depress the keys more than 9 times.)

6. 5^8 (Do not depress the keys more than 7 times and do not use the squaring key [x^2].)

7. 4.7^5 (Do not depress the keys more than 12 times.)

8. 1.3^6 (Use the fewest possible number of depressions.)

Square Roots

Exercise 6

Estimate to one significant figure the following square roots:

e.g. 1 $\sqrt{60}$ lies between 7 and 8.

e.g. 2 $\sqrt{500}$ lies between 20 and 30.

(*Note* $\surd$ is also used as a square-root sign.)

1. $\sqrt{30}$	**9.** $\sqrt{80}$	**17.** $\sqrt{200}$	**25.** $\sqrt{619}$
2. $\sqrt{70}$	**10.** $\sqrt{10}$	**18.** $\sqrt{2000}$	**26.** $\sqrt{6.8}$
3. $\sqrt{45}$	**11.** $\sqrt{52}$	**19.** $\sqrt{600}$	**27.** $\sqrt{31.6}$
4. $\sqrt{92}$	**12.** $\sqrt{39}$	**20.** $\sqrt{300}$	**28.** $\sqrt{79.8}$
5. $\sqrt{12}$	**13.** $\sqrt{110}$	**21.** $\sqrt{700}$	**29.** $\sqrt{0.4}$
6. $\sqrt{58}$	**14.** $\sqrt{85}$	**22.** $\sqrt{1000}$	**30.** $\sqrt{0.7}$
7. $\sqrt{21}$	**15.** $\sqrt{28}$	**23.** $\sqrt{9000}$	**31.** $\sqrt{0.05}$
8. $\sqrt{8}$	**16.** $\sqrt{19}$	**24.** $\sqrt{948}$	**32.** $\sqrt{0.006}$

Exercise 7

You need to use a graph of $y = x^2$. Either use the one from the second year (book 2G pp. 302, 303) or draw one. (Use a scale of 1 cm to 1 unit on the x-axis and 2 cm to 5 units on the y-axis.)

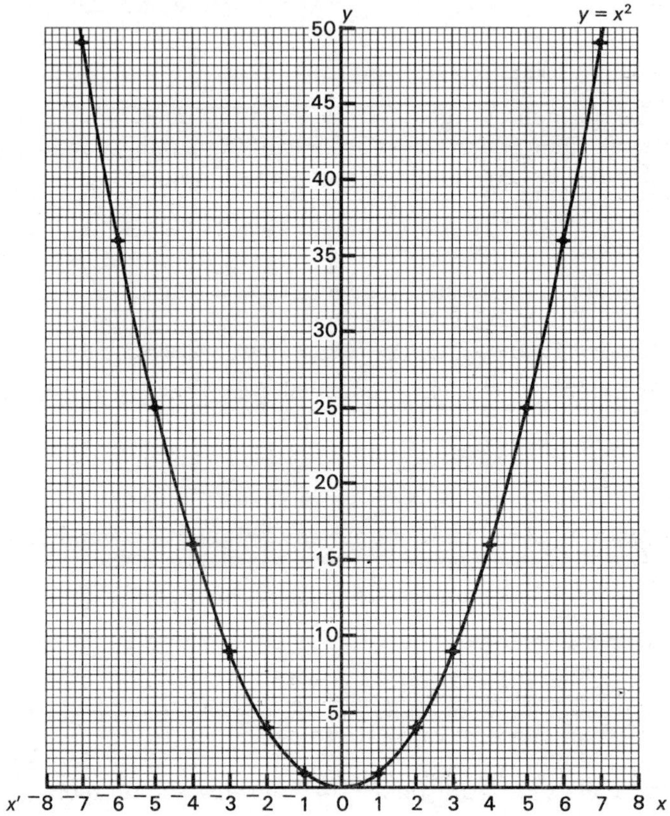

Now use your graph to find:

1. 4.5^2

2. 5.7^2

3. 3.1^2

4. 1.4^2

5. 4.3^2

6. 6.1^2

7. $\sqrt{45}$

8. $\sqrt{35}$

9. $\sqrt{24}$

10. $\sqrt{26}$

11. $\sqrt{4.4}$

12. $\sqrt{15.2}$

Exercise 8

A Use a calculator to answer the questions in Exercise 7. Give the answers to questions 7 to 12 correct to four significant figures.

B Answer these using a calculator, giving answers to 4 s.f.:

1. $\sqrt{6}$	**5.** $\sqrt{3.9}$	**9.** $\sqrt{5.8}$	**13.** $\sqrt{62.7}$
2. $\sqrt{10}$	**6.** $\sqrt{39}$	**10.** $\sqrt{265}$	**14.** $\sqrt{0.7}$
3. $\sqrt{23}$	**7.** $\sqrt{390}$	**11.** $\sqrt{807}$	**15.** $\sqrt{0.193}$
4. $\sqrt{2.3}$	**8.** $\sqrt{3900}$	**12.** $\sqrt{9.62}$	**16.** $\sqrt{0.061}$

Exercise 9

This method finds square roots without using a square-root key:

e.g. $\sqrt{3} = \boxed{?}$

First estimate $\sqrt{3} = 1.6$

$$\frac{3}{1.6} = 1.875 \text{ so } 1.6 < \sqrt{3} < 1.875$$

Second estimate $\sqrt{3} = 1.74$ (about half-way between 1.6 and 1.875)

$$\frac{3}{1.74} \approx 1.724 \text{ so } 1.724 < \sqrt{3} < 1.74$$

Third estimate $\sqrt{3} = 1.732$ (half-way between 1.724 and 1.74)

$$\frac{3}{1.732} \approx 1.7321 \text{ (which agree to 4 s.f.)}$$

Hence $\sqrt{3} = 1.732$ correct to 4 s.f.

Use the method above to calculate to 4 s.f.:

1. $\sqrt{2}$ (Try 1.4 as the first estimate.)
2. $\sqrt{5}$
3. $\sqrt{7}$
4. $\sqrt{68}$
5. $\sqrt{250}$

Exercise 10

The following square roots have whole numbers answers. Find them without using a calculator.

1. $\sqrt{64}$	**4.** $\sqrt{144}$	**7.** $\sqrt{121}$	**10.** $\sqrt{256}$
2. $\sqrt{36}$	**5.** $\sqrt{400}$	**8.** $\sqrt{225}$	**11.** $\sqrt{361}$
3. $\sqrt{81}$	**6.** $\sqrt{900}$	**9.** $\sqrt{625}$	**12.** $\sqrt{1225}$

Exercise 11

You must not use a calculator for this exercise.

A Select the correct answer:

1. $\sqrt{0.09} = \boxed{?}$
A. 0.3 B. 0.03 C. 0.003 D. 0.81 E. 0.081

2. $0.5^2 = \boxed{?}$
A. 0.0025 B. 0.025 C. 0.25 D. 2.5 E. 0.2236

3. $0.2^2 = \boxed{?}$
A. 0.0004 B. 0.004 C. 0.04 D. 0.4 E. 0.1414

4. $\sqrt{810\,000} = \boxed{?}$
A. 90 000 B. 9000 C. 900 D. 90 E. 656 100

5. $\sqrt{72} \approx \boxed{?}$
A. 26.83 B. 2.683 C. 5184 D. 8.485 E. 0.8485

B Give the answer 'TRUE' or 'FALSE':

1. $\sqrt{4900} = 70$

2. $8 < \sqrt{79} < 9$

3. $0.4 < \sqrt{0.2} < 0.5$

4. $\sqrt{2.5} = 0.5$

5. $36 < 6.5^2 < 49$

6. $\sqrt{0.049} = 0.07$

7. $\sqrt{0.9} = 0.3$

8. $0.003^2 = 0.009$

9. A square has an area of 16 cm^2. Its perimeter = 16 cm.

10. A square has an area of 25 cm^2. Its perimeter = 25 cm.

11. Doubling a number doubles its square root.

12. If $\sqrt{3} = 1.732$ and $\sqrt{30} = 5.477$ then $\sqrt{300} = 17.32$.

Standard Form

Exercise 12 M

A Write these numbers without indices:

1. 10^2 **2.** 10^5 **3.** 10^9 **4.** 10^{12} **5.** 10^{14}

B Write in index form with a base of 10:

e.g. 1 000 000 = $\underline{\underline{10^6}}$

1. 1000 **2.** 10 000 **3.** 100 000 000 **4.** 10 000 000 000

C Copy and complete these, replacing each question mark with the correct symbol, < or >:

1. 10^4 ? 10^2
2. 10^7 ? 10^4
3. 10^9 ? 10^6
4. 10^6 ? 10^5
5. 10^4 ? 10^8
6. 10 ? 10^3
7. 10^3 ? 10^{10}
8. 10^{12} ? 10^{10}
9. 10^{14} ? 10^{11}
10. 10^9 ? 10^{18}
11. 10^{13} ? 10^{14}
12. 10^{26} ? 10^{19}

D Work out:

1. 3.6×10
2. 5.73×10
3. 8.12×100
4. 7.165×100
5. 2.4×100
6. 4.5×1000
7. 1.406×1000
8. 64.3×1000
9. $18.7 \times 10\,000$
10. $296 \times 10\,000$
11. $5.88 \times 100\,000$
12. $7.06 \times 1\,000\,000$

E Copy and complete:

e.g.	1.84×10^5	$1.84 \times 100\,000$	184 000
1.	2.69×10^3	2.69×1000	?
2.	4.7×10^4	$4.7 \times 10\,000$	?
3.	8.3×10^5	$8.3 \times 100\,000$	?
4.	9.16×10^4	$9.16 \times$?	?
5.	$3.06 \times 10^{?}$	3.06×1000	3060

6.	7.97×10^2	7.97×100	?
7.	$6.245 \times 10^{?}$	6.245×100	?
8.	$1.135 \times 10^{?}$	$1.135 \times 10\,000$	?
9.	5.08×10^3	$5.08 \times$?	?
10.	$8.007 \times 10^{?}$	$8.007 \times$?	80 070

F Write each of the following numbers without indices:

e.g. $1.26 \times 10^5 = \underline{\underline{126\,000}}$

1. 4.2×10^2
2. 7.41×10^2
3. 8.03×10^4
4. 2.9×10^4
5. 1.75×10^3
6. 3.6×10^5
7. 6.18×10^6
8. 9.54×10^7
9. 3.07×10^3
10. 2.83×10^8
11. 4.1×10^6
12. 6.95×10^9

The mass of the Sun is 2 000 000 000 000 000 000 000 000 000 t. This can be written neatly as 2×10^{27} t.
This notation is called *standard form* (or *scientific notation* or *standard index form*). For the example above, instead of using the words 'standard form' some texts would state 'in the form $x \times 10^n$ where $1 \leqslant x < 10$ and where n is a positive integer'.

Exercise 13

Write the given numbers in standard form:

1. 4000
2. 4679
3. 820 000
4. 7 350 000

5. The speed of light is almost 300 000 kilometres per second.

6. Mount Everest is 8848 m high.

7. The largest diameter of the Earth is almost 12 800 km.

8. The area of the Earth is approximately 510 000 000 km^2.

9. The greatest depth to which a whale has dived is 1134 m.

10. By 1972, Evel Knievel had suffered 431 bone fractures.

11. A world record for non-stop talking was set by a man! (This was achieved by Mr Raymond Cantwell in Oxford from 4–10 Dec 1977.) He talked for 150 h.

12. The world population in 2000 AD has been forecast as 6 493 000 000.

13. The Pacific Ocean is more than 165 million km^2 in area.

14. The Earth is about 4600 million years old.

15. The mass of the Earth is 5 976 000 000 000 000 000 000 t.

Exercise 14 **M**

A 1. The star Proxima Centauri is at a distance of 40 200 000 000 000 km while Luyten's Star is at 116 000 000 000 000 km. Which star is at the greater distance?

2. The star Sirius A is at a distance of 8.17×10^{13} km and Procyon A is at 1.07×10^{14} km. Which is closer? (*Note* It is easier to compare big numbers that are written in standard form.)

B Copy these, but replace each box with $<$ or $>$ to make each statement correct:

1. $3.4 \times 10^{6}\ \boxed{?}\ 2.7 \times 10^{4}$
2. $4.2 \times 10^{5}\ \boxed{?}\ 1.9 \times 10^{7}$
3. $5.6 \times 10^{4}\ \boxed{?}\ 8.4 \times 10^{3}$
4. $7.92 \times 10^{6}\ \boxed{?}\ 4.1 \times 10^{9}$
5. $6.03 \times 10^{8}\ \boxed{?}\ 5.28 \times 10^{8}$
6. $9.6 \times 10^{10}\ \boxed{?}\ 7.89 \times 10^{10}$
7. $8.07 \times 10^{6}\ \boxed{?}\ 7.99 \times 10^{6}$
8. $1.99 \times 10^{7}\ \boxed{?}\ 2.01 \times 10^{7}$
9. $1.64 \times 10^{14}\ \boxed{?}\ 3.02 \times 10^{12}$
10. $8.41 \times 10^{12}\ \boxed{?}\ 8.39 \times 10^{12}$
11. $7.93 \times 10^{15}\ \boxed{?}\ 5.66 \times 10^{16}$
12. $2.78 \times 10^{2}\ \boxed{?}\ 9.03 \times 10$
13. $6 \times 10^{13}\ \boxed{?}\ 3.9 \times 10^{14}$
14. $9.183 \times 10^{19}\ \boxed{?}\ 4.8 \times 10^{20}$
15. $6.1 \times 10^{9}\ \boxed{?}\ 6.01 \times 10^{9}$
16. $3.07 \times 10^{13}\ \boxed{?}\ 3.009 \times 10^{13}$

Many calculators use standard form.
$40\,000 \times 6000 = 240\,000\,000 = 2.4 \times 10^8$ in standard form. Work out $40\,000 \times 6000$ on a calculator. The answer will probably be given as

2.4 08

Exercise 15

Carry out these calculations on a calculator. Give each answer as a number without using indices and in standard form:

e.g. $150\,000 \times 30\,000 = \underline{\underline{4\,500\,000\,000}} = \underline{\underline{4.5 \times 10^9}}$

1. $500\,000 \times 7000$
2. $20\,000 \times 6000$
3. $34\,000 \times 20\,000$
4. $1800 \times 300\,000$
5. $4\,000\,000 \times 540$
6. $83\,000 \times 400\,000$
7. $4\,000\,000 \times 7\,000\,000$
8. $6\,800\,000 \times 20\,000$
9. $900\,000 \times 5\,400\,000$
10. $47\,000 \times 24\,000$
11. $1\,500\,000 \times 7\,500\,000$
12. $97\,000\,000 \times 98\,500\,000$

10 Brackets and Factorising

4(3 + 5) can be worked out in different ways.

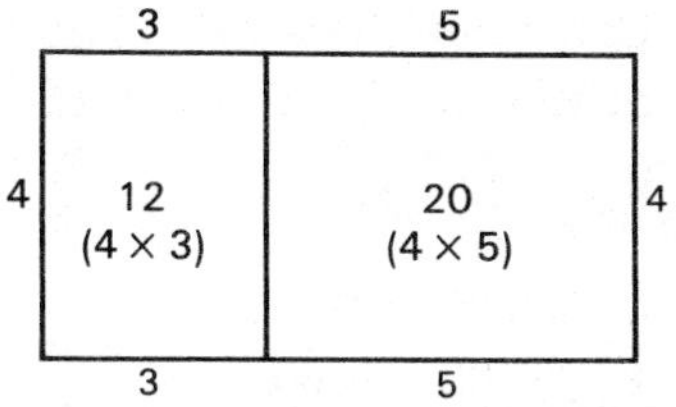

Here are two methods:

Method 1

$4(3 + 5) = 4 \times 8$ (working out the brackets first)

$= \underline{\underline{32}}$

Method 2

$4(3 + 5) = 4 \times 3 + 4 \times 5$ (by multiplying out)

$= 12 + 20$ (Each term must be worked out separately before

$= \underline{\underline{32}}$ adding. This means that multiplication must be carried out before addition.)

Exercise 1

Work these out in two different ways as shown above:

1. 5(3 + 4)
2. 7(2 + 6)
3. 2(8 + 5)
4. 6(3 + 7)
5. 4(12 + 8)
6. 3(6 + 14)
7. 9(15 + 15)
8. 2(1.2 + 8.8)

Exercise 2

Work these out in two different ways:

1. 4(9 − 2)
2. 3(7 − 4)
3. 6(8 − 3)
4. 2(14 − 5)
5. 7(15 − 5)
6. 5(23 − 14)
7. 9(46 − 36)
8. 8(9.1 − 6.1)

Exercise 3

Write each number as a product of two factors in as many different ways as possible:

e.g. $12 = 1 \times 12 = 2 \times 6 = 3 \times 4$

1. 8
2. 6
3. 10
4. 15
5. 4
6. 9
7. 18
8. 20
9. 16
10. 13
11. 24
12. 30
13. 36
14. 42
15. 75

Exercise 4 R

List the common factors of:

1. 6 and 8
2. 6 and 9
3. 4 and 8
4. 3 and 9
5. 10 and 15
6. 10 and 12
7. 25 and 15
8. 30 and 24
9. 42 and 56
10. 90 and 75
11. 4, 8 and 12
12. 10, 15 and 30
13. 6, 4 and 18
14. 24, 16 and 32
15. 30, 75 and 90

Exercise 5 R

Work these out by factorising first:

e.g.
$$\begin{aligned} &= 8 \times 12 + 8 \times 28 \\ &= 8(12 + 28) \\ &= 8 \times 40 \\ &= \underline{\underline{320}} \end{aligned}$$

1. $6 \times 17 + 6 \times 13$
2. $9 \times 83 + 9 \times 17$
3. $8 \times 29 - 8 \times 19$
4. $4 \times 35 + 4 \times 25$
5. $7 \times 21 - 7 \times 15$
6. $5 \times 42 + 58 \times 5$
7. $3 \times 254 - 54 \times 3$
8. $27 \times 66 + 27 \times 34$
9. $7 \times 6.8 + 7 \times 3.2$
10. $9 \times 24.1 - 9 \times 14.1$
11. $4.6 \times 13 + 13 \times 5.4$
12. $1.2 \times 7.8 + 1.2 \times 2.2$
13. $6.7 \times 84 + 6.7 \times 16$
14. $3.9 \times 6.2 - 4.2 \times 3.9$
15. $6.18 \times 12.4 + 6.18 \times 7.6$
16. $3.14 \times 16 - 3.14 \times 9$

The diagram shows that

$$5(x + 3) \equiv 5x + 15$$

(The sign $\equiv$ means 'is identical to'.)

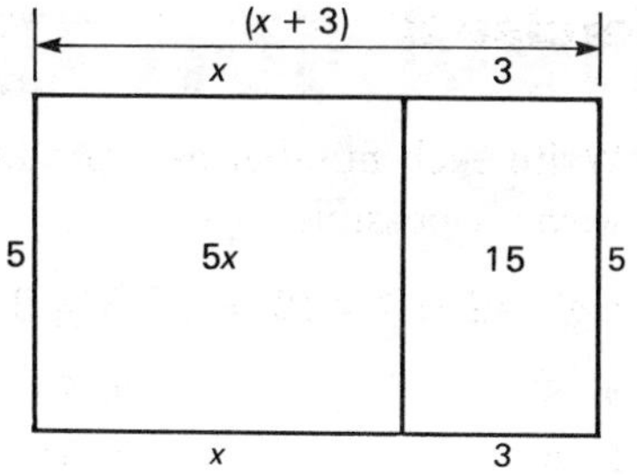

Exercise 6

R

Multiply out:

e.g. $3(2x + 6) = \underline{\underline{6x + 18}}$

1. $3(x + 4)$
2. $2(c + 6)$
3. $5(p + 7)$
4. $4(t - 3)$
5. $6(u - 2)$
6. $2(3m + 4)$
7. $7(2n - 3)$
8. $9(4 + 2k)$
9. $3(5 - 3v)$
10. $8(3 + l)$
11. $4(c + d)$
12. $3(2y + 4z)$
13. $7(4q - r)$
14. $2(9a + 7b)$
15. $5(d + 6f)$

Exercise 7

R

Factorise:

e.g. $8n - 6 = \underline{\underline{2(4n - 3)}}$

1. $3n + 9$
2. $2b + 16$
3. $4x + 6$
4. $6a - 8$
5. $6c + 12$
6. $9d - 6$
7. $8z - 20$
8. $4n - 10$
9. $15 + 10k$
10. $8g + 18$
11. $25 + 15m$
12. $24 - 30h$
13. $12e - 36$
14. $14e - 7f$
15. $4v + 2w$
16. $8l + 8p$
17. $9t - 12u$
18. $30y + 45$

Revision Exercises I to X

Revision Exercise I

1. List the set of odd numbers that lie between 15 and 28.

2. List the set of natural numbers that are less than 7.

3. List the set of whole numbers that are less than 7.

4. From set G, list the set of numbers:
   (*a*) that are bigger than 10,
   (*b*) that are factors of 28,
   (*c*) that divide exactly by 9,
   (*d*) that are multiples of 5.

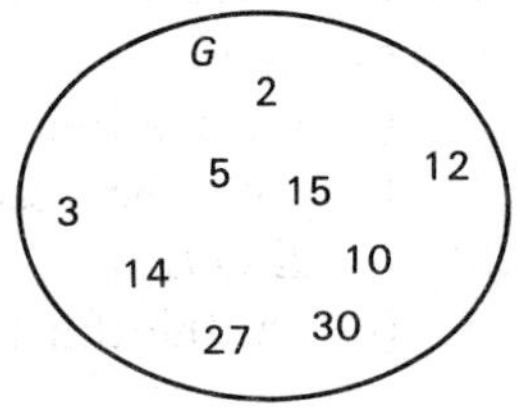

5. List the set of factors of 40.

6. List the set of negative integers that are bigger than $^-6$.

7. Draw a Venn diagram to show the set of prime numbers that are less than 18.

8. In the Venn diagram shown below, is it true that:
   (*a*) $^-2 \in P$?
   (*b*) $^-5 \in P$?
   (*c*) $^-5 \in \mathscr{E}$?
   (*d*) $^-4 \in \mathscr{E}$?
   (*e*) $7 \in P'$?
   (*f*) $n(P) = 3$?
   (*g*) $n(\mathscr{E}) = 4$?
   (*h*) $8 \in P'$?

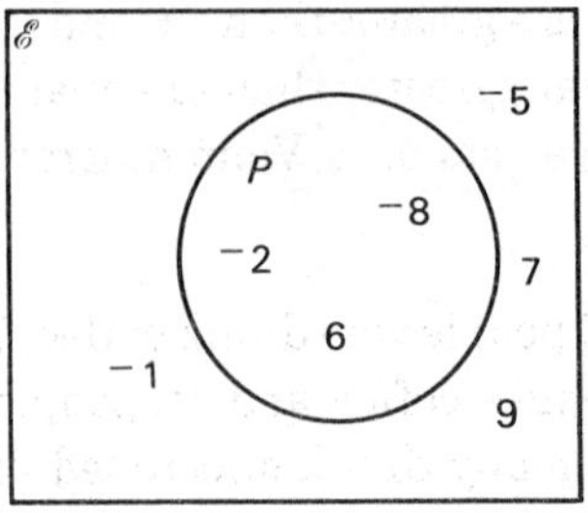

9. If V = {even numbers between 25 and 45}, are the following true?

(*a*) $31 \in V$ (*b*) $28 \notin V$ (*c*) $43 \notin V$ (*d*) $40 \in V$ (*e*) $n(V) = 20$ (*f*) $n(V) = 11$ (*g*) $n(V) = 10$ (*h*) $n(V) \neq 9$

10. $\mathscr{E}$ = {natural numbers less than 35}
A = {numbers exactly divisible by 4}
B = {factors of 32}

(*a*) Show the above sets on a Venn diagram.
(*b*) How many members has set B?
(*c*) Find $n(A)$.
(*d*) How many members has set A'?
(*e*) How many members has $(A \cap B)$?

11. Make three copies of the Venn diagram.

(*a*) On the first, shade $K \cap L$.
(*b*) On the second, shade $K \cup L$.
(*c*) On the third, shade $(K \cup L)'$.

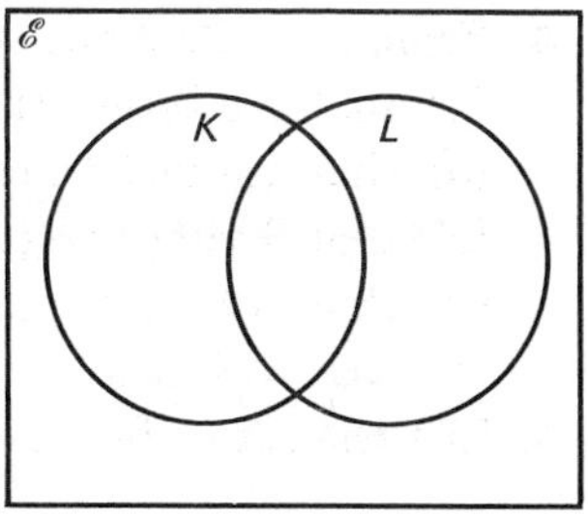

12. D = the set of odd numbers less than 8
P = the set of prime numbers less than 10
Are sets D and P equal?

13. I = {integers that are greater than $^-4$ but less than 4}
J = {$^-3$, $^-2$, $^-1$, 0, 1, 2, 3}
Does set I equal set J?

14. $\mathscr{E}$ = {integers that are greater than $^-8$ and less than 12}
F = {integers that are greater than $^-6$ and less than or equal to 3}
G = {integers that are greater than or equal to $^-2$ and less than 8}

(*a*) Show the above sets on a Venn diagram
(*b*) Find $F \cap G$.

15. In a café, out of 100 people who drank coffee, 77 drank white coffee, 49 took sugar in white coffee and 12 people drank unsweetened black coffee. How many drank sweetened black coffee?

Revision Exercise II

1. A room is 5.43 m long. Write its length correct to the nearest metre.

2. Round these numbers correct to 2 decimal places:
(*a*) 7.946 (*b*) 81.635 (*c*) 0.6282 (*d*) 2.0749

3. Round these numbers correct to 3 significant figures:
(*a*) 9.267 (*b*) 45.829 (*c*) 37.454 (*d*) 29.97

4. (*a*) Is 7×6.84 less than or greater than 7×7?
(*b*) Is 2.4×41.6 less than or greater than 2×40?

5. The answer to 4.9×6.3 lies between 24 and 35. Give two numbers between which the answer to 8.5×3.7 lies.

6. Anita worked for 29 h at £5.16 per hour. Estimate how much she earned.

Revision Exercise III

1. (*a*) Does $(4 \times 2) \times 5 = 4 \times (2 \times 5)$?
(*b*) Does $(29 - 8) - 4 = 29 - (8 - 4)$?

2. Copy and insert the correct sign, $<$, $>$ or $=$:
(*a*) $30 - 17 - 9$ [?] $30 - (17 - 9)$
(*b*) $45 - 19 - 8$ [?] $45 - (19 + 8)$
(*c*) $6 \times (4 + 3)$ [?] $6 \times 4 + 3$
(*d*) $7 \times (5 + 4)$ [?] $7 \times 5 + 7 \times 4$

3. If you take 6 from 14 then multiply the result by 4, what answer should you get?

4. Copy the statement $8 + 3 \times 6 = 66$ but insert brackets to make it correct.

5. What is the difference between the two temperatures shown in the sketch of a thermometer?

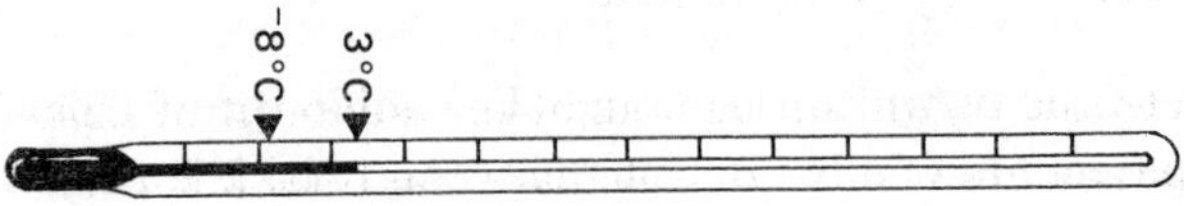

Revision Exercise IV

1. Justin worked for 34 h at £4 an hour. How much did he earn?

2. Marion earned £180 for working 30 h. Calculate her hourly rate.

3. Mr Evans earned £5.43 an hour. If he worked for 36 h how much did he earn?

4. Use the ready reckoner on p. 37 to find the earnings of someone who worked:
   (*a*) 39 h at £3.50 per hour, (*b*) 34 h at £4.10 per hour.

5. Mrs Khiroya's gross weekly pay was £161.70. If deductions totalled £38.90, calculate her net weekly wage.

6. Mr MacLeod earned £22.32 overtime. If his basic wage was £178.56, calculate his gross earnings.

7. Neal's basic hourly rate is £5 an hour. Calculate his overtime earnings if he worked:
   (*a*) 3 h overtime at double-time rate,
   (*b*) 6 h overtime at time-and-a-half.

8. If your basic rate is £4 an hour for a basic working week of 24 h and you worked 41 h in one week, how much would you earn if overtime was paid at double-time rate?

9. How much per annum is £152 per week?

10. How much per week is £7748 p.a.?

11. If your gross salary was £8150 and deductions totalled £2195, calculate your net salary.

12. A jacket costing £34.50 was sold for £27.95 in a sale. How much discount was that?

13. A bicycle costs £149.99. Find the balance payable after a deposit of £37 has been paid.

14. A finance company charges £16.50 interest on a loan of £55. What is the total HP price to be paid?

15. An electronic organ can be bought for a deposit of £295 followed by 36 payments of £16.70. Calculate the total HP cost.

Revision Exercise V

1. A film lasts 1 h 55 min. If it starts at 20.10, at what time does it finish?

2. A timer needs to be set for 2 h 25 min. How many minutes is that?

3. If 10 May was a Wednesday, what would be the date of the first Wednesday in June of the same year?

4. The length of a matchstick is about:
   A. 23 mm   B. 46 mm   C. 78 mm   D. 10 cm

5. Mr Steele jogged 7.2 km per day for 7 days. How far was that altogether?

6. A 30 cm plastic ruler weighs about:
   A. 15 g   B. 40 g   C. 100 g   D. 180 g

7. Find the mass in kilograms of 5 tins of beans if each weighs 288 g.

8. A milk bottle holds about:
   A. 170 mℓ   B. 300 mℓ   C. 570 mℓ   D. 70 cℓ

9. A fountain-pen sac holds 4 mℓ of ink. How many times can the pen be filled from a bottle containing 60 mℓ of ink?

10. To make a ginger cake I need 225 g of flour. How many kilograms of flour are needed to make 6 ginger cakes?

11. A bottle holds 250 mℓ. What is its volume in cubic centimetres?

12. A tank has a volume of 48 000 cm^3. How many litres does it hold?

Revision Exercise VI

1. Answer these using the table in Exercise 1 on p. 67:
   (*a*) Find the length of the Ohio.
   (*b*) How many kilometres longer than the Saskatchewan is the Red River?

2. Using the table in Exercise 2 on p. 68, find the minimum distance of the Earth from the Sun.

3. Using the table in Exercise 3 on p. 69, find:
   (*a*) The average height of a 13-year-old girl.
   (*b*) The difference in mass in grams of 14-year-old girls and boys.

4. Using the table in Exercise 4 on p. 70, find:
   (*a*) the height and (*b*) the time of the morning tide on 19 October.

5. Find the waist measurement of a 13-year-old boy (in centimetres and inches) using the table in Exercise 5 on p. 72.

6. Using the table in Exercise 6 on p. 73, find:
   (*a*) The value of an investment of £20 per month over 5 years.
   (*b*) The amount of interest obtained from saving £100 per month over 1 year.

7. Using the table in Exercise 7 on p. 74, find:
   (*a*) The number of tablespoons that will fill a cup.
   (*b*) How to measure 50 mℓ by filling spoons as few times as possible.

8. Using the timetables on p. 75, find:
   (*a*) The time of arrival at Newark Castle of a train that leaves Burton Joyce at 18.53.
   (b) The time of departure from Bleasby of the train that leaves Carlton for Nottingham at 13.29.

9. Using the conversion graph on p. 76, find:
   (*a*) The number of metres in 21 ft.
   (*b*) The number of feet in 10 m.

Revision Exercise VII

1. The diagram is of a triangular-based prism lying on one face.

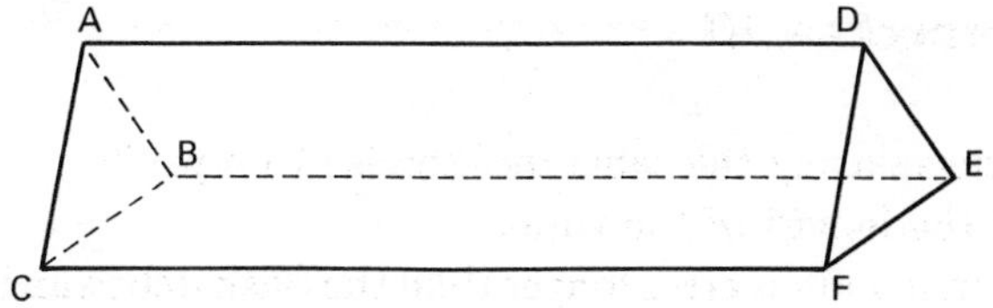

   (*a*) What shape is face BEFC?
   (*b*) What shape is face ABED?
   (*c*) If AB = BC, which edge of face DEF equals DE?

2. Find the angles labelled with letters:

(*a*)

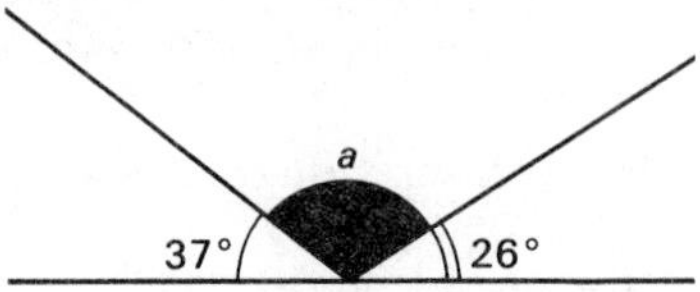

(*b*)

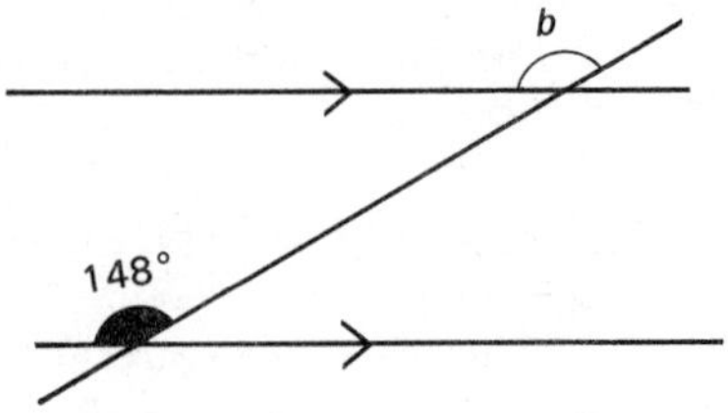

3. Calculate the missing angles:

(*a*)

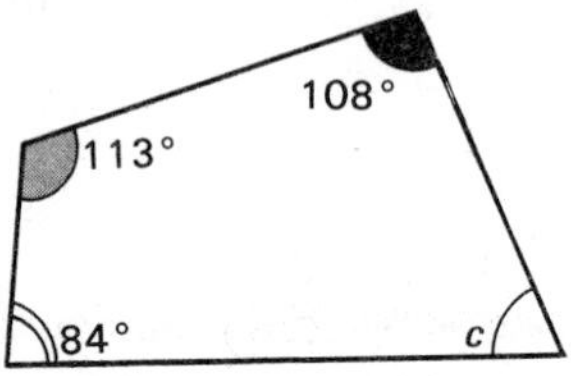

(*b*)

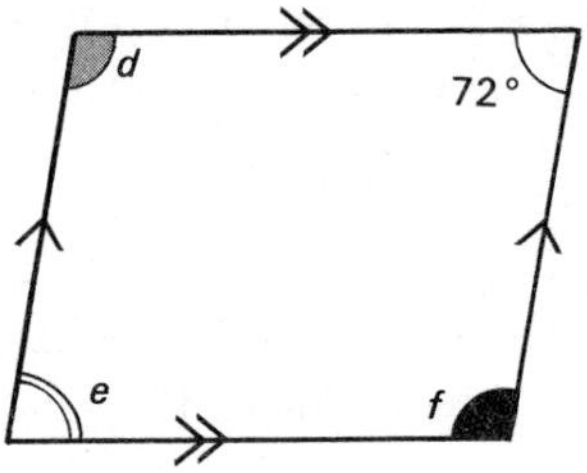

4. Calculate the sum of the interior angles of a 7-sided polygon.

5. Calculate each interior angle of a regular hexagon.

6. Calculate each exterior angle of a regular decagon (a 10-sided polygon).

Revision Exercise VIII

1. Construct $\triangle$TUV where TU = 45 mm, UV 68 mm, and T$\hat{U}$V = 28°. Using a pair of compasses, bisect angle TUV and let the bisector meet TV at W. Measure TW.

2. Construct a right-angled triangle PQR as shown, where QR = 25 mm, P$\hat{Q}$R = 72° and angle at R is a right-angle. How long is PR?

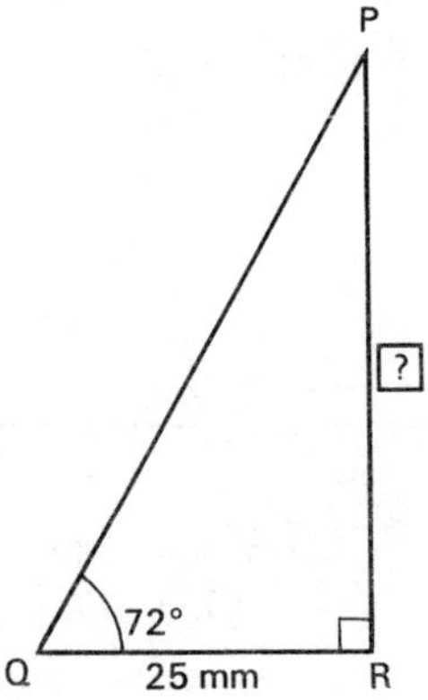

3. Calculate the labelled angles (O is the centre of the circle):

(*a*)

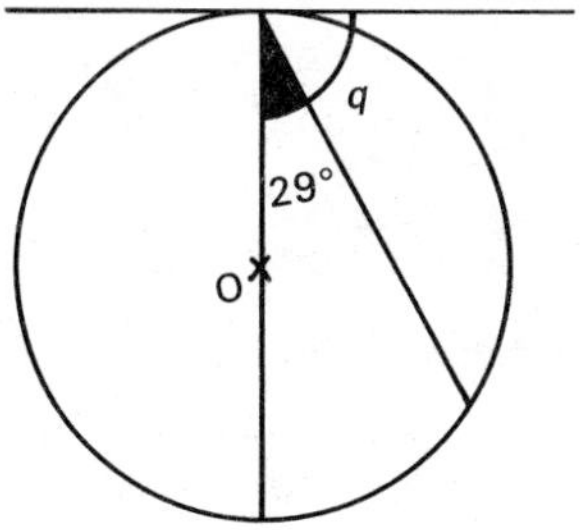

(*b*)

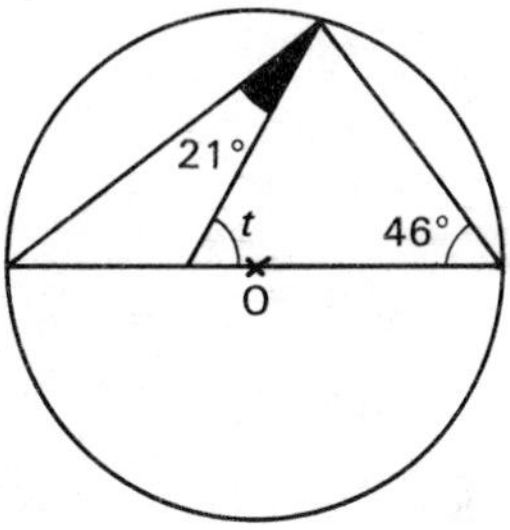

4. XY is a diameter of the circle centre O. YZ is a tangent at Y. Z is joined to O, and P is a point on the circle.

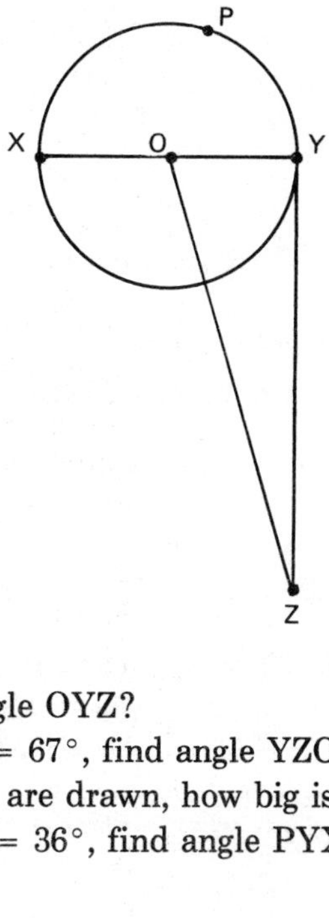

(*a*) How big is angle OYZ?
(*b*) If angle YOZ = 67°, find angle YZO.
(*c*) If XP and YP are drawn, how big is angle XPY?
(*d*) If angle PXY = 36°, find angle PYX.

Revision Exercise IX

1. Find the value of: (*a*) 8^2 (*b*) 5^3

2. Which is bigger, 3^4 or 4^3?

3. Simplify, leaving answers in index form:

(a) $c^4 \times c^3$

(b) $4^7 \times 4^5$

(c) $u^{10} \div u^4$

(d) $\frac{m^9}{m^2}$

(e) $3x \times 4x$

(f) $2t^3 \times 4t^2$

4. $V = l^3$ gives the volume of a cube with edge l units. Find the volume of a cube with edge 9 cm.

5. Find the value of:
(a) 2^2 (b) 0.2^2 (c) 0.02^2

6. Use a calculator to find the following. Give your answers correct to 3 significant figures.

(a) 8.3^2

(b) $\sqrt{48}$

(c) $\sqrt{0.9}$

(d) 5.29^2

7. Without using a calculator, find $\sqrt{324}$.

8. (a) Is it true that $1 < \sqrt{3} < 2$?
(b) Is it true that $0.1 < \sqrt{0.3} < 0.2$?

9. (a) Work out $7.92 \times 10\,000$.
(b) Write 6.47×10^3 as a number without using indices.

10. Write the number 59 000 000 in standard form.

11. (a) Which is smaller, 7.4×10^6 or 6.9×10^7?
(b) Which is bigger, 8.03×10^9 or 8.11×10^9?

12. Work out $170\,000 \times 40\,000$ on a calculator giving the answer (a) in standard form, (b) as a number without using indices.

Revision Exercise X

1. (a) Work out $6(7 + 5)$.
(b) Work out $6 \times 7 + 6 \times 5$.

2. Work these out by factorising first:

(a) $7 \times 15 + 7 \times 5$

(b) $4 \times 76 + 4 \times 24$

(c) $9 \times 64 - 9 \times 54$

(d) $14 \times 52 + 14 \times 48$

(e) $6 \times 7.3 - 6 \times 5.3$

(f) $4.8 \times 2.7 + 4.8 \times 7.3$

(g) $5.4 \times 9 + 4.6 \times 9$

(h) $3.14 \times 25 - 3.14 \times 15$

3. Multiply out:

(*a*) $2(x \times 8)$

(*b*) $3(m - 6)$

(*c*) $3(2t + 5)$

(*d*) $4(3u + 1)$

(*e*) $5(2 + 5k)$

(*f*) $2(7d - e)$

4. Factorise:

(*a*) $2n + 8$

(*b*) $5g - 15$

(*c*) $6k - 3$

(*d*) $12p + 18$

(*e*) $12 + 8y$

(*f*) $14a - 21b$

11 Loci

Exercise 1

1. Joanne throws a ball to Dean. Draw a sketch to show the path of the ball.

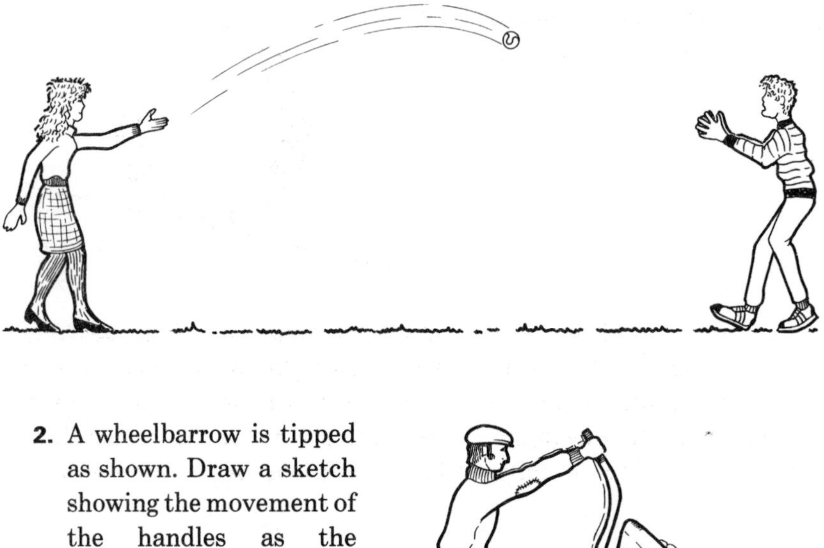

2. A wheelbarrow is tipped as shown. Draw a sketch showing the movement of the handles as the wheelbarrow is tipped.

In Exercise 1, the path drawn to show the movement of the ball is called the *locus* of the ball. Likewise the path drawn to show the movement of the handles of the wheelbarrow as it is tipped is called the locus of the handles. The plural of *locus* is *loci* (pronounced 'low sigh').

Exercise 2

1. Sketch the locus of a mark on a window as the window is opened.

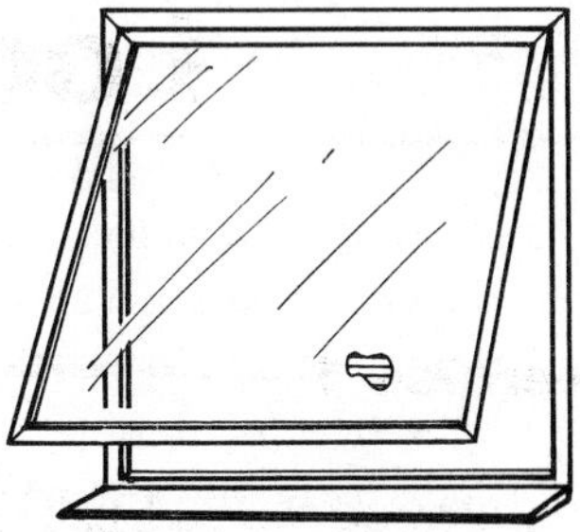

2. Sketch the locus of the centre of a wheel as it rolls down a hill.

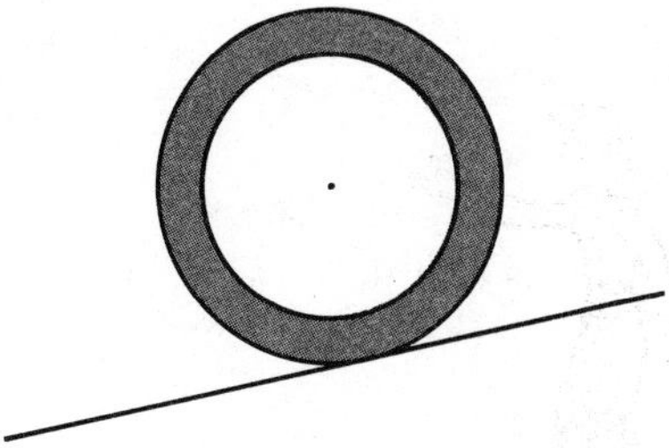

In Exercises 1 and 2 the loci have only been sketched. Sometimes they need to be accurately drawn. A locus must follow a particular rule or condition that will be given and any drawing instruments may be used to make accurate drawings. Before drawing (or plotting) an accurate locus, it is useful to carefully read the conditions and sketch the locus first.

Exercise 3 gives some basic loci that will help with later problems.

Exercise 3

1. Mark a point on your page with at least 30 mm space all around it. This point will be called a fixed point and the rule for the locus will refer to the point.

   Plot the locus of a point that moves so that it is always 25 mm from a fixed point.

2. Draw a line segment that is 56 mm long. Plot the locus of a point which moves so that it is always 20 mm from that line segment.

3. Mark two points 72 mm apart. Now construct the locus of a point which moves so that it is always equidistant from these two fixed points. (Remember that a sketch may help. Also, try to remember some of the constructions you have carried out.)

4. Draw two intersecting lines as shown. (Make each one about 80 mm long.) Now construct the locus of a point which moves so that it is always equidistant from these two lines.

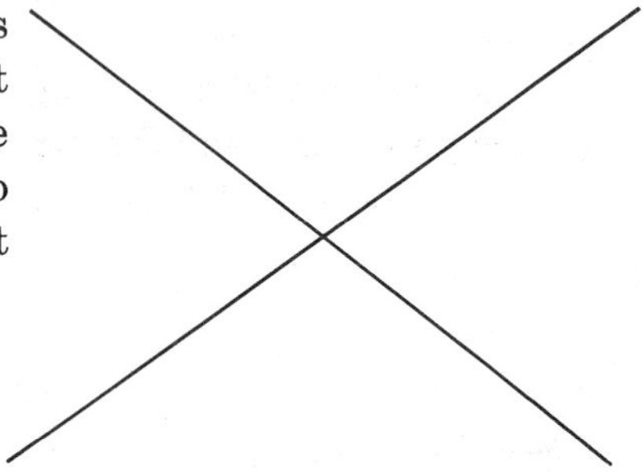

5. Draw a pair of parallel lines that are 30 mm apart. Now draw the locus of a point which moves so that it is always equidistant from these two lines.

Exercise 4

1. For one-day county cricket, discs are placed on the ground to form a special boundary inside which at least four fielders, the bowler and wicket keeper must stand.

The discs are placed 30 yd away from the wicket line which is an imaginary straight line joining the two middle stumps, a distance of 22 yd.

Using a scale of 1 in to 20 yd mark the position of the wickets on your page as shown. (If your ruler does not have inches on it, then use a scale of 1 cm to 10 yd.)

(*a*) Draw a faint line to show all possible positions of the discs.
(*b*) Position a set of discs as for a game. Space them out with 7–10 yd between adjacent discs.

2. A ball was thrown vertically into the air from a point 1 m above the ground. It reached a height of 6 m. Draw the locus of the ball using your own choice of scale. Write on your page the scale used.

3. The sketch shows a parallelogram linkage.
(Make one out of geo-strips.)
It could be a model of a swing.
Fasten positions P and Q down and move the rest of the linkage to see how it does model a swing.

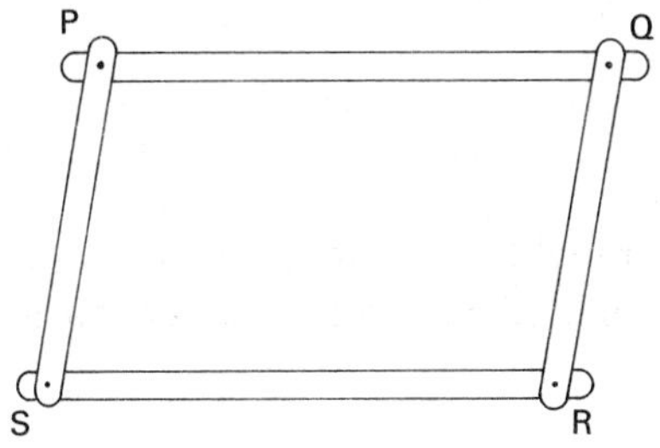

(*a*) Draw the locus of a point R.
(*b*) Draw the locus of point S.
(*c*) Draw the locus of the mid-point of RS.
(*d*) Draw the locus of any other point on RS.

4. This linkage is a quadrilateral linkage in which PS = QR.
Make one. Once again fasten down positions P and Q.

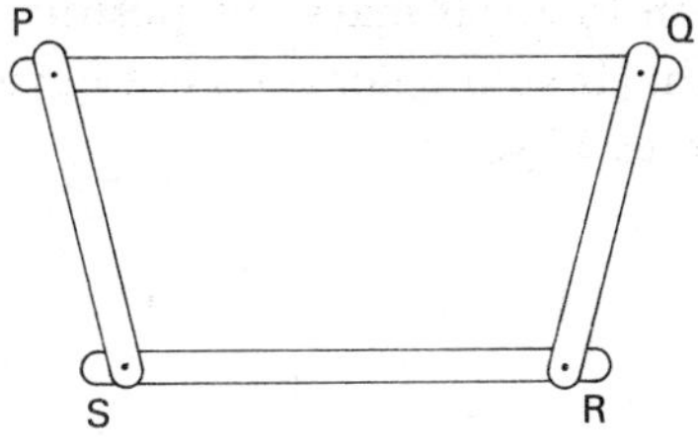

Now repeat all four parts of question 3 for this linkage.

5. This quadrilateral linkage is the same as in question 4 but is upside down.
Fix P and Q and repeat all four parts of question 3 for this linkage.

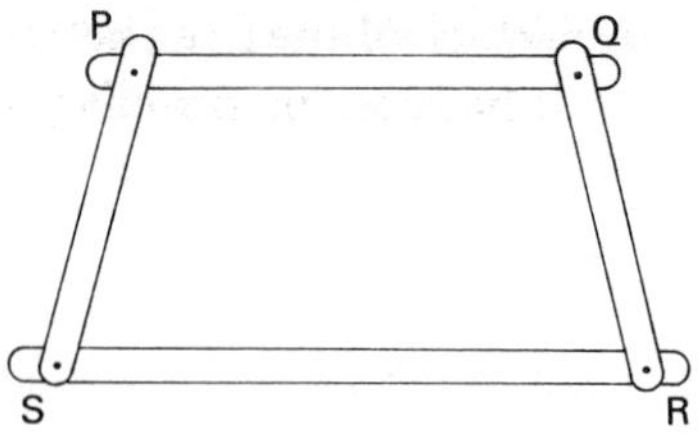

6. Here is another quadrilateral linkage. This time, all the bars are of different length.
Once again, fix P and Q then answer the four parts of question 3 for this linkage.

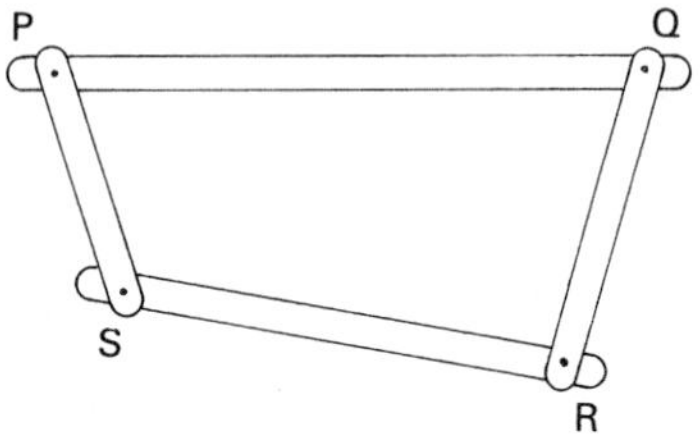

7. A ladder 6 m in length is placed against a wall as shown. It begins to slip. The foot of the ladder slides along the ground while the top of the ladder slides down the wall. It continues to slip until it lies flat on the ground.

(*a*) Which of the five sketches below shows the locus of a man's feet if he remains standing on the middle rung as the ladder slips?

A.

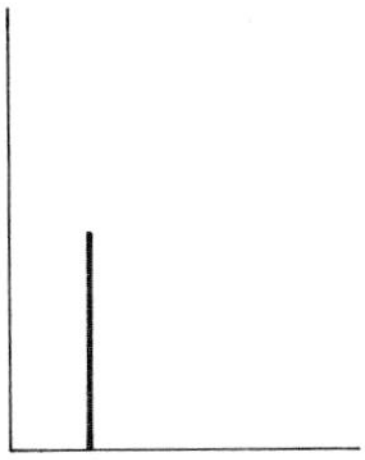

D.

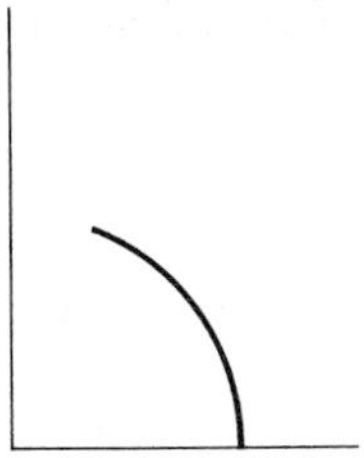

B.

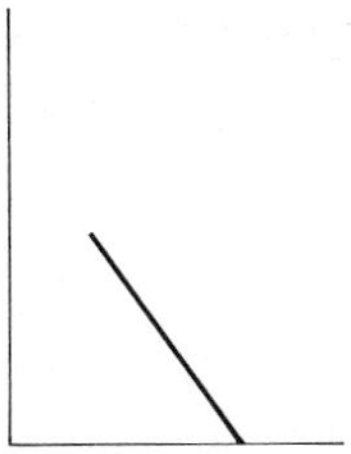

E.

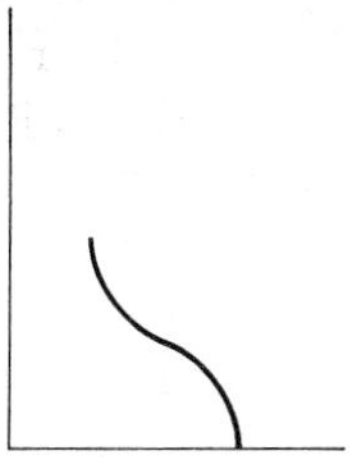

C.

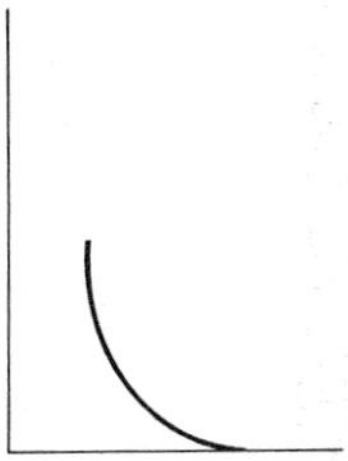

(*b*) Make a scale drawing to show the locus. Use a scale of 1 cm to 1 m. Draw the ladder in several different positions. In each position it touches both the wall and the ground. (Remember, it must be 6 m long – it is not an extending ladder!) Draw the ladder faintly and clearly mark its mid-point in each position.

8. In discus throwing, the discus must be thrown from inside a circle of diameter 2.5 m and must land between two straight lines which are at an angle of 45° to each other as shown in the diagram (it is not drawn to scale).

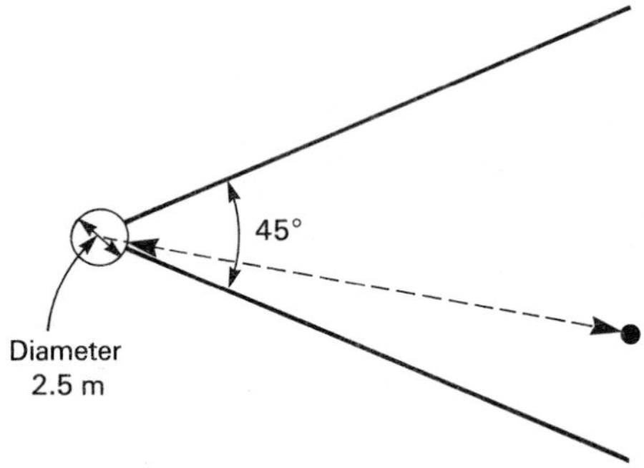

The total length of a throw is measured in a straight line from the circumference of the throwing circle to where the discus lands. If this straight line was produced, it would pass through the centre of the throwing circle. Lines are marked on the ground to show certain lengths of throw. Copy the given diagram using a scale of 1 cm to 10 m and draw lines to show all the possible landing points for throws of the following distances (that is, for each distance given, draw the locus showing that distance from the circumference of the throwing circle).

(*a*) 40 m (*b*) 50 m (*c*) 60 m (*d*) 70 m (*e*) 80 m

Exercise 5

1. Draw a circle of radius 30 mm. Faintly draw several radii and mark the mid-point of each. Draw the locus of the mid-points of the radii.

2. Draw a straight line, AB, 60 mm in length. Plot the locus of a point P which moves so that ∠APB is always 90°.

3. Draw a straight line, JK, 6 cm in length. Draw the locus of a point L such that the area of △JKL is always 9 cm^2.

4. Draw a square of side 60 mm. Draw the locus of a point that is always 20 mm from the sides of the square.

5. On your page, mark two points, X and Y, 80 mm apart. Now plot the locus of a point which moves so that the sum of its distances from X and Y is always 100 mm.

6. Draw a straight line, CD, 30 mm in length. Construct the locus of a point E which moves so that $\triangle CDE$ is always an isosceles triangle.

Exercise 6

1. Mark two points about 40 mm apart. Position a set square (any; 45° or 30°/60°) as shown to touch both points.

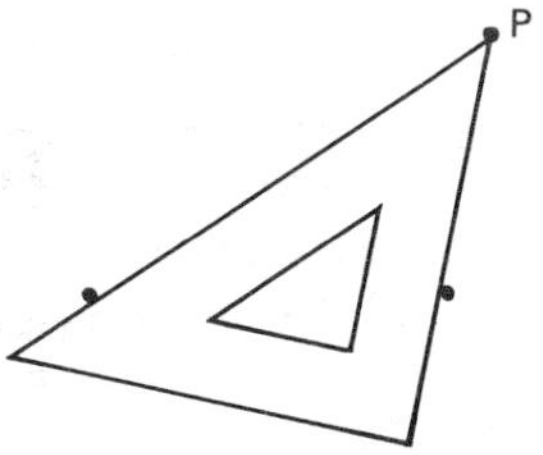

Mark the position of the point labelled P. Move the set square so that the same edges touch the same points and again mark the position of P. Repeat this as many times as necessary to plot the locus of P. What shape is the locus?

2. Cut out of card, a right-angled triangle. (The two shorter sides should be about 30 mm and 60 mm in length.)

Label the vertices on both sides of the card-triangle using Y for the vertex at the right-angle, X for the vertex at the larger acute angle and P for the remaining vertex.

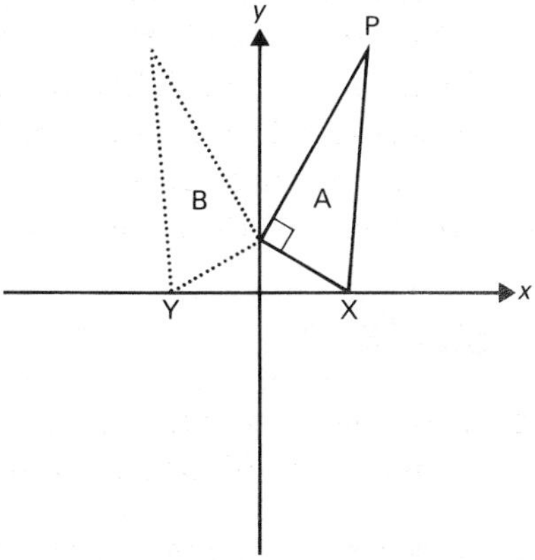

Draw a pair of axes as shown, each being about 140 mm long (70 mm in each direction from the origin).

Plot the locus of vertex P when vertex Y moves along and is always in contact with the positive part of the y-axis and at the same time vertex X moves along the whole of the x-axis and remains in contact with it.

In the figure above, A shows the position of the triangle to obtain the right-hand part of the locus while B shows the position for the left-hand part of the locus.

3. Draw the locus of a point on the circumference of a bicycle wheel as it moves in a straight line along a level surface.

To answer this you probably need to make a model. You need a cardboard disc with a mark on its edge and a ruler. Place the ruler and the cardboard disc flat on a page of your exercise book so that the mark on the edge of the disc touches one edge of the ruler (as shown in the diagram). Roll the disc along the edge of the ruler and at various intervals, mark a dot on your page next to the mark on the edge of the disc. Joining the dots will give the locus which is a curve called a *cycloid*. (You need to be careful that the disc does not slip. You may need a friend to hold the ruler.)

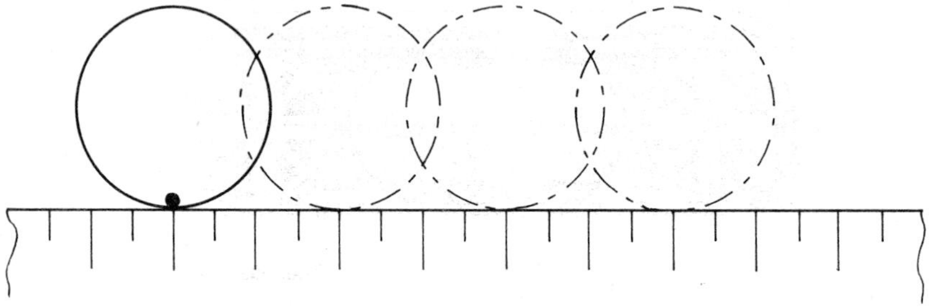

Exercise 7

Sketch the loci of the following:

1. A mark on the cover of a hard-backed textbook as the book is fully opened from the closed position.

2. The stylus (or needle) of a record-player when a record is being played.

3. A point on the track of a track-laying vehicle, such as on the caterpillar track of a tracked tractor as it travels in a straight line on level ground.

Tracked tractor

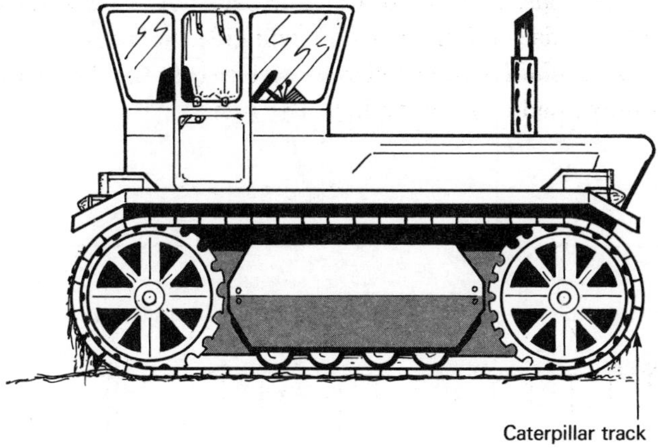

12 Area and Volume

Reminders:

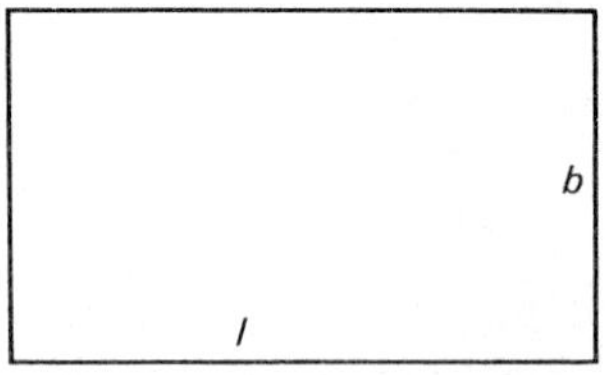

Area of a rectangle = lb

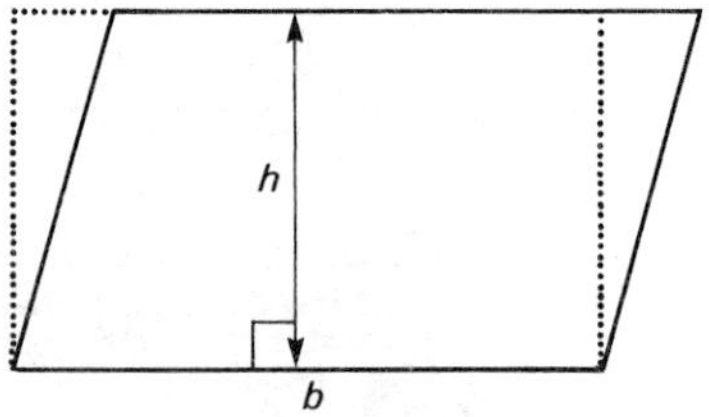

Area of a parallelogram = bh

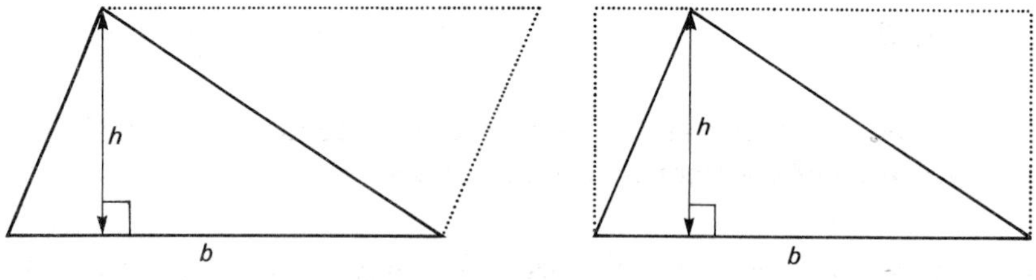

Area of a triangle = $\frac{1}{2}bh$

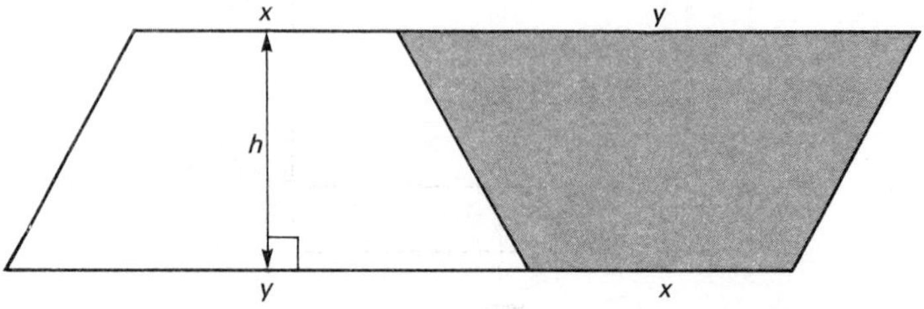

Area of a trapezium = $\frac{1}{2}(x + y)h$

Exercise 1

1. A rectangular jigsaw puzzle measures 60 cm by 42 cm. Find the area of the card out of which it was cut if there was no waste.

2. A bedroom is 5 m long and 3.5 m wide. What area of carpet is needed to cover the whole floor?

3. A basketball court measures 26 m by 14 m. Calculate its area.

4. A postage stamp measures 2.5 cm by 2 cm.
   (*a*) Calculate the area of one stamp.
   (*b*) Calculate the area of 20 of the stamps.
   (*c*) If I buy 20 stamps in a rectangular block, ignoring the perforations, list the possible sizes of the rectangle. (One possible answer is: 20 cm by 5 cm.)

5. A pane of glass measures 76 cm by 58 cm. Calculate its area.

Exercise 2

1. A carpet measuring 4 m by 3 m is placed in a room 6 m by 4 m. What is the area of the floor that is not covered?

2. A car is 4.3 m long and 1.6 m wide. When it is in a garage of length 6 m and width 2.5 m, what is the area of the floor space that is left?

3. A path, 1.2 m wide, fits along two sides of a lawn as shown.

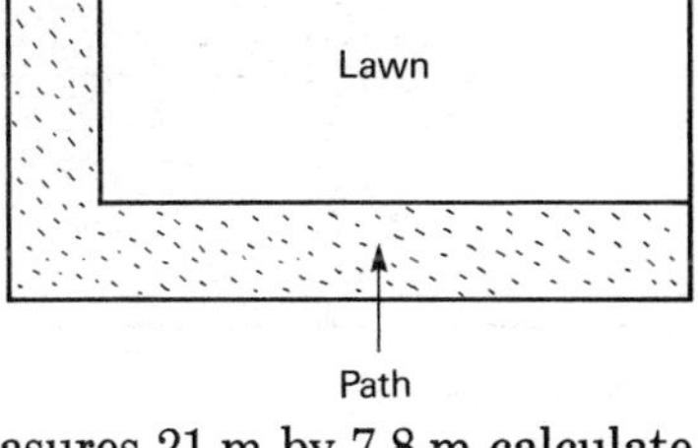

If the lawn measures 21 m by 7.8 m calculate the area of the path.

Exercise 3

1. A bathroom floor measuring 2.1 m by 1.5 m is to be tiled with 15 cm square tiles.

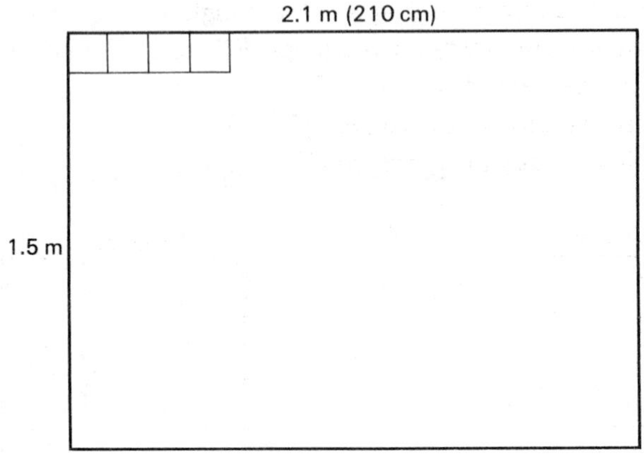

How many tiles are needed?

2. How many 600 mm square paving stones are needed to pave an area measuring 4.8 m by 3 m?

3. What is the greatest number of dusters that can be cut out of a piece of material measuring 3 m by 2.4 m if the dusters are 60 cm long and 40 cm wide?

4. Dusters measuring 60 cm by 40 cm are to be cut from a piece of material measuring 5.4 m by 3 m. What is the greatest number of dusters that can be cut out? Note that the dusters can be cut out in any direction. Make a drawing to show how you would cut them out.

Exercise 4

1. A rectangular room of length 4 m has an area of 12 m^2. How wide is it?

2. A classroom is 5 m wide. If it has an area of 55 m^2 how long is it?

3. A square handkerchief has a perimeter of 1.6 m. Calculate its area in square centimetres.

Exercise 5 **M**

A 1. (*a*) What is the perimeter of rectangle P?
(*b*) What is the perimeter of rectangle Q?
(Note that a square is a special rectangle.)
(*c*) What is the perimeter of rectangle R?
(*d*) What is the area of rectangle P?
(*e*) What is the area of rectangle Q?
(*f*) What is the area of rectangle R?

Rectangle P

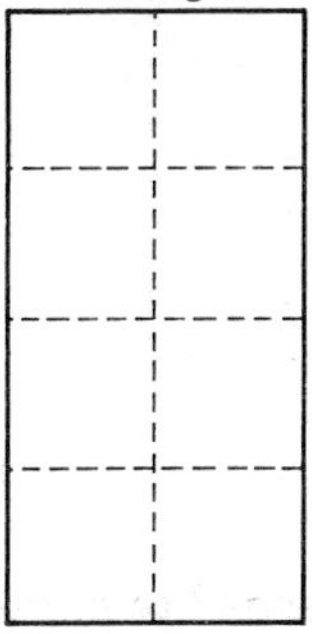

Rectangle Q

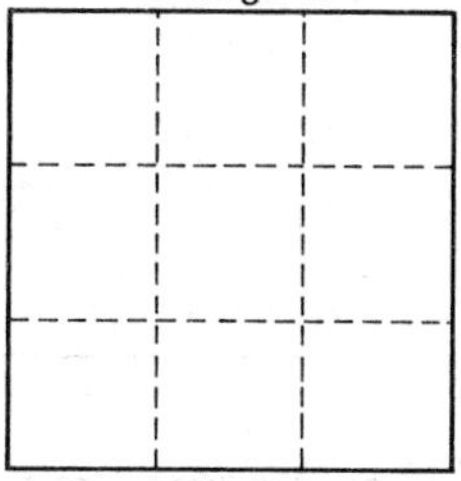

Rectangle R

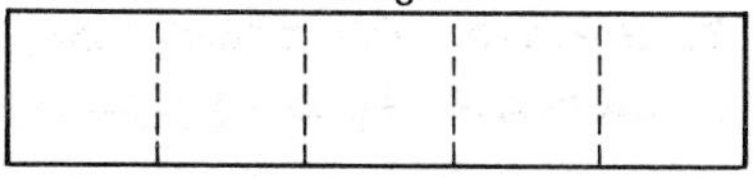

Note Although the perimeters are the same, the rectangles have different areas.

2. (*a*) Find as many different rectangles as you can that have a perimeter of 24 cm and whose sides have whole number lengths. One possible rectangle is 10 cm by 2 cm. You may write the answers in this way or draw the rectangles.
(*b*) Which of the rectangles has the biggest area?
(*c*) Copy and complete the table, shown below, for rectangles with a perimeter of 24 cm.

Length of rectangle, l (cm)	1	2	3	4	5	6	7	8	9	10	11
Breadth of rectangle, b (cm)	11	10									
Area of rectangle, A (cm^2)		20						32			11

(*d*) Draw a pair of axes as shown. Use a scale of 1 cm to 1 cm for the length and 1 cm to 5 cm^2 for the area. Using the table of question 2(*c*), plot the graph of area against length.

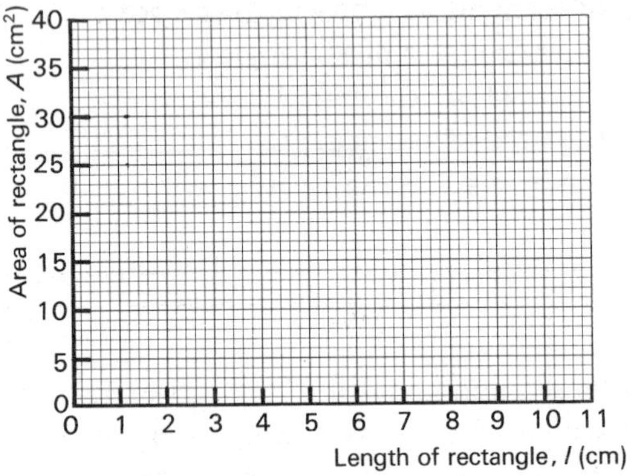

(*e*) Use your graph to find which rectangle has the largest area. (Give both its length and breadth.)

3. (*a*) Try other perimeters such as 16 cm, 36 cm, 40 cm, 100 cm. In each case, find the rectangle that has the largest area.

(*b*) For a given perimeter, what do you notice about the rectangle that gives the biggest area?

4. A farmer has 200 m of fencing. He wants to fence off a paddock using all the fencing. He would like the fenced paddock to be rectangular and to have the largest possible area. How must the farmer arrange his fencing to create the largest possible area?

5. Suppose the sides of the rectangles need not be whole numbers. Find the dimensions of the rectangles giving the largest possible areas for perimeters of:

(*a*) 18 cm (*b*) 30 cm (*c*) 150 m

6. Find the largest possible area of a rectangle that has a perimeter of:

(*a*) 28 cm (*b*) 60 cm (*c*) 50 cm

7. A rectangle has an area of 144 cm^2. Find the smallest perimeter it can have.

B **1.** I should like to make a rectangular flower bed using a wall for one side and laying stone for the other three sides. I have enough stone for a total distance of 24 m so the length and two breadths of the rectangle must add up to 24 m.

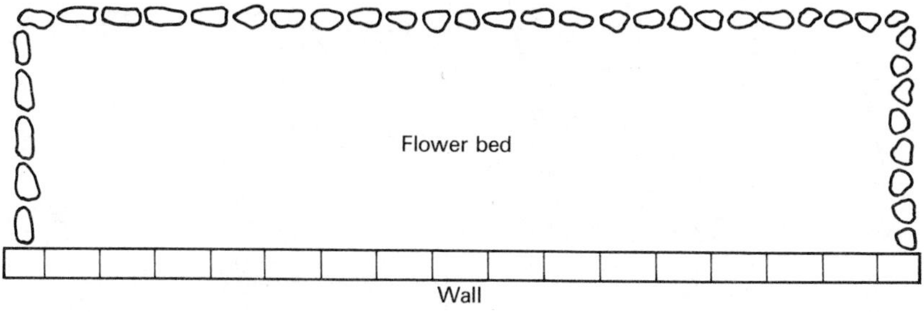

(*a*) Find the length and breadth of the rectangle that encloses the biggest possible area. It may be helpful to sketch some different flower beds where three of the sides total 24 m.

(*b*) Copy and complete the following table for a rectangular flower bed where three sides total 24 m.

Length	1	2	3	4	5	6	7	10	11	12	13	14	16	18	20	23
Breadth	11.5	11	10.5										4		2	0.5
Area	11.5	22	31.5		47.5											11.5

(*c*) Draw a pair of axes as shown using a scale of 1 cm to 2 m for the length and 1 cm to 10 m^2 for the area. Using the table above, plot a graph of area against length.

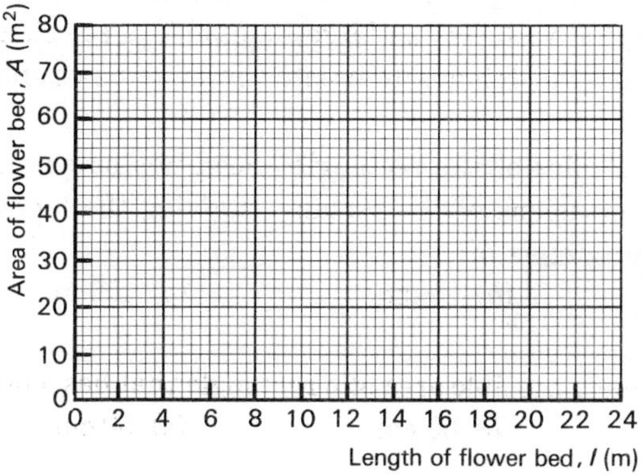

(*d*) Use your graph to find the rectangle that has the largest area. (Give its length, breadth and area.)

Exercise 6 **R**

Calculate the areas of the following shapes:

1.

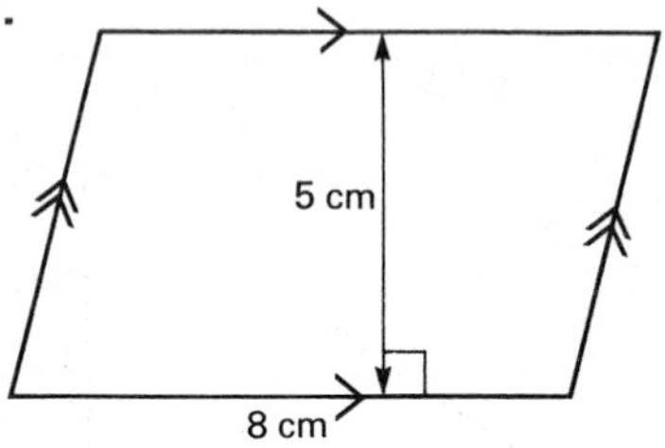

2.

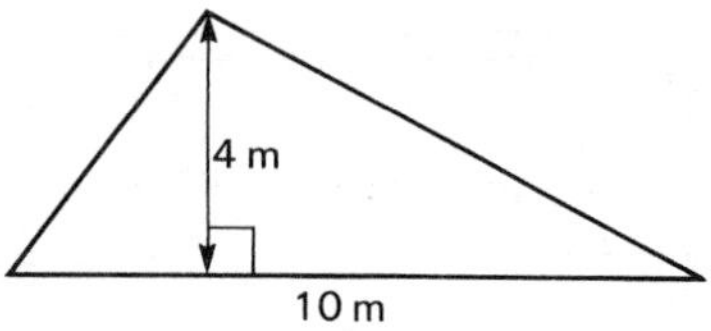

3.

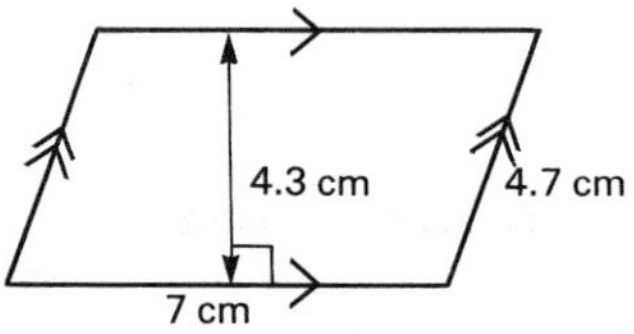

4.

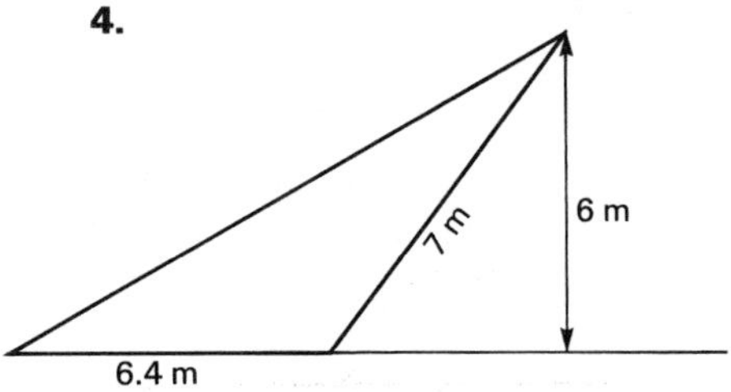

5. A parallelogram with base 9 m and perpendicular height 4.2 m.

6. A parallelogram with base 50 mm and perpendicular height 36 mm.

7. A triangle with base 62 mm and perpendicular height 30 mm.

8. A triangle with base 7.7 cm and perpendicular height 5.1 cm.

9.

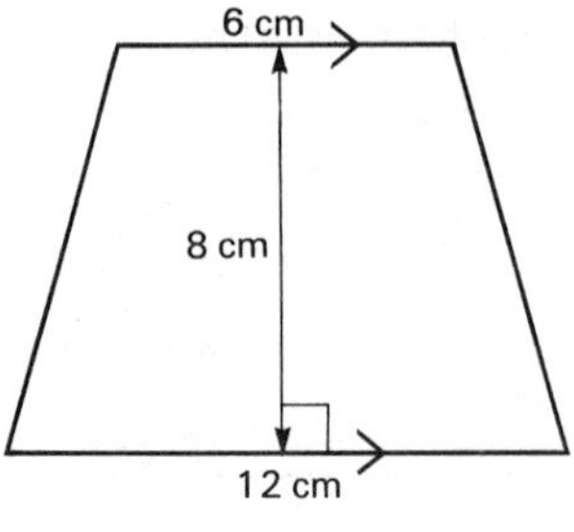

10.

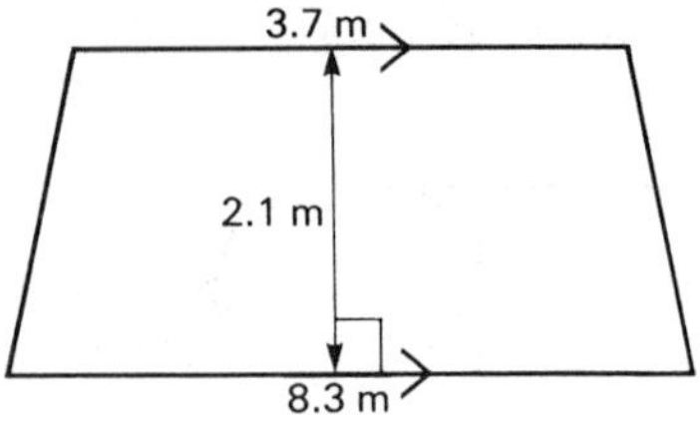

Exercise 7

Calculate the missing base or perpendicular height:

1. Area $= 84\ cm^2$

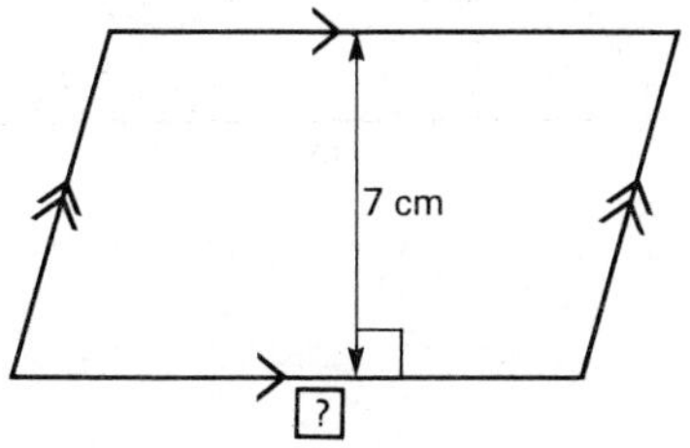

2. Area $= 10.4\ m^2$

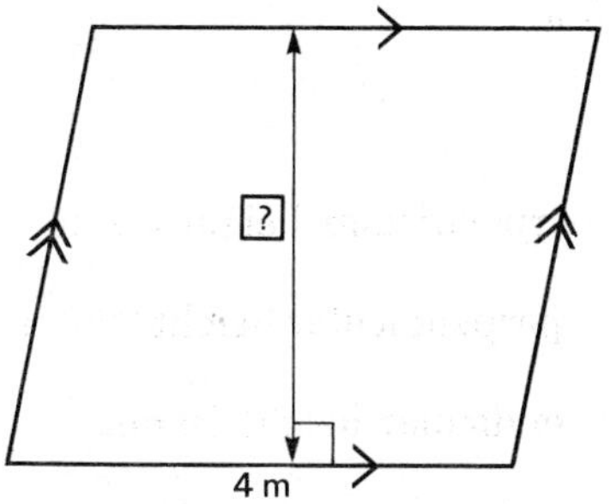

3. Area $= 44.7\ cm^2$

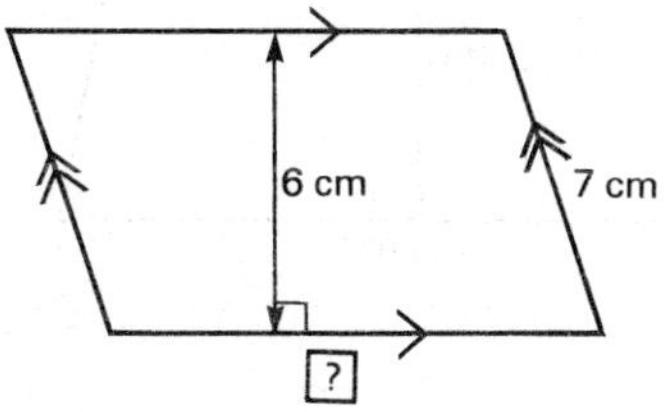

4. Area $= 340\ mm^2$

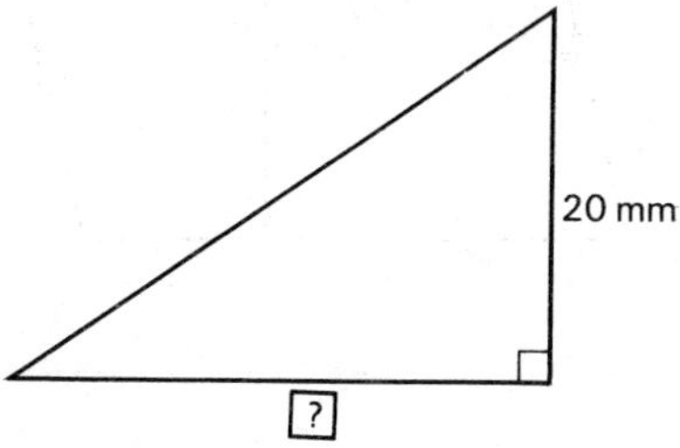

5. Area $= 6\ cm^2$

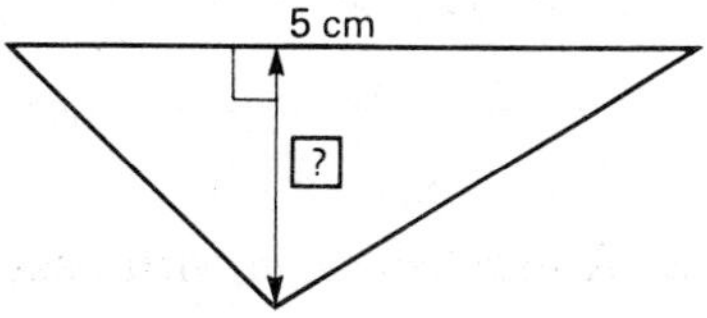

6. Area $= 30\ m^2$

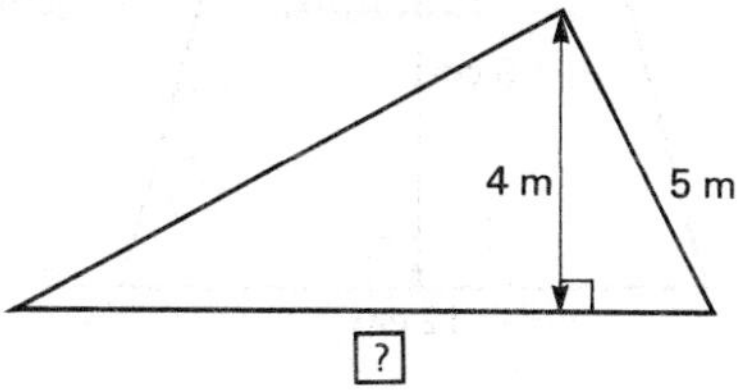

Exercise 8

By measuring then calculating, find the area of each of the following shapes:

1.

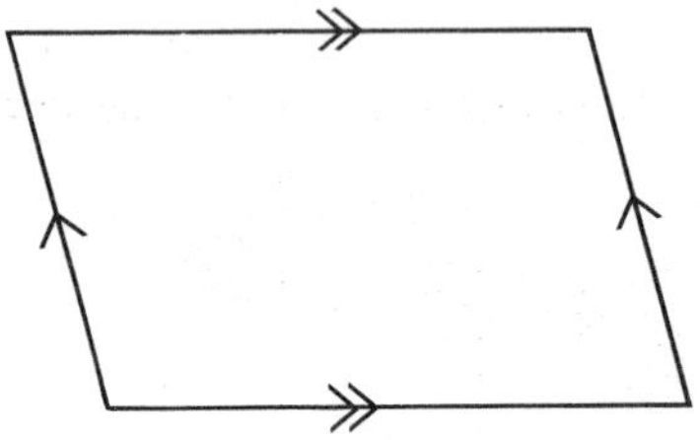

3.

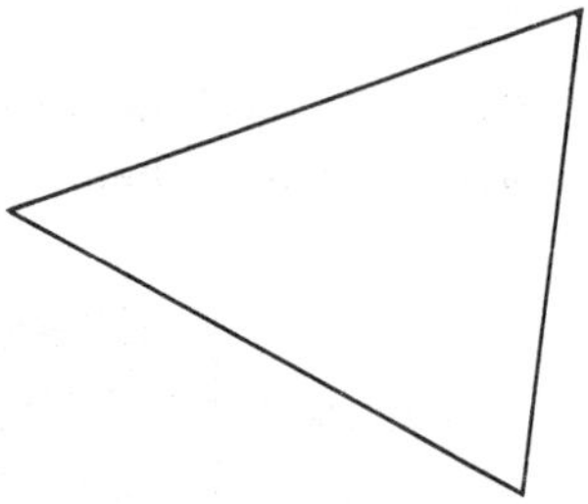

2.

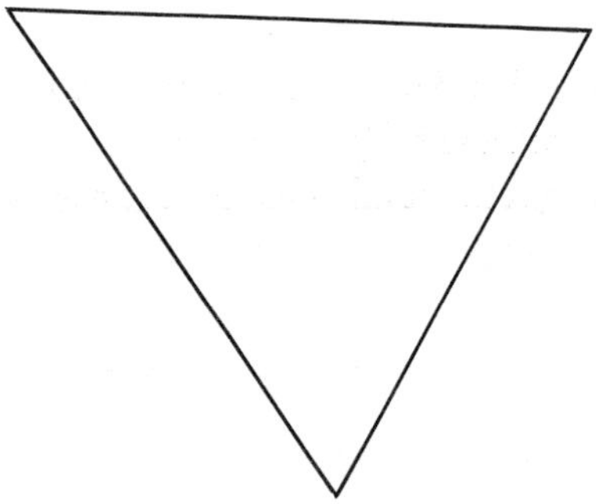

4.

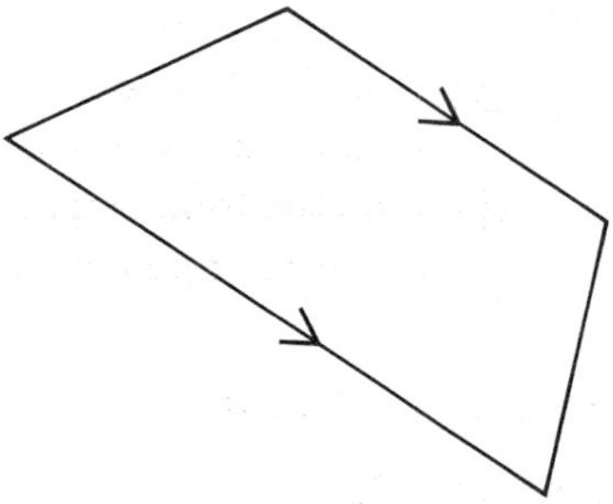

Exercise 9

R

Reminder: Circumference of a circle, $C = \pi d$.

1. A circular cycle track has a diameter of 120 m. Find its circumference using $\pi = 3$.

2. A cylindrical waste-paper bin, as shown, has a diameter of 20 cm. Calculate the distance around the bin using $\pi = 3.14$.

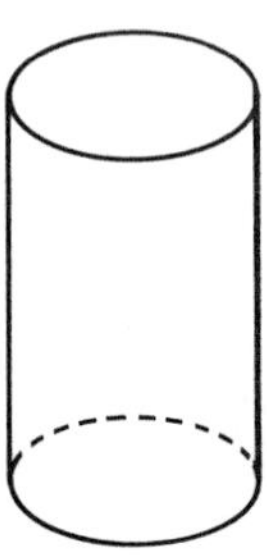

3. A circular shaving mirror with diameter 14 cm has a metal rim. How long is the rim? (Use $\pi = 3\frac{1}{7}$.)

4. The sketches show some kitchen containers with two metal bands around each of them:

The diameter of each container is: tea 90 mm, coffee 120 mm, sugar 144 mm and flour 168 mm.

(*a*) Calculate the length of each metal band using $\pi = 3.142$. (Give each answer correct to three significant figures.)

(*b*) Find the total length of all eight metal bands giving the answer in metres rounded to 3 s.f.

Area of a Circle

Exercise 10

A 1. Cut two circles out of coloured, gummed paper. Use two different colours and make the circles the same size; the diameters should be less than 50 mm.

2. Divide both circles into sixteen equal sectors but do not cut them out.

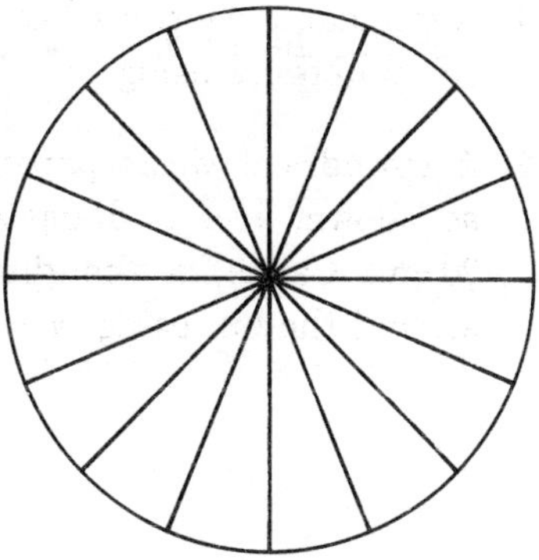

3. Cut both circles in half, giving four semi-circles.

4. Cut out the sectors of two of the semi-circles, one of each colour. (You should now have two semi-circles, one of each colour, eight sectors in one colour and eight sectors in the other colour.)

5. Stick the two semi-circles on to your page to give a full circle then stick the sectors on to your page as shown in the following sketches:

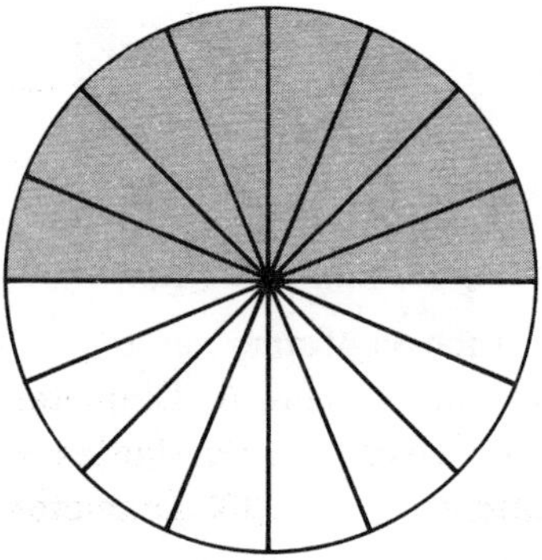

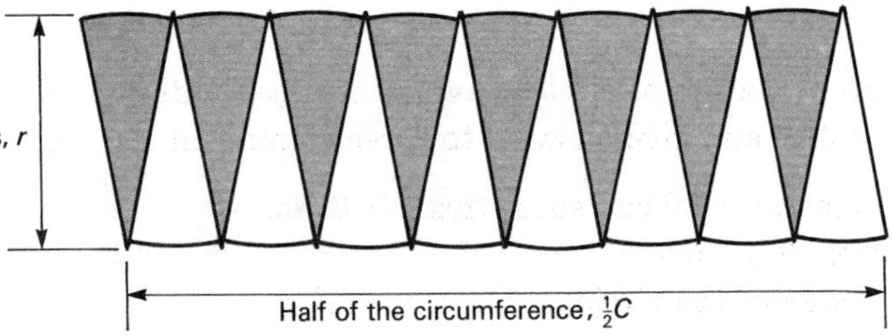

$$
\begin{aligned}
\text{Area of the circle} &= \text{area of the parallelogram} \\
&= b \times h \\
&= \tfrac{1}{2}C \times r \\
&= \tfrac{1}{2}\pi d \times r \qquad (\text{since } C = \pi d) \\
&= \tfrac{1}{2}\pi \times 2r \times r \quad (\text{since } d = 2r) \\
&= \pi \times r \times r \\
\text{so the area of a circle} &= \underline{\underline{\pi r^2}}
\end{aligned}
$$

6. Copy the above text that shows how to obtain a formula for the area of a circle.

Exercise 11

Calculate the area of each circle using $\pi = 3$:

1.

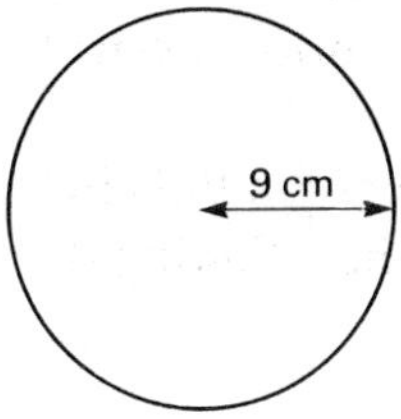

3.

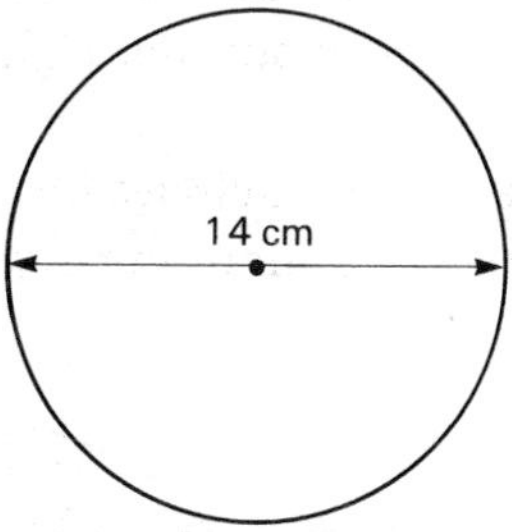

2.

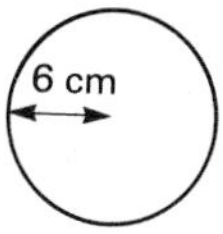

4.

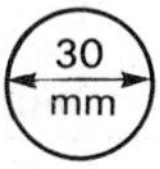

5. Radius = 11 cm
6. Radius = 12 m
7. Diameter = 120 mm
8. Diameter = 2 m
9. Radius = 4.5 cm
10. Diameter = 8.2 cm

Exercise 12

Calculate the areas of circles having the given radius or diameter. Use $\pi = 3.14$ and give answers to three significant figures.

e.g. diameter = 16 cm so radius r = 8 cm.

Area of a circle $= \pi r^2$

so area of the circle $= 3.14 \times 8^2 \text{ cm}^2$

$= 3.14 \times 64 \text{ cm}^2$

$= 200.96 \text{ cm}^2$

$= \underline{\underline{201 \text{ cm}^2 \quad \text{(to 3 s.f.)}}}$

1.

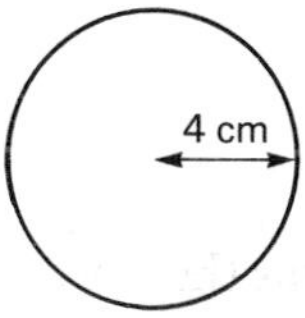

2.

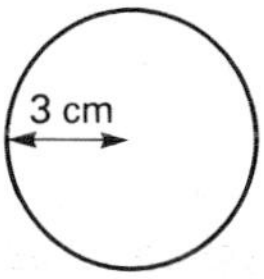

3.

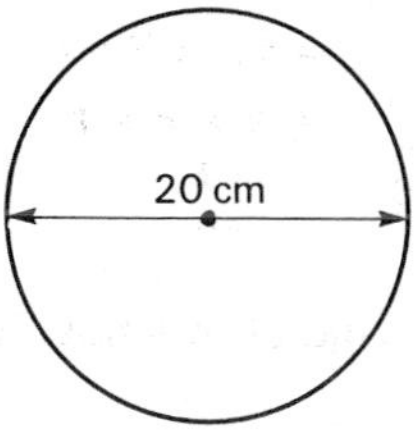

4.

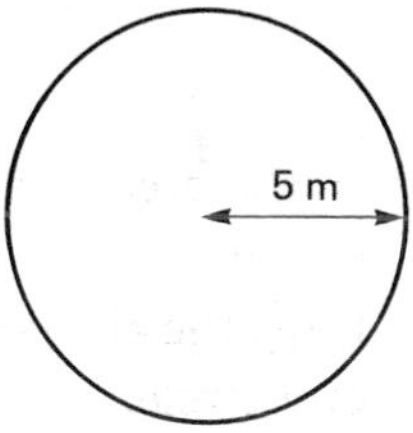

5. Diameter = 18 m
6. Radius = 3.5 cm
7. Diameter = 9.4 m
8. Radius = 28 mm
9. Radius = 8.3 cm
10. Radius = 79 mm

Exercise 13

Work out the following, giving answers correct to 3 significant figures:

1. A circular flower bed has a diameter of 4 m. Find its area. (Use $\pi = 3.14$.)
2. An LP record has a diameter of 12 in. Using $\pi = 3.14$, find the area of one side in square inches.
3. The radius of the lid of a paint tin is 45 mm. What area of metal is needed to make it? (Use $\pi = 3.142$ and presume that the lid is flat.)

4. The shaving mirror in Exercise 9, p. 139 has a diameter of 14 cm. Find its area using $\pi = \frac{22}{7}$.
5. The diameter of a circular window in a church is 1.8 m. What area of glass was used in making it ($\pi = 3.142$)?
6. A circular metal tray has a radius of 16 cm. Find the area of metal used in making it ($\pi = 3.14$).
7. A circular plastic template has a radius of 23 mm. Find its area using $\pi = 3.14$.
8. A pastry cutter has a diameter of 7.5 cm. Find the area of the top of each piece of pastry that is cut out to make scones ($\pi = 3.14$).

Exercise 14

In the Rhind Papyrus (about 1580 BC) a scribe (in problem 50), wrote how to calculate the area of a circle. He wrote: 'Subtract from the diameter its one-ninth part and square the remainder.'

This can be written as a formula using symbols as follows:

$$\text{Area of a circle, } A = \left(d - \frac{d}{9}\right)^2 \text{ where } d \text{ is the diameter.}$$

Use the Egyptian formula to find the area of some of the circles in Exercise 12, pp. 141–2 (give the answers to three significant figures). Compare the answers obtained using the Egyptian formula with those obtained in Exercise 12.

Exercise 15

Investigate the following:

1. If the radius of a circle is doubled, its diameter is also doubled.
2. If the diameter of a circle is doubled, its circumference is also doubled.
3. If the radius of a circle is doubled then its area is also doubled.
4. The area of a circle can be found using the formula $A = \dfrac{\pi d^2}{4}$ where d is the diameter of the circle.

Exercise 16 Areas of Combinations of Shapes

1. Find the area of the L-shaped room:

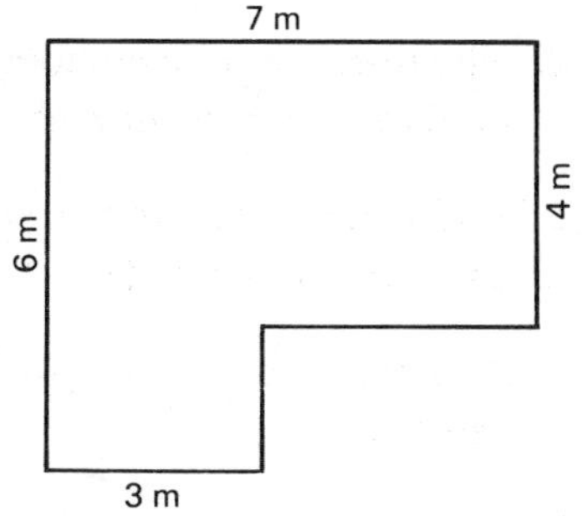

2. A kitchen worktop is shown. Calculate its area (it is 500 mm wide).

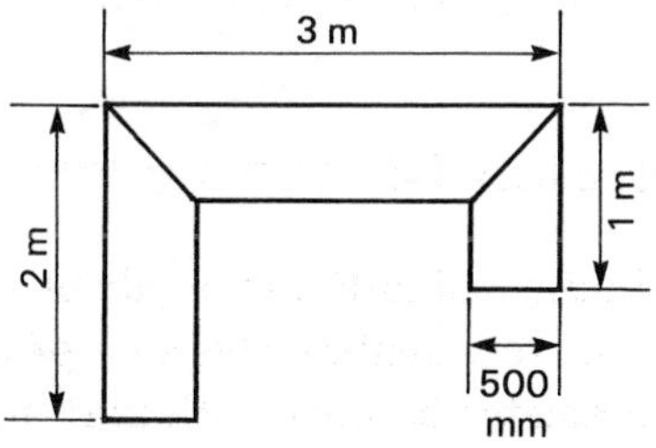

3. Find the area of the gable end of the house:

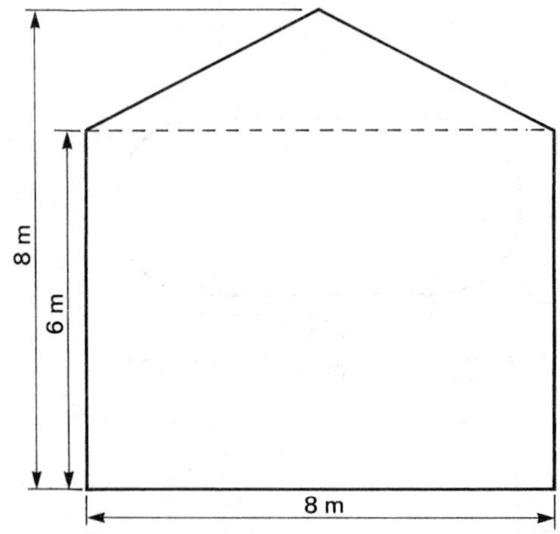

4. Two identical trapezoidal tables are placed together as shown. Calculate the total area of the top.

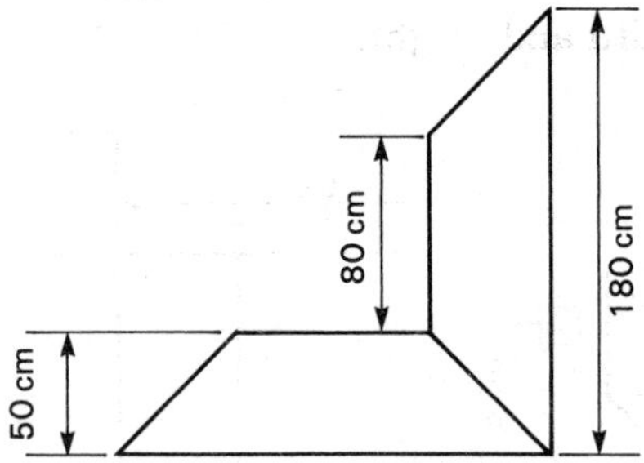

5. Find the area of plastic needed to make a protractor as shown. (Use $\pi = 3.14$.) It is formed with a semi-circle and rectangle.

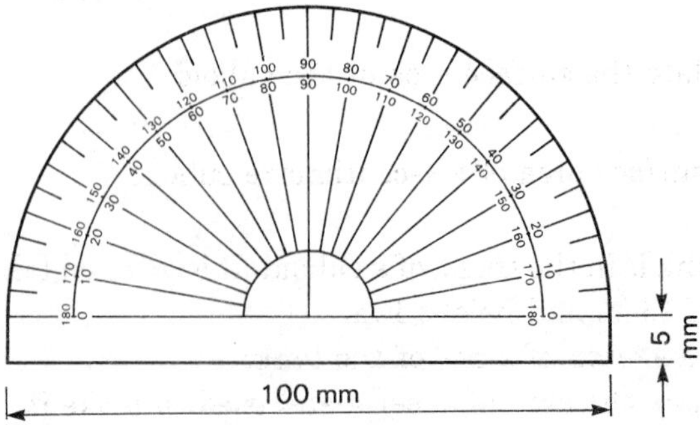

6. A dining-room table has semi-circular ends. Calculate the area of the top. (Use $\pi = 3.14$.)

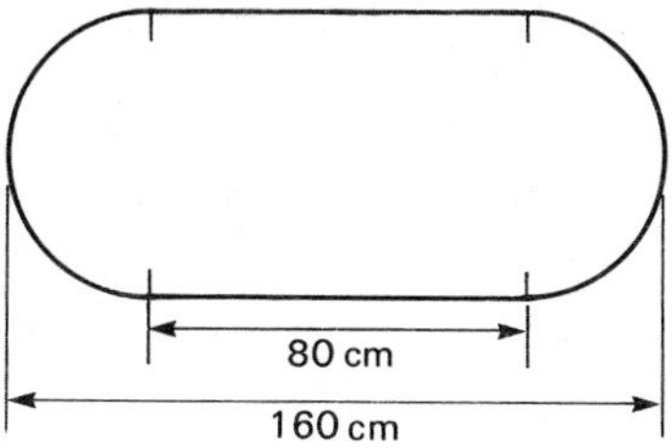

Exercise 17 Surface Area of Cuboids

1. (*a*) Here is a drawing of a cuboid and its net. Copy the cuboid but not the net. On your drawing of the cuboid, mark the size of its length, breadth and height.

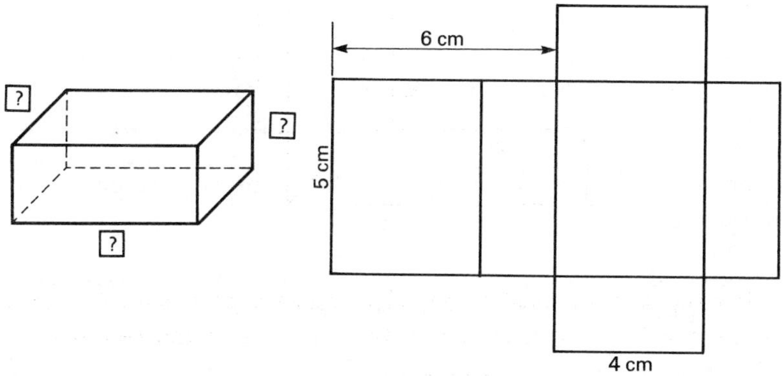

(*b*) Calculate the surface area of the cuboid.

2. Find the surface area of a 4-centimetre cube.

3. A water tank is in the shape of a cuboid. It is an open tank of length 2 m, width 1.5 m and height 1 m.
(*a*) Draw a sketch of a net of the tank.
(*b*) Calculate the area of sheet metal used to make it.

4. A classroom is 10 m long, 8 m wide and 3.5 m high. One long wall, both short walls and the ceiling are to be painted. Calculate:
   (*a*) the total area to be painted,
   (*b*) the number of litres of paint needed if 1 ℓ of paint covers 14 m^2 and if two coats of paint are used.

Exercise 18 Volumes of Cuboids

A 1. Calculate the volume of air in a room that measures 7 m by 5 m by 3 m.

2. Calculate the volume of air in a room that measures 5 m × 4 m × 2.5 m.

3. A pack of butter measures 10 cm by 6.5 cm by 4 cm. Calculate:
   (*a*) its volume, (*b*) the volume of 12 packs.

4. A crate measures 1.5 m × 1 m × 0.75 m. Calculate its volume.

5. A sand-pit measures 180 cm by 100 cm and is 20 cm deep. Calculate the volume of the sand.

B 1. A petrol tank in the shape of a cuboid measures 70 cm × 30 cm × 20 cm. How many litres of petrol does it hold? (Remember that a volume of 1000 cm^3 holds 1 ℓ of liquid.)

2. A fish tank measures 40 cm by 30 cm by 20 cm. How many litres of water does it hold?

3. A water cistern is 2 m long, 1.5 m wide and 1 m high. How many litres of water does it hold when half full?

4. A gold bar is 15 cm long, 10 cm wide and 2 cm thick. How heavy is it if 1 cm^3 of gold weighs 19 g? (Give the answer in kilograms.)

5. How many tonnes of sand are needed to fill a long-jump pit that measures 10 m by 2.75 m and is 30 cm deep, if 1 m^3 of sand has a mass of 1.6 t?

13 Percentages

Equivalence between Vulgar, Decimal and Percentage Fractions

The relationships between certain frequently used vulgar, decimal and percentage fractions ought to be learnt off by heart, without the need for any method of conversion. Most of these are used in Exercise 1.

Exercise 1

On the left of the page is a list of percentages. Copy the list. Next to each percentage, write its decimal and vulgar-fraction equivalents. Choose your answers from the lists on the right. The first has been done for you.

1. 50% = 0.5 = $\frac{1}{2}$	0.1	$\frac{1}{5}$
2. 25%	0.05	$\frac{1}{8}$
3. 75%	0.7	$\frac{1}{10}$
4. 10%	0.875	$\frac{3}{4}$
5. 20%	0.25	$\frac{3}{20}$
6. 70%	0.025	$\frac{1}{2}$
7. 30%	0.375	$\frac{1}{40}$
8. 80%	0.5	$\frac{7}{10}$
9. 5%	$0.\dot{3}$	$\frac{7}{8}$
10. 15%	0.075	$\frac{1}{4}$
11. $2\frac{1}{2}$%	0.2	$\frac{3}{40}$
12. $12\frac{1}{2}$%	0.8	$\frac{1}{20}$
13. $7\frac{1}{2}$%	0.75	$\frac{3}{8}$
14. $37\frac{1}{2}$%	0.15	$\frac{1}{3}$
15. $87\frac{1}{2}$%	0.3	$\frac{4}{5}$
16. $33\frac{1}{3}$%	0.125	$\frac{3}{10}$

Exercise 2 **M**

Here is a board game that should help you to learn the equivalences between vulgar, decimal and percentage fractions. A copy of the board is given shown opposite.

Copies of the spinners are given here.

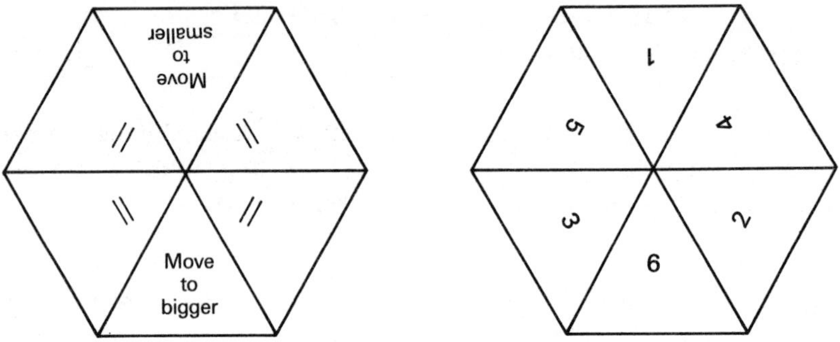

A larger board and larger spinners (to be cut out) are given in *3G Copy Masters*.

Also required are either 1, 2, 3 or 4 counters (transparent, coloured plastic is best) for each of the two players. Each player should have a different colour. The rules of the game are the same however many counters are used. I suggest that each player should use two counters when they first play.

Rules
The first player's counters are placed on the shaded hexagons at one end of the board. If less than four counters are used the player can choose which of the four shaded hexagons to use. The second player does the same at the other end of the board and the game can begin.

Player 1 spins both spinners. The number on the spinner shows that player 1 should move any *one* of his counters that number of places in any direction. (The counter may be moved forwards, backwards and sideways during the one move, but should not visit the same hexagon twice during that move.) The other spinner shows player 1 the type of hexagon the counter should be moved to ('=' to the same value, 'move to bigger' value or 'move to smaller' value). At any time during the game, if it is possible to move somewhere, the player must move, even if it means moving backwards.

Player 2 now plays in the same way.

Board for Percentages Game

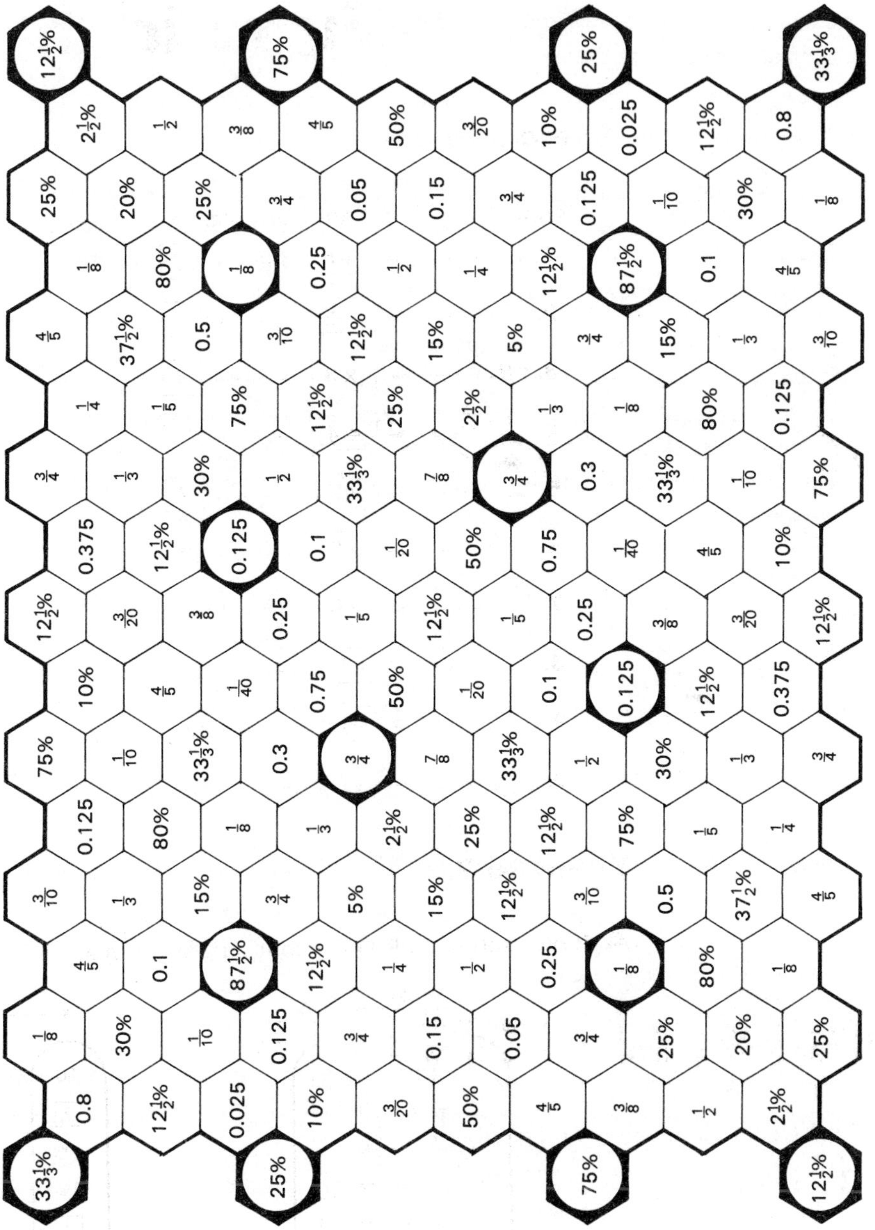

Play continues following the same rules for moving as for the first move.

The winner is the person whose counters first reach the shaded hexagons at the opposite end of the board. When a counter reaches the other end it is 'home' and is never moved again.

All of a player's counters may be in play at once. However, at any one move, only one counter may be moved.

If at any time, the spinner shows a six, the player who obtained the six is allowed another turn. However, a move of six must be made before taking the extra turn. If at any time a player is unable to move then it is the other player's turn.

The shaded hexagons are 'safe' positions. Other hexagons are unsafe. If player 1 has a counter on a hexagon that is unsafe and player 2 is able during a move to get to that position, the move can be made to that hexagon. Player 1 must return the counter that was at that position to any one of the four starting hexagons. However, if a player's counter is on a 'safe' hexagon then the other player is not allowed to move to that position.

Exercise 3 Conversions between Vulgar, Decimal and Percentage Fractions

You may use a calculator where necessary in any part of this exercise.

A Write each percentage as a decimal:

1. 23%	**6.** 92%	**11.** 28%	**16.** 61%
2. 95%	**7.** 63%	**12.** 87%	**17.** 7%
3. 76%	**8.** 51%	**13.** 19%	**18.** 4%
4. 14%	**9.** 36%	**14.** 73%	**19.** $12\frac{1}{2}\%$
5. 88%	**10.** 45%	**15.** 34%	**20.** $2\frac{1}{2}\%$

B Write each decimal as a percentage:

1. 0.98	**5.** 0.83	**9.** 0.03
2. 0.39	**6.** 0.66	**10.** 0.065
3. 0.16	**7.** 0.48	**11.** 0.58
4. 0.54	**8.** 0.625	**12.** 0.058

C Write each vulgar fraction as a percentage:

1. $\frac{12}{25}$ **4.** $\frac{9}{25}$ **7.** $\frac{11}{40}$ **10.** $\frac{23}{80}$ **13.** $\frac{3}{16}$

2. $\frac{17}{20}$ **5.** $\frac{7}{50}$ **8.** $\frac{37}{40}$ **11.** $\frac{67}{80}$ **14.** $\frac{15}{16}$

3. $\frac{11}{20}$ **6.** $\frac{21}{25}$ **9.** $\frac{23}{40}$ **12.** $\frac{17}{80}$ **15.** $\frac{13}{32}$

D Write each percentage as a vulgar fraction in its simplest terms:

1. 82% **3.** 9% **5.** 24% **7.** 65% **9.** 16%

2. 4% **4.** 45% **6.** 64% **8.** 88% **10.** 95%

E Change each vulgar fraction to a decimal:

1. $\frac{9}{10}$ **4.** $\frac{5}{8}$ **7.** $\frac{13}{40}$ **10.** $\frac{19}{32}$ **13.** $\frac{5}{9}$

2. $\frac{27}{100}$ **5.** $\frac{9}{20}$ **8.** $\frac{5}{16}$ **11.** $\frac{2}{3}$ **14.** $\frac{2}{9}$

3. $\frac{3}{5}$ **6.** $\frac{22}{25}$ **9.** $\frac{11}{16}$ **12.** $\frac{3}{7}$ **15.** $\frac{7}{9}$

F Change each decimal to a vulgar fraction in its lowest terms:

1. 0.7 **4.** 0.38 **7.** 0.12 **10.** 0.08 **13.** 0.015

2. 0.1 **5.** 0.42 **8.** 0.55 **11.** 0.006 **14.** 0.865

3. 0.4 **6.** 0.94 **9.** 0.85 **12.** 0.056 **15.** 0.475

G Change each decimal to a vulgar fraction in its lowest terms:

1. (*a*) 0.3 (*b*) 0.30 (*c*) 0.300

2. (*a*) 0.8 (*b*) 0.80 (*c*) 0.800

3. (*a*) 0.1 (*b*) 0.10 (*c*) 0.100

4. (*a*) 0.25 (*b*) 0.250 (*c*) 0.2500

5. (*a*) 0.72 (*b*) 0.720 (*c*) 0.7200

6. (*a*) 0.9 (*b*) 0.90

7. (*a*) 0.2 (*b*) 0.200

8. (*a*) 0.18 (*b*) 0.180

9. (*a*) 0.68 (*b*) 0.6800

10. (*a*) 0.32 (*b*) 0.320 00

Write what you notice about the answers to each question in part G.

H Change each decimal into a vulgar fraction in its lowest terms:

1. (*a*) 0.9	(*b*) 0.09	(*c*) 0.009
2. (*a*) 0.2	(*b*) 0.02	(*c*) 0.002
3. (*a*) 0.5	(*b*) 0.05	(*c*) 0.005
4. (*a*) 0.75	(*b*) 0.075	(*c*) 0.0075
5. (*a*) 0.25	(*b*) 0.025	(*c*) 0.0025
6. (*a*) 0.36	(*b*) 0.036	(*c*) 0.0036
7. (*a*) 0.92	(*b*) 0.092	(*c*) 0.0092
8. (*a*) 0.52	(*b*) 0.052	(*c*) 0.0052
9. (*a*) 0.46	(*b*) 0.046	(*c*) 0.0046
10. (*a*) 0.65	(*b*) 0.065	(*c*) 0.0065
11. (*a*) 0.6	(*b*) 0.06	
12. (*a*) 0.76	(*b*) 0.076	
13. (*a*) 0.44	(*b*) 0.0044	
14. (*a*) 0.28	(*b*) 0.000 28	
15. (*a*) 0.84	(*b*) 0.000 84	

16. 0.016
17. 0.0096
18. 0.0008
19. 0.000 56
20. 0.000 000 005

Percentages of Money

Exercise 4

A Find 10% of each sum of money:

1. £20	**10.** £19	**19.** £9.20
2. £70	**11.** £28	**20.** £36.40
3. £400	**12.** £603	**21.** £89.30
4. £500	**13.** £199	**22.** £14.10
5. £760	**14.** £4	**23.** £72.60
6. £240	**15.** 60 p	**24.** £499.90
7. £2000	**16.** 50 p	**25.** £608.80
8. £5600	**17.** £0.70	**26.** £511.30
9. £60	**18.** £2.50	**27.** £899.50

B Find:

1. 50% of £40
2. 50% of £90
3. 50% of £300
4. 50% of £24
5. 50% of £8
6. 25% of £12
7. 25% of £600
8. 20% of £35
9. 60% of £20
10. 30% of £50
11. 75% of £16
12. 10% of £80
13. 5% of £80
14. 5% of £100
15. 5% of £400
16. 50% of £7
17. 50% of £2.50
18. 25% of £3
19. 25% of £10.20
20. 75% of £1.80
21. 20% of £12
22. 20% of £8.40
23. 80% of £4.50
24. 30% of £12.70
25. 50% of £2.36
26. 40% of £61.30
27. 90% of £256
28. 70% of £133
29. 60% of £91.80
30. 15% of £29.60

C Find:

1. $33\frac{1}{3}$% of £96
2. $33\frac{1}{3}$% of £4.50
3. 10% of £7
4. 5% of £7
5. $2\frac{1}{2}$% of £10
6. $2\frac{1}{2}$% of £24
7. $7\frac{1}{2}$% of £20
8. $7\frac{1}{2}$% of £30
9. $12\frac{1}{2}$% of £76
10. $12\frac{1}{2}$% of £39.20

Exercise 5

Work these out giving each answer correct to the nearest penny:

e.g. 1 10% of £7.98 = 80 p (to the nearest penny)

e.g. 2 50% of £4.29 = £2.15 (to the nearest penny)

1. 10% of £4.99
2. 10% of £6.72
3. 25% of £2.25
4. 25% of £15.81
5. 50% of £2.47
6. 30% of £9.45
7. 20% of £21.66
8. 15% of £5.70
9. 45% of £19.76
10. 7% of £41.50
11. 12% of £36.75
12. 17% of £118.70
13. $33\frac{1}{3}$% of £6.40
14. $33\frac{1}{3}$% of £47
15. $2\frac{1}{2}$% of £15.12
16. $12\frac{1}{2}$% of £9.99

VAT

VAT stands for *value added tax*. It is a tax on most goods or services and is set by the government. Sometimes VAT is added to the cost of single items and sometimes prices are given without VAT being added. In this case the total cost of the goods is found and the VAT on the total amount is added at the end. The VAT rate is given as a percentage.

Exercise 6

Throughout this exercise VAT is at 15%.
The price before VAT is given. Find the VAT. (It should be rounded to the nearest penny.)

1. A rubber costing 40 p.

2. A pencil sharpener costing 55 p.

3. A dress costing £26.07.

4. A cinema ticket costing £1.91.

5. A meal costing £6.52.

6. A washing machine costing £247.78.

7. A cassette costing £5.21.

8. A plumber's bill when materials and labour total £53.18.

Exercise 7

In this exercise, the pre-VAT price is given.
Find the price inclusive of VAT, if the rate is 15%. (Round to the nearest penny.)

1. A pack of pencils at £1.71.

2. A writing-pad at 74 p.

3. A fishing-rod at £25.91.

4. A telephone bill at £56.39.

5. A theatre ticket at £3.91.

6. A carpet at £179.80.

7. A holiday at £207.83.

8. A pair of jeans at £17.35.

9. A computer at £139.12.

10. A TV repair at £36.89.

Exercise 8 Discount **M**

In this exercise, give your answers to the nearest penny.

1.

Calculate the discount and the sale price of the items below if the normal selling price is given:

(*a*)

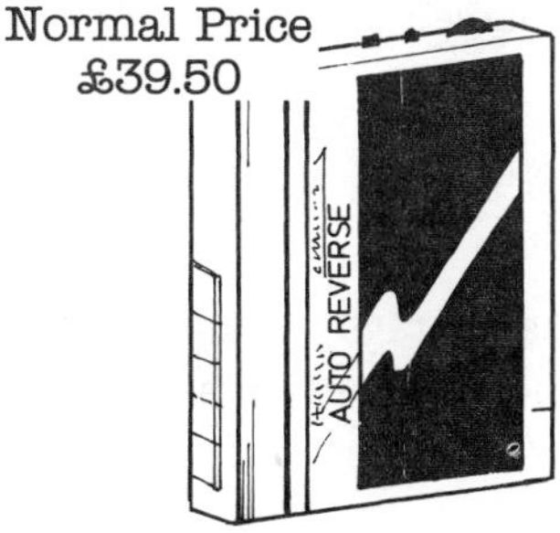

(*b*)

2. The normal full price of kitchen cabinets is shown below.

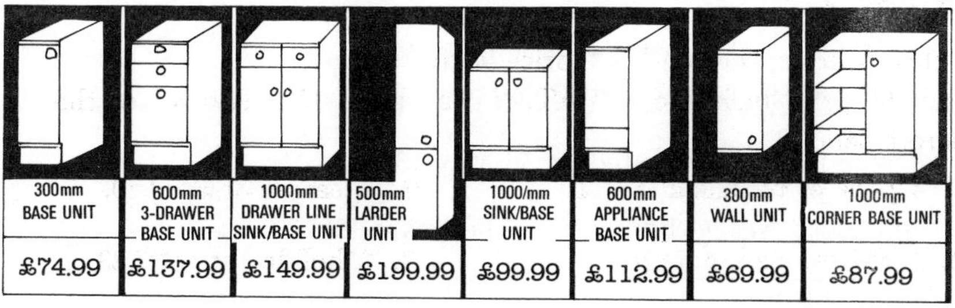

300mm BASE UNIT	600mm 3-DRAWER BASE UNIT	1000mm DRAWER LINE SINK/BASE UNIT	500mm LARDER UNIT	1000/mm SINK/BASE UNIT	600mm APPLIANCE BASE UNIT	300mm WALL UNIT	1000mm CORNER BASE UNIT
£74.99	£137.99	£149.99	£199.99	£99.99	£112.99	£69.99	£87.99

(*a*) Calculate the discount off each item and the sale price of each item if there is a discount of 20%.

(*b*) Calculate the discount off each item and the sale price of each item if there is a discount of 15%.

Savings and Interest

When you put money in a savings *account* in a bank or a building society your money earns you *interest*. Interest is money paid to you by the bank or building society for letting them use your money. It is paid into your *account*. The amount of money in your account is usually recorded in a *passbook* which you keep. (Most banks send you a *statement*, probably monthly, instead of using a passbook.) The passbook (or statement) contains a record of your *transactions*, that is, whether you have made a *deposit* (put money into your account) or a *withdrawal* (taken money out of your account).

The amount of money you have in your account at any particular time is called the *balance*. The amount of interest you get can vary. It depends on the *interest rate* at the time. The interest rate is a percentage. Your interest is a small percentage of the money saved. The interest rate is stated as a certain percentage *per annum* (per year).

e.g. 6% p.a. means that you get 6% interest on the money that has been in your account throughout the year.

Although the interest rate is stated as a percentage per annum, banks and building societies usually calculate their interest on a daily basis. It is, however, normally paid into your account yearly or half-yearly.

Exercise 9 **M**

A copy of a page from a passbook is shown opposite:

Use it to help you to answer these questions:

1. What was the balance on 23 January 1987?

2. How much was deposited on 16 May 1987?

3. How much was withdrawn on 7 February 1987?

4. Was the transaction on 1 April 1987, a deposit or a withdrawal?

5. If interest is paid into the account annually, what was the amount of interest for 1986?

6. What was the total deposit for April 1987?

Branch: 305 GARSTANG Account Number: 041637/50
Name: Mr Ian S. Rich

Date	*Cashier*	*Details*	*Deposits*		*Withdrawals*		*Balance*	
12 DEC 86	JK	Brought forward					284	56
31 DEC 86	BD	Interest	10	89			295	45
8 JAN 87	JK	Cash	71	36			366	81
23 JAN 87	JK	Cash	26	80			393	61
7 FEB 87	BD	Repaid			46	50	347	11
12 MAR 87	BD	Cash	55	41			402	52
1 APR 87	BD	Cheque	43	72			?	
23 APR 87	JK	Cash	18	95			465	19
9 MAY 87	BD	Repaid			69	90	?	
16 MAY 87	JK	Cash	38	68			433	97
30 MAY 87	BD	Cash	82	76			?	
5 JUN 87	JK	Cheque	?				567	18
10 JUN 87	JK	Repaid			94	75	?	
16 JUN 87	JK	Cash	15	19			487	62

7. What was the total of the withdrawals shown on the given page of the passbook above?

8. In the details column when deposits were made, the entry 'cash' or 'cheque' is written. Explain what is meant by (*a*) cash, (*b*) cheque.

9. What balance will be *carried forward* to the next page?

10. Work out what the five missing entries in the table should be.

Exercise 10

For each question, assume the savings have been in the account for a year. Work out in each case the amount of interest per annum using the given rates of interest. Where necessary, round answers to the nearest penny.

e.g. Savings = £240 Interest rate = 7% p.a.
Interest = 7% of £240
= 0.07 × £240
= £16.80

1. Savings = £400 Interest rate = 10% p.a.
2. Savings = £800 Interest rate = 6% p.a.
3. Savings = £650 Interest rate = 8% p.a.
4. Savings = £720 Interest rate = 7% p.a.
5. Savings = £2500 Interest rate = 11% p.a.
6. Savings = £4200 Interest rate = 9% p.a.
7. Savings = £960 Interest rate = 7.0% p.a.
8. Savings = £198 Interest rate = 12.5% p.a.
9. Savings = £324 Interest rate = 9.5% p.a.
10. Savings = £1375 Interest rate = 8.50% p.a.
11. Savings = £16 280 Interest rate = 7.25% p.a.
12. Savings = £846 Interest rate = 8.75% p.a.
13. Savings = £560 Interest rate = 10.18% p.a.
14. Savings = £829 Interest rate = 11.79% p.a.
15. Savings = £4736 Interest rate = 8.57% p.a.

Loans

When you borrow money, interest must be paid on the loan, that is, you must repay the loan together with the interest (an extra sum of money). This interest is calculated from the amount of the loan and the interest rate (a percentage). The interest rate on a loan is usually very much higher than the interest rate for savings. As with savings, the interest rate on loans is also normally stated as a certain percentage per annum.

Exercise 11

For each question, calculate, to the nearest penny, the interest charges per annum:

e.g. Amount borrowed = £1400
*Flat rate of interest = 12% p.a.

Interest = 12% of £1400
= 0.12 × 1400 pounds
= £168

	Amount borrowed (£)	Interest rate (flat rate) (% p.a.)
1.	1000	12
2.	4500	10
3.	2000	15
4.	250	14
5.	400	13
6.	3000	11
7.	5600	12
8.	1500	12.5
9.	4260	13.5
10.	675	11.5

* See the glossary, p. 383.

14 Symmetry

Bilateral and Rotational Symmetry

Exercise 1 R

A For each shape, write its number of lines of bilateral symmetry (there may not be any):

1.

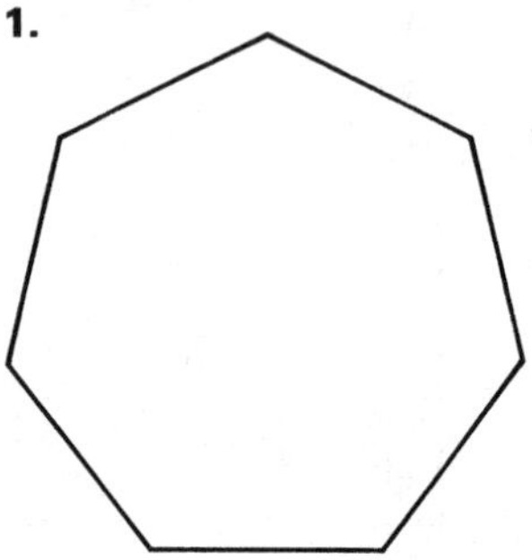

2.

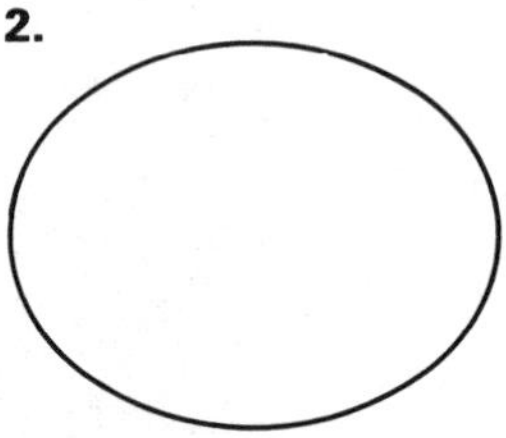

3.

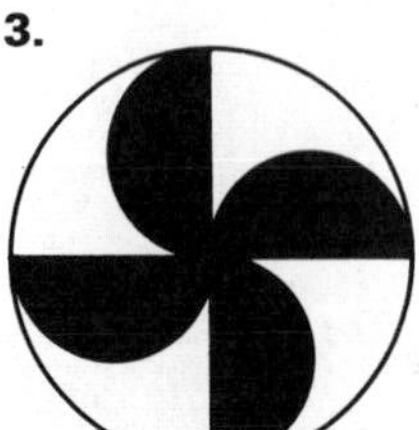

4.

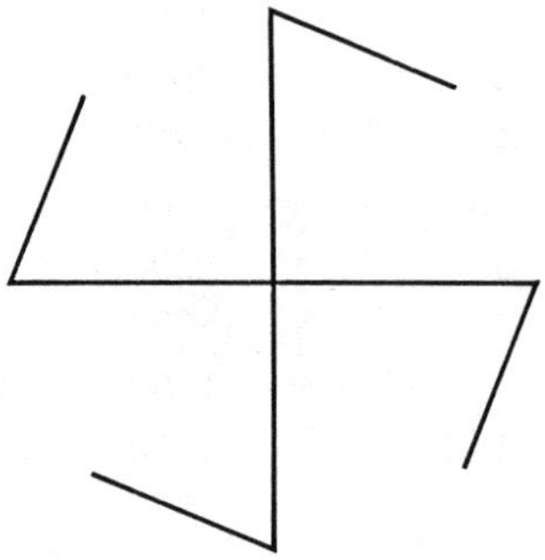

5.

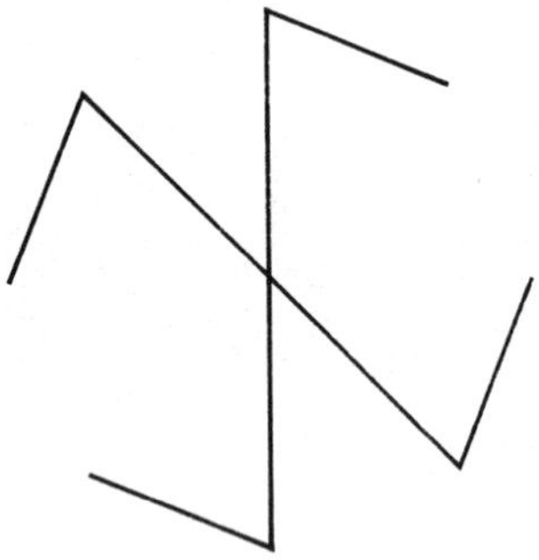

6.

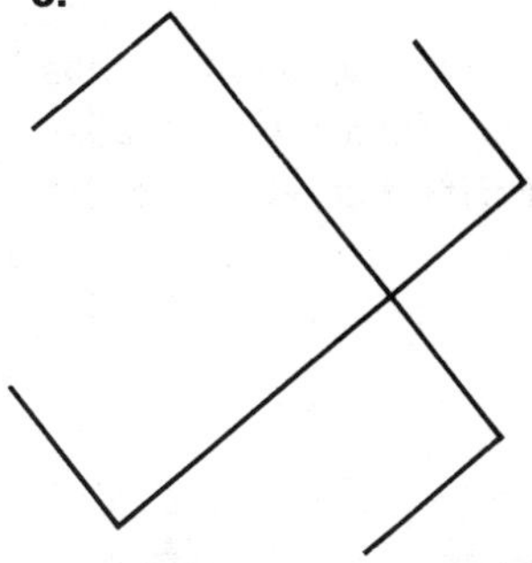

8.

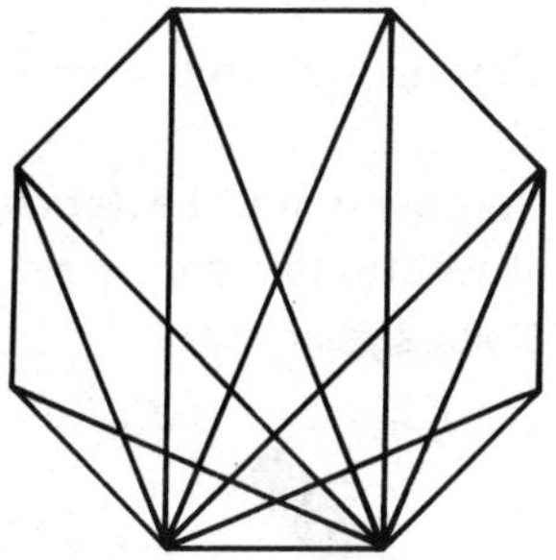

7.

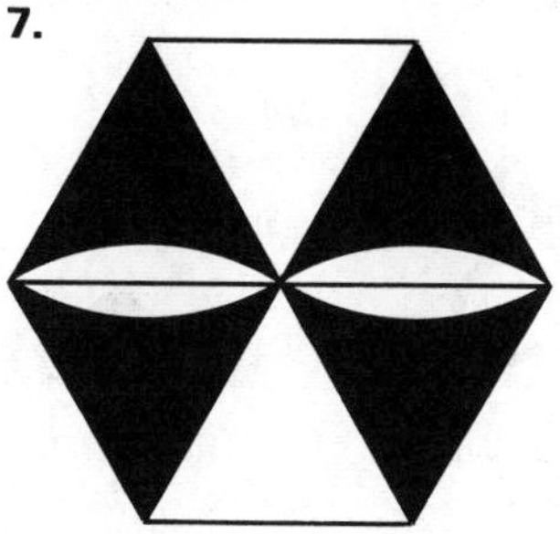

9.

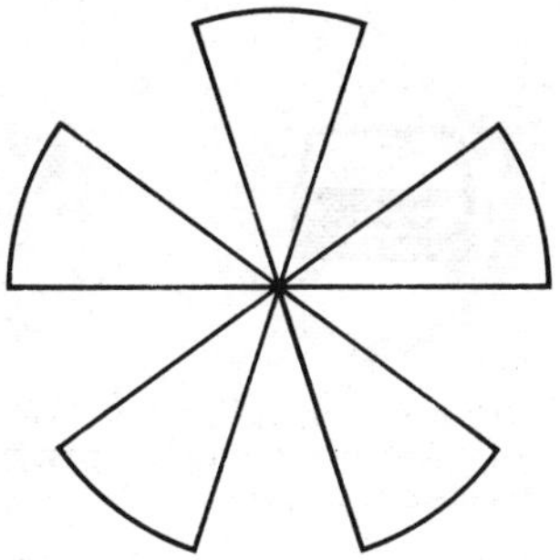

10.

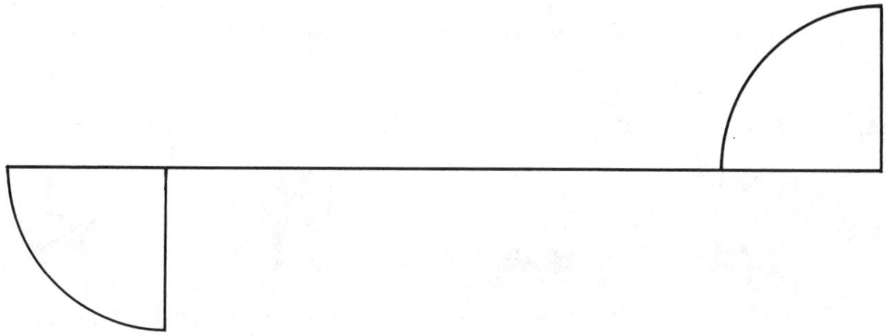

B For each of the shapes in part A, write its order of rotational symmetry if its order of rotational symmetry is greater than 1.

Exercise 2

Throughout this exercise, check whether or not a given item has bilateral symmetry; if it has, write the number of axes. Check also, whether or not the item has rotational symmetry; if it has, give its order of rotational symmetry.

A Road signs:

1.

National speed limit applies

2.

No motor vehicles except solo motorcycles scooters or mopeds

3.

No entry for vehicular traffic

4.

No stopping (clearway)

5.

Keep left

6.

Vehicles may pass either side

7.

Mini-roundabout

8.

Uneven road

9.

Crossroads

10.

Roundabout

11.

Dual carriageway ends

12.

Road narrows on both sides

13.

Two-way traffic straight ahead

14.

Hump bridge

15.

Cattle

16.

Low-flying aircraft or sudden aircraft noise

B Maths symbols:

1. $+$ **3.** $\times$ **5.** $=$ **7.** $\bumpeq$ **9.** $\cap$

2. $-$ **4.** $\div$ **6.** $\approx$ **8.** $\in$ **10.** $\cup$

C Ordnance Survey symbols:

1.  Church or chapel with spire
2.  Church or chapel with tower
3.  Church or chapel without tower or spire
4.  Youth hostel
5.  Bus or coach station

D Flags (ignore the edging for hanging the flags):

1. 

Canada

2. 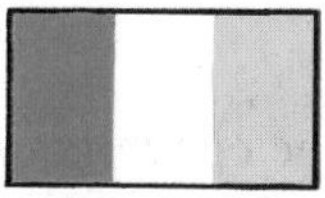

Ireland

3. 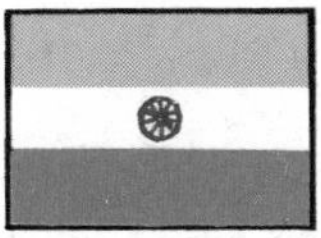

India

4. 

Jamaica

5. 

Turkey

6. 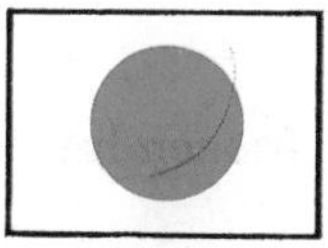

Japan

7. 

Denmark

8. 

Switzerland

9. 

Trinidad & Tobago

10. 

Israel

11. 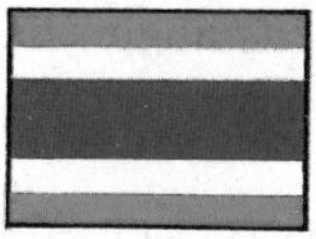

Thailand

12. 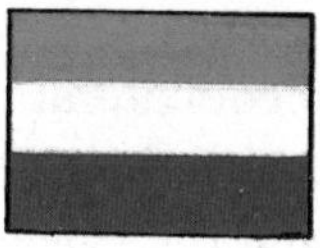

Netherlands

13. 

Morocco

14. 

Sierra Leone

15. 

Belgium

16. 

United Kingdom

Properties of Triangles and Quadrilaterals related to their Symmetries

Exercise 3

A **1.** Copy the given diagram.

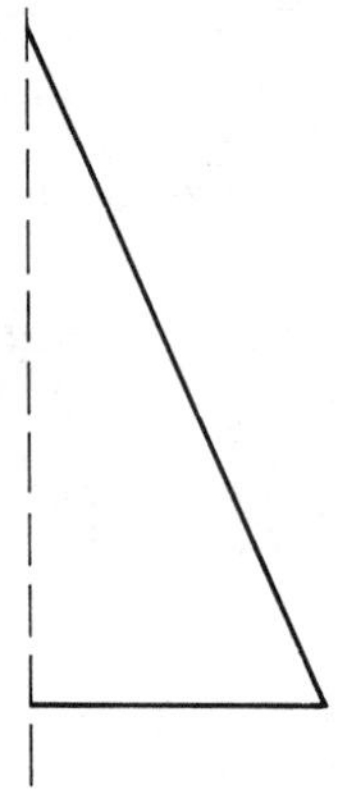

2. Complete your copy so that the broken line is a line of symmetry.

3. What sort of triangle have you obtained?

4. Mark on your triangle the sides that are equal.

5. Mark on your triangle the angles that are equal.

B **1.** Carefully construct an equilateral triangle with sides that measure 50 mm, and label its vertices P, Q and R (labelling clockwise).

2. Draw the lines of bilateral symmetry and label the point of intersection of these lines of symmetry as C.

3. If an identical equilateral triangle was cut out and placed on top of your drawing with their vertices matching, P on top of P, Q on Q and R on R, and the cut-out was then rotated anticlockwise about C through $\frac{2}{3}$ of a turn:

(*a*) On which side would side PQ of the cut-out lie?
(*b*) On which angle would angle R land exactly on top of?

Exercise 4 M

A Copy and complete these diagrams where the broken lines are lines of symmetry:

1.

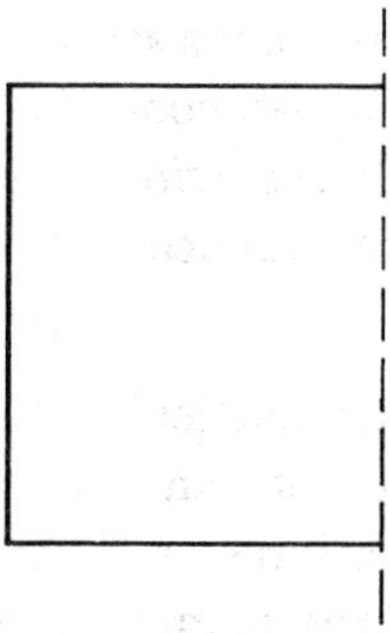

4.

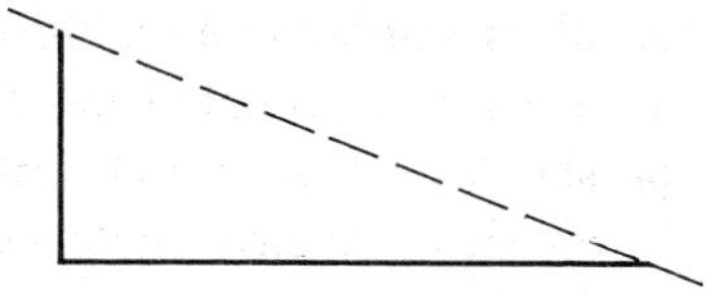

2.

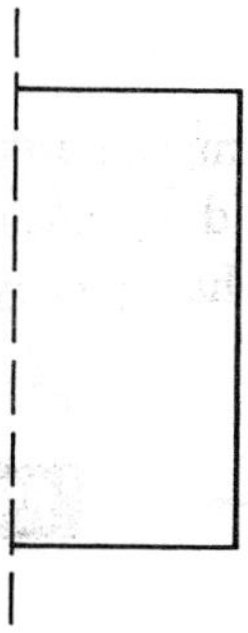

5.

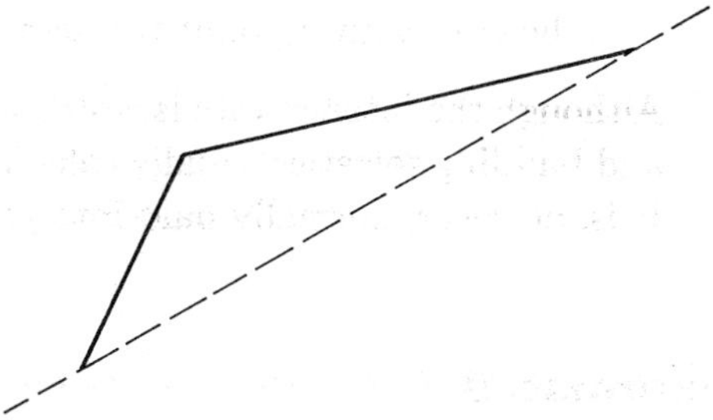

3.

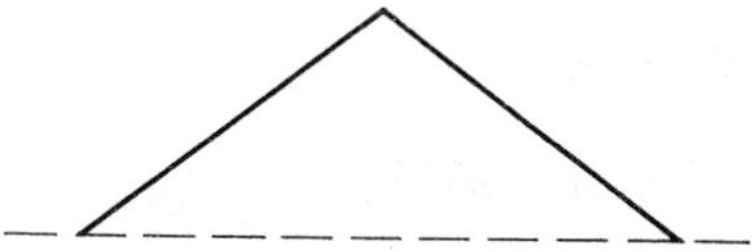

6.

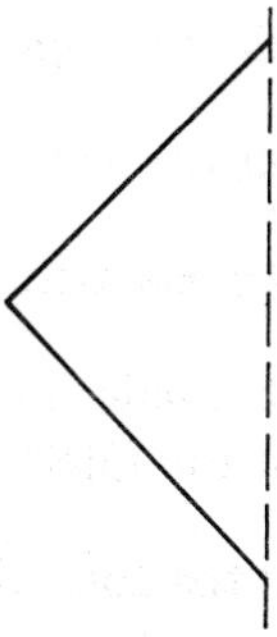

7.

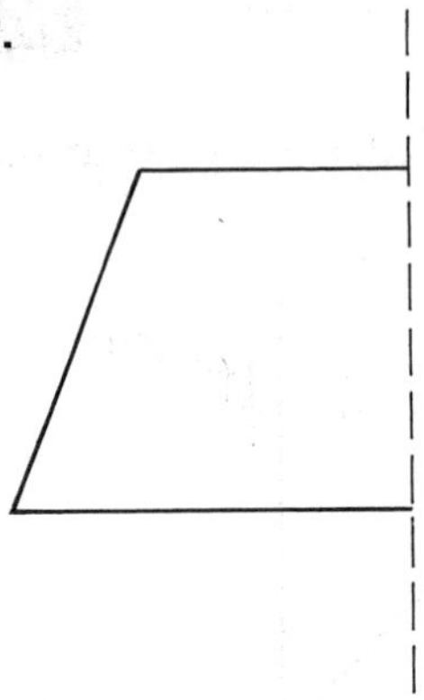

10.

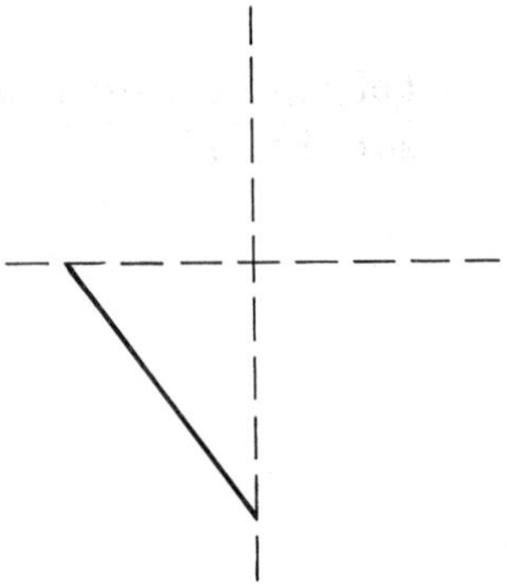

8.

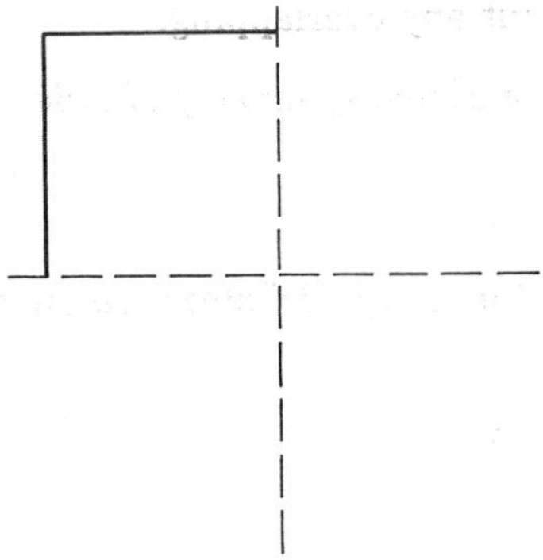

11.

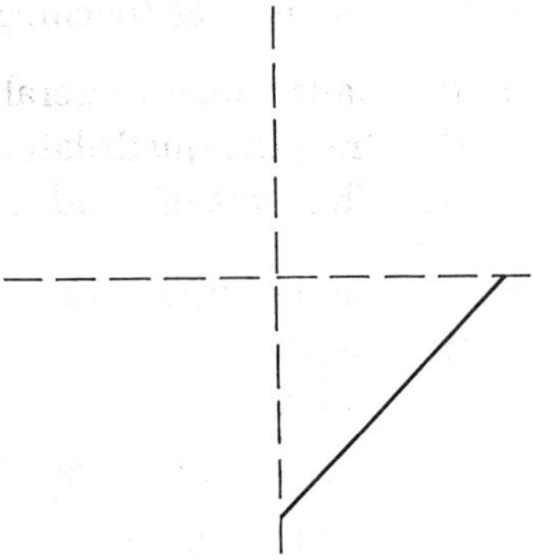

9.

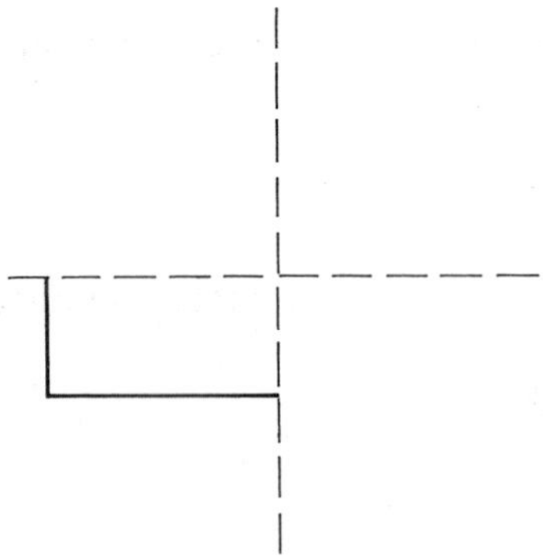

12.

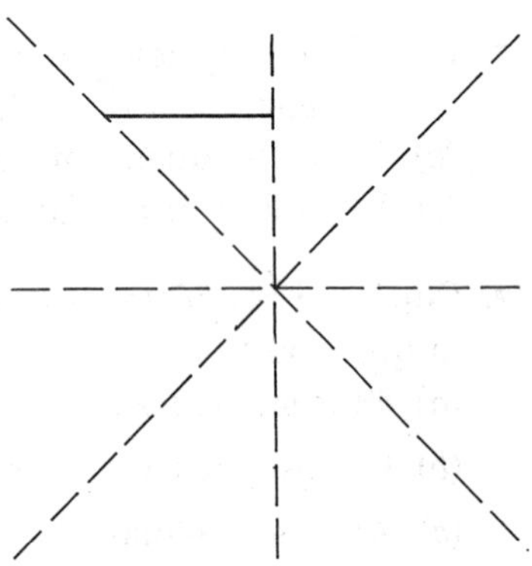

B Write the names of the quadrilaterals obtained in part A.

Exercise 5 **M**

Cut out of paper or card, four identical right-angled, isosceles triangles of the size shown here.

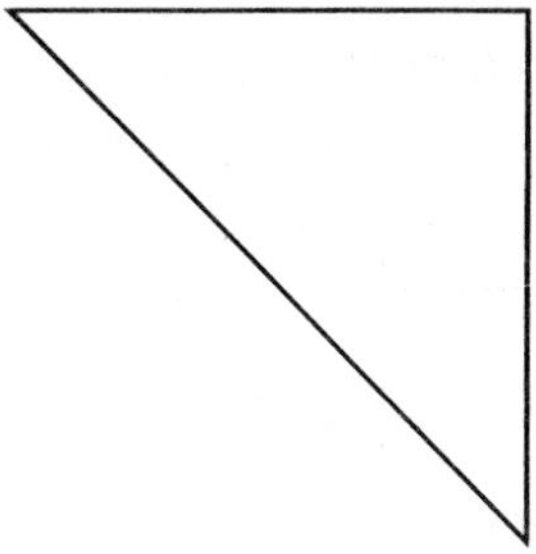

Throughout this exercise use all four triangles. They must be placed together with sides touching and without any overlapping.

A **1.** (*a*) Make a quadrilateral that has rotational symmetry of order 4.
(*b*) Draw the quadrilateral.
(*c*) What sort of quadrilateral is it?

2. Copy and complete these sentences for the quadrilateral obtained in question 1:
(*a*) All sides are [?] in length.
(*b*) Opposite sides are [?].
(*c*) All four angles are [?].
(*d*) The diagonals are [?] in length.
(*e*) The diagonals [?] each other at [?].

B **1.** (*a*) Make a quadrilateral that has exactly two axes of bilateral symmetry.
(*b*) Draw the quadrilateral.
(*c*) What sort of quadrilateral is it?

2. Copy and complete these sentences for the quadrilateral obtained in question 1:
(*a*) Opposite sides are [?] in length.
(*b*) Opposite sides are also [?].
(*c*) All angles equal [?] °.
(*d*) The diagonals [?] each other.
(*e*) The diagonals are [?] in length.

C **1.** (*a*) Make a quadrilateral that has rotational symmetry but not bilateral symmetry.
(*b*) Draw the quadrilateral.
(*c*) What sort of quadrilateral is it?

2. Copy and complete for the quadrilateral obtained in question 1.
(*a*) Opposite sides are [?] in length.
(*b*) Opposite sides are also [?].
(*c*) Opposite angles are [?].
(*d*) Diagonals [?] each other.

D Make any other quadrilaterals. Draw each quadrilateral and write about those you are able to make.

E Make a right-angled isosceles triangle and draw it.

F Make a shape that has rotational symmetry of order 4 but does not have bilateral symmetry. Draw it.

G Make any other symmetrical shapes. Draw each one and describe its symmetry.

Exercise 6

Cut out of paper or card four identical right-angled, scalene triangles of the size shown here.

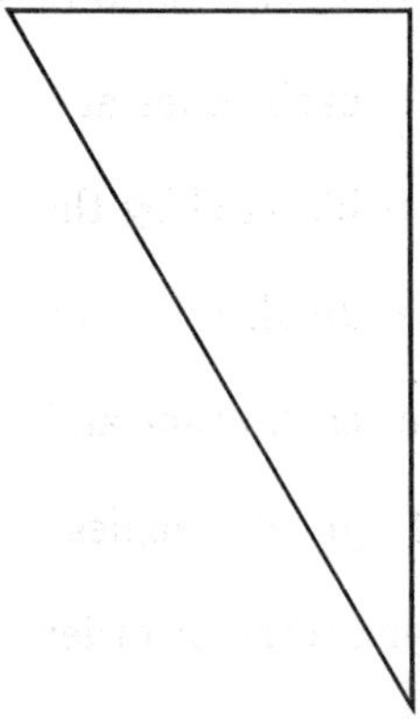

Throughout this exercise use all four triangles. They must be placed together with sides touching and without any overlapping.

A 1. Make a quadrilateral that has both rotational and bilateral symmetry but does not contain a right-angle.

2. Draw the quadrilateral.

3. What sort of quadrilateral is it?

B Make any other quadrilaterals that you can find. Draw each one.

C Make any other symmetrical shapes. Draw each one and describe its symmetry.

Exercise 7

Copy each statement then next to it write the names of the quadrilaterals suggested by that property. (Sometimes there may only be one quadrilateral.)

1. All four sides are equal.
2. Only opposite sides are equal and parallel, and all the angles are right-angles.
3. There is exactly one pair of parallel sides.
4. All four angles are right-angles.
5. The diagonals are of equal length.
6. Opposite angles are equal but are not right-angles.
7. There are four equal sides but no right-angles.
8. The diagonals bisect each other at right-angles.
9. Only one diagonal is bisected by the other.
10. Diagonals are perpendicular.
11. The diagonals bisect each other and are of different length.
12. Exactly one pair of opposite angles are equal.
13. It has rotational symmetry of order 2 and the diagonals are of equal length.
14. It has rotational symmetry of order 2 but does not have bilateral symmetry.

Exercise 8

Calculate the angles labelled with letters:

1.

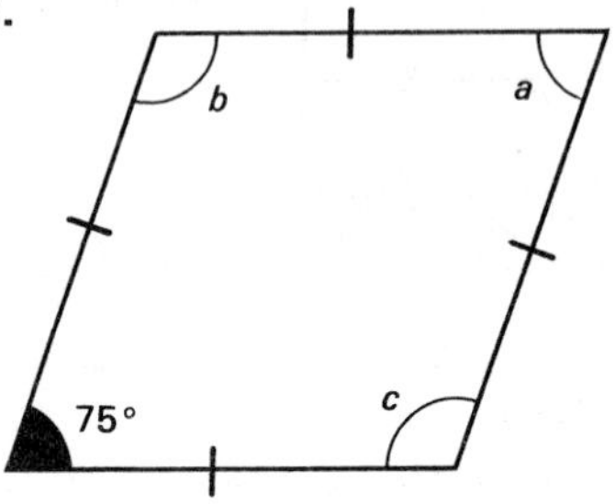

2.

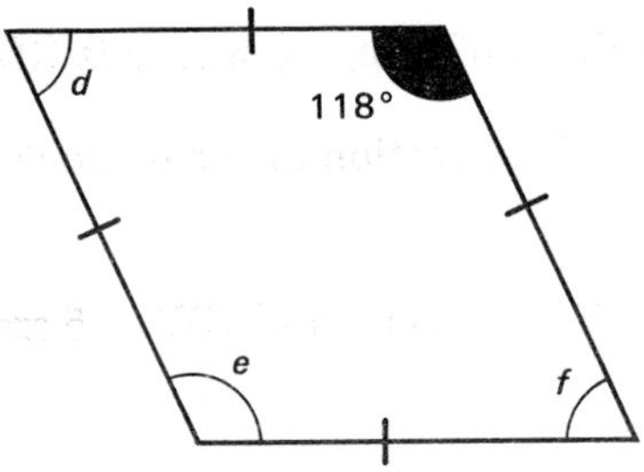

3.

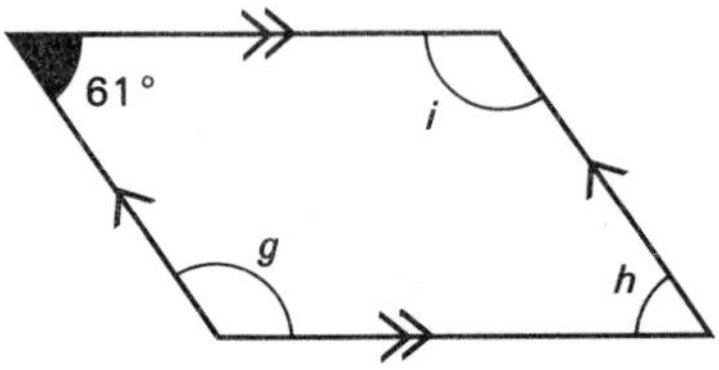

4.

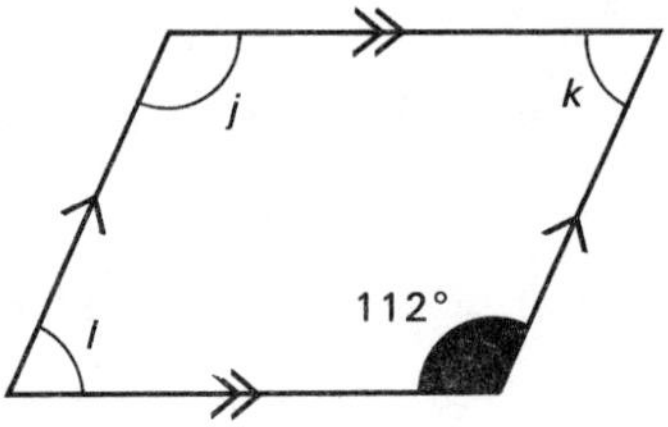

5.

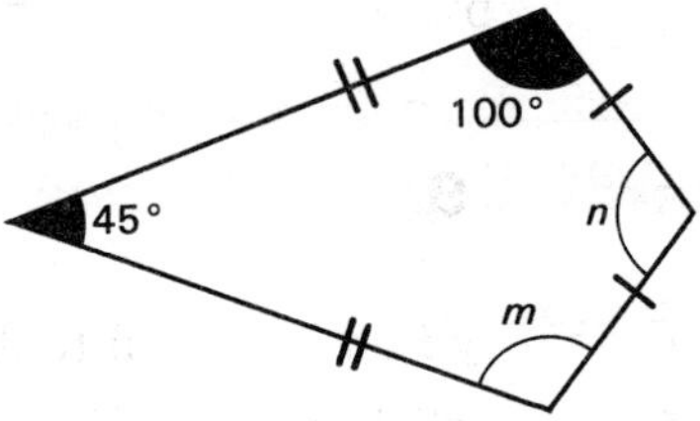

6.

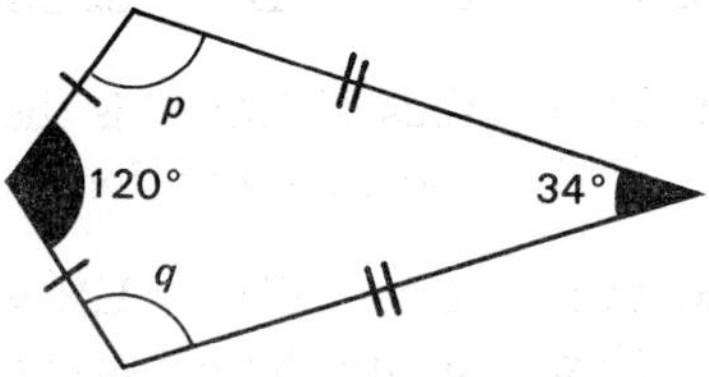

7.

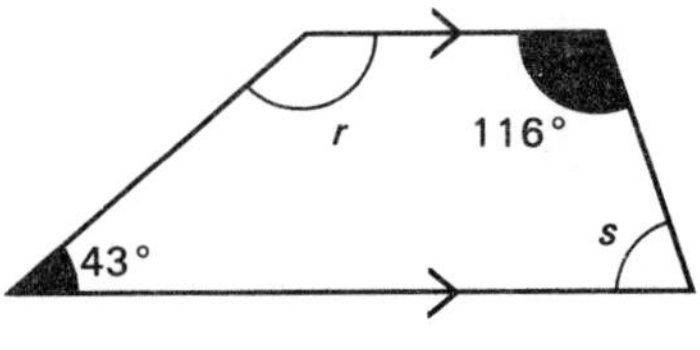

8.

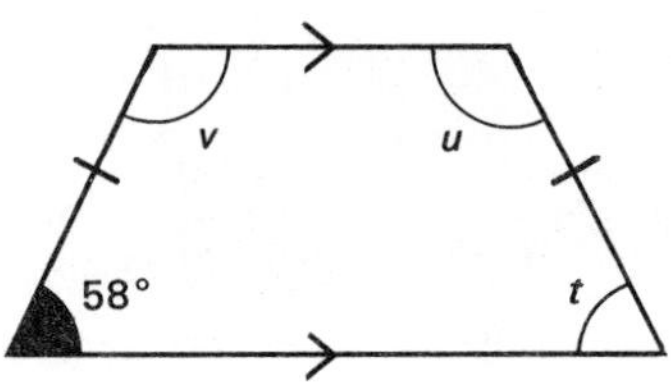

Remember: Plane shapes should be labelled cyclically (going around in one direction, clockwise or anticlockwise).

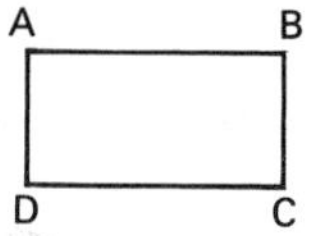

is correct.

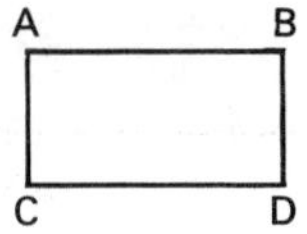

is incorrect.

Exercise 9

(You may find it helpful to draw sketches.)

1. In parallelogram ABCD, AB = 6 cm and BC = 4 cm. How long is AD?

2. In square PQRS, PR = 5 cm. How long is QS?

3. In kite DEFG, DE = 82 mm and EF = 37 mm. How long is GD?

4. In rhombus JKLM, P is the point of intersection of the diagonals. If JL = 46 mm how long is PJ?

5. In rectangle UVWX, UV = 4 cm, VW = 3 cm and UW = 5 cm. How long are the following?

(*a*) UX
(*b*) VX
(*c*) WX

15 Functions

Exercise 1

Find the missing input or output:

1. 7 ⟶ [+5] ⟶ [?]

2. 8 ⟶ [−2] ⟶ [?]

3. 9 ⟶ [×3] ⟶ [?]

4. 36 ⟶ [÷4] ⟶ [?]

5. 12 ⟶ [+9] ⟶ [?]

6. [?] ⟶ [×7] ⟶ 42

7. [?] ⟶ [×9] ⟶ 54

8. [?] ⟶ [+13] ⟶ 24

9. [?] ⟶ [−11] ⟶ 13

10. [?] ⟶ [÷6] ⟶ 8

Exercise 2 **M**

A Copy and complete the mapping diagrams:

1.

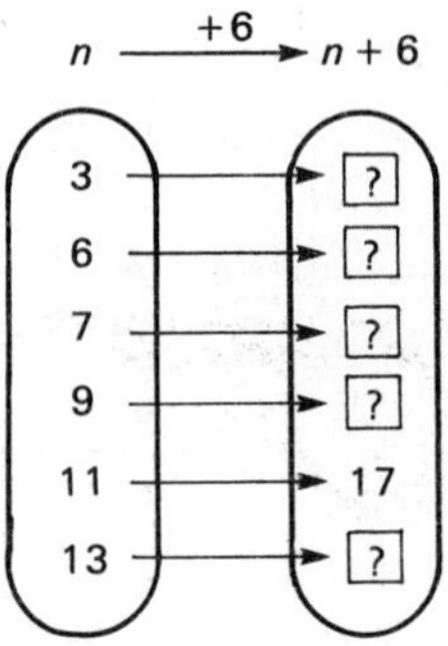

2.

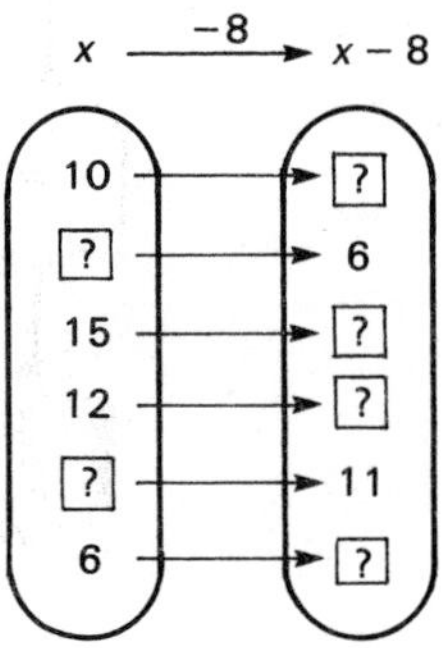

3.

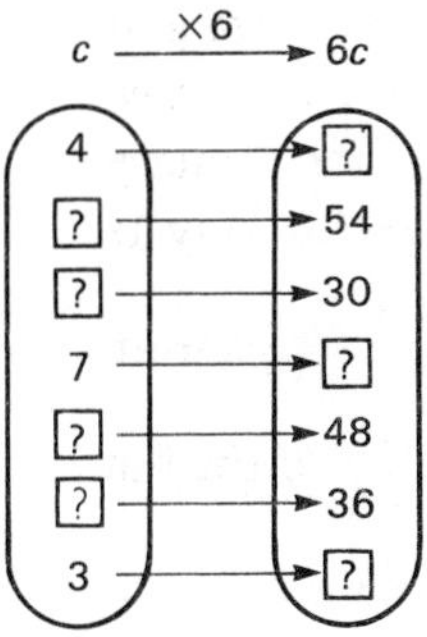

4.

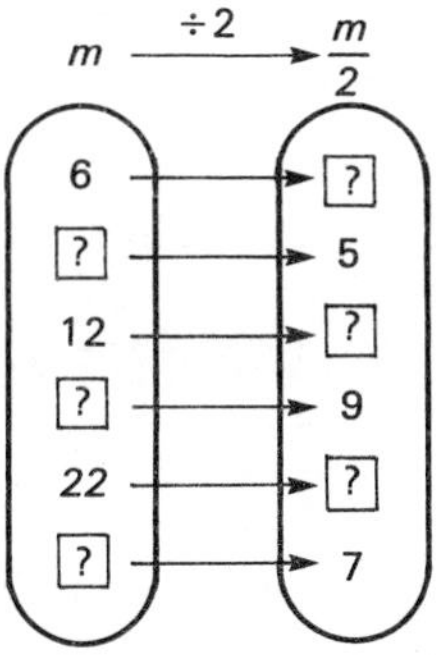

B **1.** Copy and complete the given mapping diagram to show the function* $f(x) = 5x$ using the domain $\{3, 5, 6, 7, 9, 10\}$.

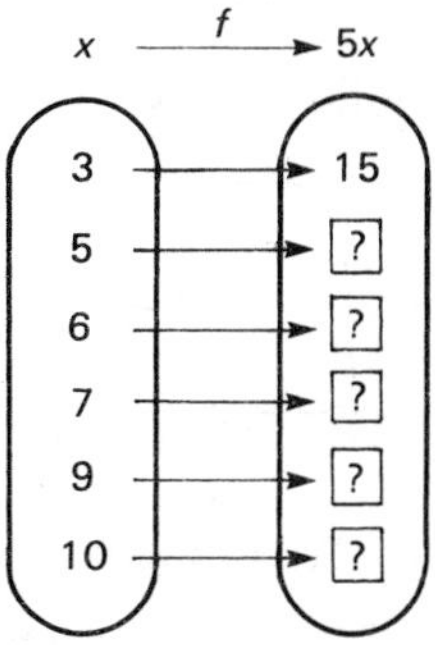

2. Draw a mapping diagram to show the function $g(x) = x + 8$ using the domain $\{4, 5, 6, 8, 10, 12\}$.

C **1.** If $y = 8x$, find the value of y when:

(*a*) $x = 2$
(*b*) $x = 6$
(*c*) $x = 9$
(*d*) $x = 10$

2. If $y = x - 4$ find the value of y when:

(*a*) $x = 10$
(*b*) $x = 12$
(*c*) $x = 15$
(*d*) $x = 4$

In all the questions in Exercises 1 and 2, when a number is the input, something is done to it (depending on the function) and another number is the output. Function keys on a calculator can be used to show this. A number can be keyed in (the input), then after a function key is pressed (such as the $\boxed{x^2}$ or $\boxed{\sqrt{\ }}$ keys), a number appears on

* See the glossary, p. 383.

the display (the output). Note that many function keys are normally pressed *after* a number has been input. Also note that *some* calculators need a special function key (possibly marked [F] or [f]) or perhaps an inverse key, [INV], to be pressed before the normal function keys can be used. (If your calculator does not appear to work properly then read the instructions.)

[+], [−], [×] and [÷] are also called function keys but they require two numbers to be input and [=] to be pressed to work. You may have seen 'four-function calculators' on sale in the shops. Such calculators have the four functions $+$, $-$, $\times$ and $\div$ on them. Scientific calculators have many function keys on them. So far, in books 1G, 2G and in earlier chapters of this book, we have used the calculator functions $+$, $-$, $\times$, $\div$, x^y, x^2 and $\sqrt{}$. If your calculator has the function key [$1/x$] on it then you will be able to use it in the next two exercises.

Exercise 3

A Try this on a calculator: [AC] [5] [$1/x$]

If the display shows 0.2 then you are using the [$1/x$] key correctly. If the display does not show 0.2 then try:

[AC] [5] [F] [$1/x$] or [AC] [5] [INV] [$1/x$]

or try to find out how the [$1/x$] key works on the calculator you are using.

B Try these on a calculator:

1. (*a*) [AC] [1] [÷] [2] [=] (*b*) [AC] [2] [$1/x$]
2. (*a*) [AC] [1] [÷] [4] [=] (*b*) [AC] [4] [$1/x$]
3. (*a*) [AC] [1] [÷] [8] [=] (*b*) [AC] [8] [$1/x$]
4. (*a*) [AC] [1] [÷] [1] [0] [=] (*b*) [AC] [1] [0] [$1/x$]
5. (*a*) [AC] [1] [÷] [2] [5] [=] (*b*) [AC] [2] [5] [$1/x$]
6. (*a*) [AC] [1] [÷] [1] [6] [=] (*b*) [AC] [1] [6] [$1/x$]
7. (*a*) [AC] [1] [÷] [7] [=] (*b*) [AC] [7] [$1/x$]
8. (*a*) [AC] [1] [÷] [3] [=] (*b*) [AC] [3] [$1/x$]

C **1.** Try some questions of your own (as in part B).
2. Explain what the [$1/x$] key does.

[$^1/_x$] is called the *reciprocal* key.

$^1/_x$ can be read 'the reciprocal of x'.

$^1/_4$ can be read 'the reciprocal of 4'.

Exercise 4

A Try these on a calculator:

1. [AC] [2] [$^1/_x$] [$^1/_x$]

2. [AC] [4] [$^1/_x$] [$^1/_x$]

3. [AC] [5] [$^1/_x$] [$^1/_x$]

4. [AC] [8] [$^1/_x$] [$^1/_x$]

5. [AC] [2] [0] [$^1/_x$] [$^1/_x$]

6. [AC] [2] [5] [$^1/_x$] [$^1/_x$]

7. [AC] [1] [6] [$^1/_x$] [$^1/_x$]

8. [AC] [3] [2] [$^1/_x$] [$^1/_x$]

B Write what you notice about your answers to part A.

Exercise 5

e.g. Find the value of $f(4)$ when $f(x) = 2x - 3$:

$$\begin{aligned} f(x) &= 2x - 3 \\ f(4) &= 2 \times 4 - 3 \\ f(4) &= 8 - 3 \\ f(4) &= \underline{\underline{5}} \end{aligned}$$

1. Find the value of $f(4)$ when $f(x) = 3x$.

2. Find the value of $f(3)$ when $f(x) = x + 9$.

3. Find the value of $f(2)$ when $f(t) = 2t$.

4. Find the value of $f(6)$ when $f(g) = 2g + 4$.

5. Find the value of $f(9)$ when $f(u) = 5u - 7$.

6. Given that $f(n) = 3n + 2$, find the value of:
(*a*) $f(4)$ (*b*) $f(7)$ (*c*) $f(5)$ (*d*) $f(9)$

7. If $g(x) = 2x - 4$, find the value of:
(*a*) $g(2)$ (*b*) $g(8)$ (*c*) $g(9)$ (*d*) $g(4)$

8. If $h(x) = 4x - 8$, find the value of:
(*a*) $h(2)$ (*b*) $h(8)$ (*c*) $h(9)$ (*d*) $h(4)$

Exercise 6

1. $y = 4x$. Find the value of y when $x = 6$.

2. $y = x + 7$. Find the value of y when $x = 4$.

3. $y = x - 9$. Find the value of y when $x = 15$.

4. $y = 2x - 5$. Find the value of y when $x = 7$.

5. $y = 3x - 3$. Find the value of y when $x = 2$.

6. Given that $y = 4x + 3$, find the value of y when:
(*a*) $x = 3$ (*b*) $x = 6$ (*c*) $x = 1$ (*d*) $x = 7$

7. Given that $y = 2x + 6$, find the value of y when:
(*a*) $x = 1$ (*b*) $x = 5$ (*c*) $x = 8$ (*d*) $x = 4$

8. Given that $y = 3x - 5$, find the value of y when:
(*a*) $x = 2$ (*b*) $x = 5$ (*c*) $x = 6$ (*d*) $x = 9$

Exercise 7

1. If $f(x) = 2x - 6$, find the value of:
(*a*) $f(4)$ (*b*) $f(3)$ (*c*) $f(0)$ (*d*) $f(1)$

2. If $f(x) = 4 - x$, find the value of:
(*a*) $f(1)$ (*b*) $f(4)$ (*c*) $f(7)$ (*d*) $f(10)$

3. If $f(x) = x - 5$, find the value of:
(*a*) $f(5)$ (*b*) $f(2)$ (*c*) $f(0)$ (*d*) $f(^-3)$

4. If $f(x) = 6x$, find the value of:
(*a*) $f(2)$ (*b*) $f(^-2)$ (*c*) $f(0)$ (*d*) $f(^-4)$

5. If $f(x) = x + 4$, find the value of:
(*a*) $f(^-2)$ (*b*) $f(^-7)$

6. Find the value of $f(^-3)$ when $f(x) = x - 1$.

7. Find the value of $f(^-4)$ when $f(x) = 2 - x$.

8. Find the value of $f(^-2)$ when $f(x) = 4x$.

Exercise 8

1. If $y = x - 3$, find the value of y when:
   (a) $x = 7$ (b) $x = 3$ (c) $x = {}^-2$ (d) $x = {}^-5$

2. If $y = 3 - x$, find the value of y when:
   (a) $x = 2$ (b) $x = 3$ (c) $x = 8$ (d) $x = 10$

3. If $y = 7x$, find the value of y when:
   (a) $x = 3$ (b) $x = {}^-3$ (c) $x = 0$ (d) $x = 8$

4. If $y = 2x - 2$, find the value of y when:
   (a) $x = 7$ (b) $x = 1$ (c) $x = 0$ (d) $x = {}^-2$

5. If $y = x + 8$, find the value of y when:
   (a) $x = {}^-6$ (b) $x = {}^-10$

6. If $y = x - 2$, find the value of y when $x = {}^-5$.

7. If $y = 1 - x$, find the value of y when $x = {}^-2$.

8. If $y = 5x$, find the value of y when $x = {}^-3$.

Exercise 9

If $y = x^2$, find the value of y when:

1. $x = 4$	4. $x = 1$	7. $x = {}^-2$	10. $x = {}^-6$
2. $x = 9$	5. $x = 7$	8. $x = {}^-4$	11. $x = {}^-8$
3. $x = 0$	6. $x = 6$	9. $x = {}^-1$	12. $x = {}^-12$

Exercise 10

A If $y = 2x^2$, find the value of y when:

1. $x = 1$	4. $x = 5$	7. $x = 10$	10. $x = {}^-4$
2. $x = 3$	5. $x = 7$	8. $x = {}^-1$	11. $x = {}^-7$
3. $x = 0$	6. $x = 6$	9. $x = {}^-2$	12. $x = {}^-5$

B If $f(x) = 3x^2$, find the value of:

1. $f(2)$	4. $f(3)$	7. $f({}^-2)$	10. $f({}^-4)$
2. $f(1)$	5. $f(5)$	8. $f({}^-1)$	11. $f({}^-9)$
3. $f(0)$	6. $f(10)$	9. $f({}^-3)$	12. $f({}^-7)$

16 Base Systems

Exercise 1

A Here is a set of four natural numbers: $\{1, 2, 3, 9\}$
Here are two simple rules:

i Numbers from the set may be added.
ii Any number in the set may be used on its own.

By using the two rules above, various numbers can be made.

e.g. $12 = 9 + 2 + 1$ (or $12 = 9 + 3$)
$3 = 3$ (or $3 = 2 + 1$)
$4 = 3 + 1$

Note that each number in the set is only allowed to be used once in each sum, so $4 = 2 + 2$ is not allowed (2 is used twice here).

1. Try to make:
(*a*) 13 (*b*) 6 (*c*) 8 (*d*) 10

2. What is the biggest number that can be made using the set above?

3. Which numbers up to that biggest number cannot be made from the set above?

B Discover your own set of four natural numbers. Find a set that gives every natural number up to and including 15 (using the same addition rule as in part A).

C Discover a set of five natural numbers that will give, by addition, every natural number up to and including 31.

D Discover a set of five different natural numbers that will give, by addition, every natural number up to and including but not exceeding:

1. 25 **2.** 20 **3.** 15

Reminder: The binary (base 2) number $1\,1\,0\,0\,1_2$ stands for the base ten number 25. This can be seen by examining the number $1\,1\,0\,0\,1_2$ written with its base 2 place-value headings:

16	8	4	2	1	
1	1	0	0	1	
↕	↕			↕	
16 +	8 +			1	$= 25_{ten}$

Exercise 2

R

A Convert the following numbers from base 2 to base ten:

1. $1\,1_2$
2. $1\,1\,0_2$
3. $1\,0\,1\,1_2$
4. $1\,1\;0\,0\,0_2$
5. $1\,1\;0\,1\,1_2$
6. $1\,0\,0\;0\,0\,0_2$
7. $1\,0\,0\;1\,1\,0_2$
8. $1\,0\,1\;1\,1\,1_2$
9. $1\,1\,1\;0\,0\,1_2$
10. $1\;0\,0\,0\;0\,1\,0_2$
11. $1\;0\,1\,1\;0\,0\,1_2$
12. $1\;1\,0\,0\;1\,0\,1_2$

B Convert the following numbers from base ten to base 2:

1. 5_{ten}
2. 8_{ten}
3. 23_{ten}
4. 29_{ten}
5. 37_{ten}
6. 42_{ten}
7. 48_{ten}
8. 50_{ten}
9. 74_{ten}
10. 85_{ten}
11. 99_{ten}
12. 110_{ten}

C
1. Convert 7_{ten} to base 2.
2. Convert $1\,1\,0\,0_2$ to base ten.
3. Convert 15_{ten} to base 2.
4. Convert 18_{ten} to base 2.
5. Convert $1\,1\,1\,0_2$ to base ten.
6. Convert $1\,0\;0\,1\,1_2$ to base ten.
7. Convert 30_{ten} to base 2.
8. Convert $1\,0\,0\;0\,1\,0_2$ to base ten.
9. Convert $1\,1\,0\;1\,0\,0_2$ to base ten.
10. Convert 40_{ten} to base 2.
11. Convert 72_{ten} to base 2.
12. Convert $1\;0\,1\,1\;1\,0\,1_2$ to base ten.

When a key is depressed on a computer keyboard, a signal is sent to the computer. This signal is in the form of a binary code. The most commonly used code is ASCII*. The ASCII code for A is 1 0 0 0 0 0 1 which has 7 *bits* (binary digits). A is called an *upper case* letter (a capital letter) while small letters, such as a, are called *lower case*. Here are the ASCII codes for various letters and numbers:

Lower case	Binary	ASCII	Upper case	Binary	ASCII	Number	Binary	ASCII
a	1	1 1 0 0 0 0 1	A	1	1 0 0 0 0 0 1	1	1	0 1 1 0 0 0 1
b	10	1 1 0 0 0 1 0	B	10	1 0 0 0 0 1 0	2	10	0 1 1 0 0 1 0
c	11	1 1 0 0 0 1 1	C	11	1 0 0 0 0 1 1	3	11	0 1 1 0 0 1 1
d	100	1 1 0 0 1 0 0	D	100	1 0 0 0 1 0 0	4	100	0 1 1 0 1 0 0
e	101	1 1 0 0 1 0 1	E	101	1 0 0 0 1 0 1	5	101	0 1 1 0 1 0 1
f	110	1 1 0 0 1 1 0	F	110	1 0 0 0 1 1 0	6	110	0 1 1 0 1 1 0
g	111	1 1 0 0 1 1 1	G	111	1 0 0 0 1 1 1	7	111	0 1 1 0 1 1 1
h	1000	1 1 0 1 0 0 0	H	1000	1 0 0 1 0 0 0	8	1000	0 1 1 1 0 0 0
i	1001	1 1 0 1 0 0 1	I	1001	1 0 0 1 0 0 1	9	1001	0 1 1 1 0 0 1

- Code for lower case letters
- Binary for letter position
- Code for upper case letters
- Binary for letter position
- Code for numbers
- Binary for the numbers

Note: If the first 2 bits are 1 1 the character is a lower case letter; if the first 2 bits are 1 0 the character is an upper case letter; if the first 3 bits are 0 1 1 the character is a number.

* See the glossary, p. 381.

Exercise 3

A In each question, the ASCII code for a word or number has been given. Find that word or number:

1. 1 001 100
1 000 101
1 010 100

2. 1 010 000
1 010 010
1 001 001
1 001 110
1 010 100

3. 0 110 000
0 110 000
0 110 111

4. 1 001 101
1 100 001
1 110 100
1 101 000
1 110 011

5. 1 100 001
1 110 010
1 100 011

6. 0 110 111
0 110 000
0 110 100
0 110 001
0 111 001

B Write these words and numbers using ASCII code:

1. Circle
2. square
3. NEXT
4. help
5. Angle
6. 8236

Exercise 4 R

A Convert these numbers from base 8 to base ten:

1. 13_8
2. 21_8
3. 34_8
4. 40_8
5. 47_8
6. 52_8
7. 63_8
8. 71_8
9. 75_8
10. 127_8
11. 231_8
12. 514_8

B Convert these numbers from base ten to base 8:

1. 15_{ten}
2. 22_{ten}
3. 29_{ten}
4. 36_{ten}
5. 41_{ten}
6. 45_{ten}
7. 50_{ten}
8. 55_{ten}
9. 62_{ten}
10. 80_{ten}
11. 130_{ten}
12. 200_{ten}

Exercise 5

In base ten, ten different symbols are used for the digits:

0, 1, 2, 3, 4, 5, 6, 7, 8 and 9

How many different symbols are needed for the digits in the following?

1. Base 2
2. Base 8
3. Base 5
4. Base 16

Base 16 is called *hexadecimal* (*hex* for short). Sixteen different symbols are needed for the digits (0 to 9 plus six others). Hex and octal are both used in computing (for data, instructions and addressing).

Long strings of binary digits can be shortened and become easier for a programmer to handle if they are written in hex or octal.

In some computers, when a program is being loaded into the computer from tape, the number of the block being loaded at that instant is shown on the screen. The numbering is probably in hex. The six extra symbols used are usually the first six letters of the alphabet. Here are some numbers in base ten and in hex.

Base ten	Hex	Base ten	Hex
1	1	17	11
2	2	18	12
3	3	19 (16 + 3)	13
4	4	20 (16 + 4)	14
5	5	21 (16 + 5)	15
6	6	22	16
7	7	23 (16 + 7)	17
8	8	24	18
9	9	25 (16 + 9)	19
10	A	26 (16 + 10)	1A
11	B	27 (16 + 11)	1B
12	C	28	1C
13	D	29 (16 + 13)	1D
14	E	30	1E
15	F	31 (16 + 15)	1F
16	10	32	20

Exercise 6

A Convert the following numbers from hexadecimal to base ten:

e.g. 1 $32_{hex} = 3 \times 16 + 2 = 48 + 2 = \underline{\underline{50}}_{ten}$

e.g. 2 $2C_{hex} = 2 \times 16 + 12 = 32 + 12 = \underline{\underline{44}}_{ten}$

1. 14_{hex}
2. 27_{hex}
3. $1D_{hex}$
4. $2E_{hex}$
5. 39_{hex}
6. $3F_{hex}$
7. $4A_{hex}$
8. $5B_{hex}$

B Convert the following numbers from base ten to hexadecimal:

e.g. $77_{ten} = 4D_{hex}$ (Since $4 \times 16 + 13 = 77$.)

1. 22_{ten}
2. 26_{ten}
3. 31_{ten}
4. 36_{ten}
5. 40_{ten}
6. 55_{ten}
7. 94_{ten}
8. 100_{ten}

Revision Exercises XI to XVI

Revision Exercise XI

1. Draw a circle with radius 30 mm. Plot the locus of a point that moves so that it is always 10 mm from the circle.

2. Draw a circle with radius 20 mm. Plot the locus of a point that moves so that it is always 20 mm from the circle.

3. Draw a simple pendulum as shown.

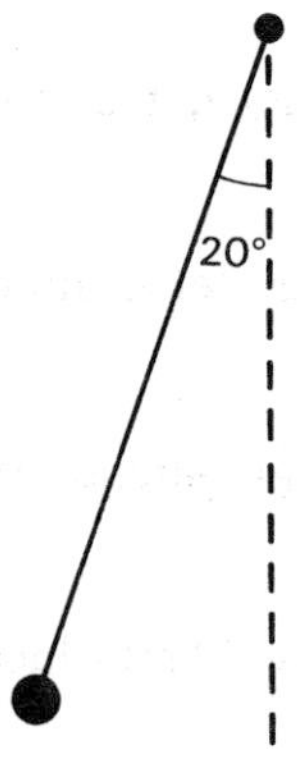

Now draw the locus of the bob as it moves if its starting position is such that the thread makes an angle of 20° with the vertical.

Revision Exercise XII

1. Wendy fitted a piece of card into the back of a frame while framing a picture. Calculate the area of the card if it measured 40 cm by 30 cm.

2. A rectangular jigsaw measures 47 cm by 33 cm. Calculate its area.

3. Calculate the area of the lawn using the dimensions given in the diagram.

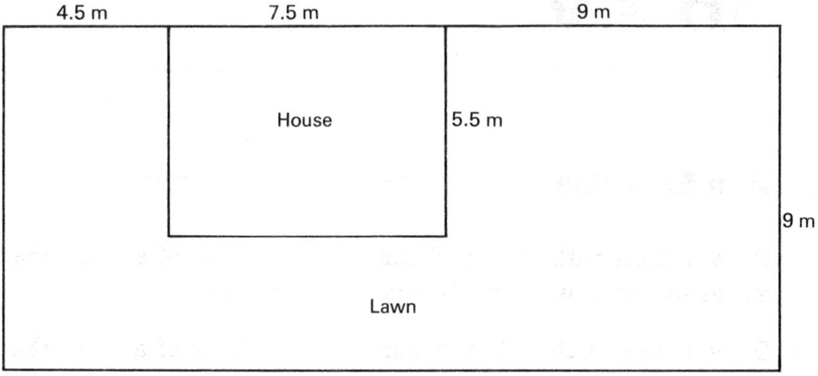

4. Part of a bathroom wall is to be tiled with 15 cm square tiles. If the area to be tiled is rectangular and measures 1.8 m by 1.2 m, how many tiles are needed?

5. A painting, 80 cm in length, has an area of 4000 cm^2. Find its breadth.

6. Calculate the area of a parallelogram with base 7 cm and perpendicular height 5.6 cm.

7. Calculate the area of a right-angled triangle with sides measuring 7 cm, 24 cm and 25 cm.

8. A parallelogram with base 60 mm has an area of 2820 mm^2.

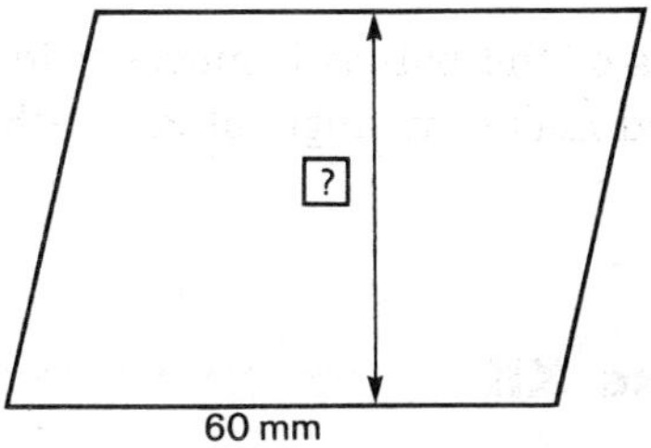

Calculate its perpendicular height.

9. How many kerbstones are needed to go around a roundabout with diameter 21 ft if each kerb is 3 ft long? (Use $\pi = 3.142$.)

10. The top of a circular table has a diameter of 1.2 m. Calculate the area of the table top:

(*a*) using $\pi = 3$, (*b*) using $\pi = 3.14$.

11. The worktop on some kitchen units is as shown.

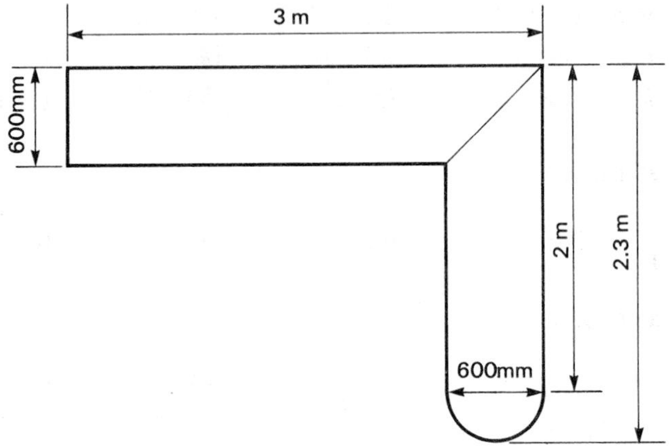

Calculate the area of the work surface. (Use $\pi = 3.142$.)

12. A fish tank, as shown, measuring 60 cm × 30 cm × 30 cm is $\frac{3}{4}$ full of water.

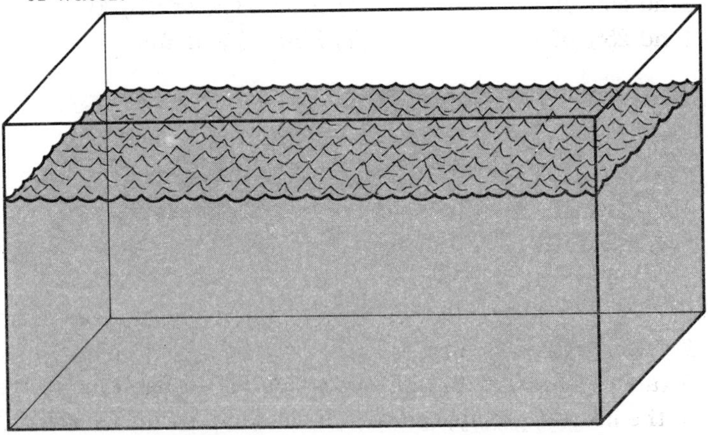

(*a*) Draw a net of the tank. (It is an open tank.)
(*b*) Calculate the area of glass used in making it.
(*c*) Calculate the volume of the water in the tank.
(*d*) Find the number of litres of water in the tank.

Revision Exercise XIII

1. Write as decimals without using calculating aids:

(*a*) 40%	(*c*) 69%	(*e*) 33%	(*g*) 27%	(*i*) $22\frac{1}{2}\%$
(*b*) 13%	(*d*) 97%	(*f*) 71%	(*h*) 56%	(*j*) $87\frac{1}{2}\%$

2. Write as common fractions in their lowest terms:

(*a*) 50%	(*c*) 40%	(*e*) 94%	(*g*) 56%	(*i*) $66\frac{2}{3}\%$
(*b*) 75%	(*d*) 60%	(*f*) 27%	(*h*) $33\frac{1}{3}\%$	(*j*) $12\frac{1}{2}\%$

3. Write as percentages:

(*a*) $\frac{29}{100}$ (*b*) $\frac{43}{50}$ (*c*) $\frac{3}{50}$ (*d*) $\frac{8}{25}$ (*e*) $\frac{3}{8}$

4. Write as decimals:

(*a*) $\frac{3}{10}$ (*b*) $\frac{2}{5}$ (*c*) $\frac{7}{8}$ (*d*) $\frac{3}{25}$ (*e*) $\frac{1}{3}$

5. Write as vulgar fractions in their lowest terms:

(*a*) 0.9 (*b*) 0.6 (*c*) 0.74 (*d*) 0.48 (*e*) 0.15

6. (*a*) Find 10% of £120.
(*b*) Find 10% of £4.50.
(*c*) Find 20% of £70.
(*d*) Find 25% of £36.
(*e*) Find 25% of £25.60.
(*f*) Find 70% of £49.
(*g*) Find $33\frac{1}{3}\%$ of £13.20.
(*h*) Find $2\frac{1}{2}\%$ of £16.

7. Find correct to the nearest penny:
(*a*) 30% of £5.46
(*b*) 35% of £16.73
(*c*) 72% of £4.25
(*d*) 2% of £49.99

8. (*a*) If VAT is at 15%, calculate the VAT on a pair of shoes costing £17.38 giving your answer correct to the nearest penny.
(*b*) A table lamp costs £14.77 before VAT is added. Find, correct to the nearest penny, the cost of the lamp inclusive of VAT if the VAT rate is 15%.

9. A watch costing £17.80 is sold at a discount of 25% in a sale. Calculate its sale price.

10. Using the passbook page given on p. 157 find:
(*a*) how much was withdrawn on 9 May 1987,
(*b*) the balance on 8 January 1987,
(*c*) the deposit on 30 May 1987

11. If £350 is saved for 1 year at 9% p.a., calculate the interest.

12. £2500 was borrowed at the flat rate of interest of 12% p.a. Calculate the interest charges.

Revision Exercise XIV

1. In the diagrams below, the broken lines are lines of symmetry:

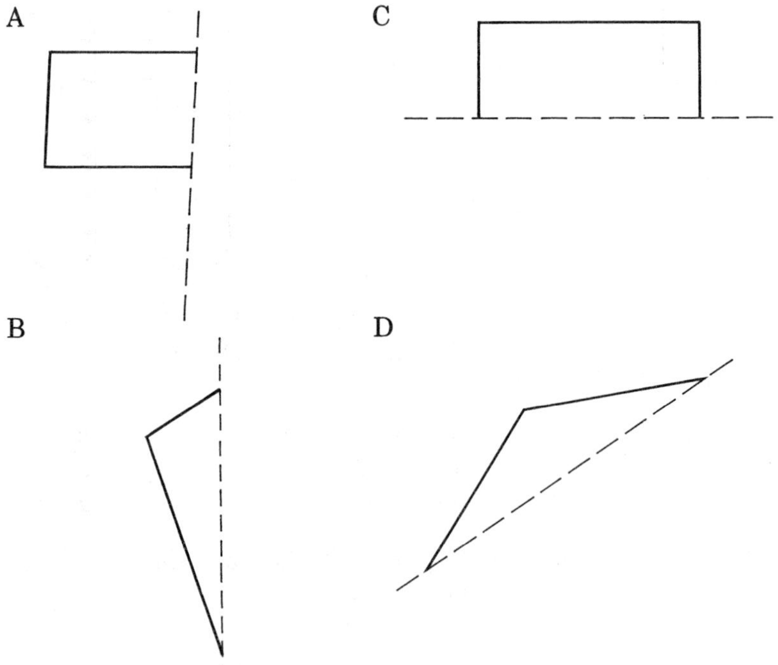

When the shapes are completed, which shape (or shapes) *if any*, are:
(*a*) a rectangle?
(*b*) a kite?
(*c*) a parallelogram?
(*d*) a rhombus?

2. Which quadrilaterals have rotational symmetry of order 2?

3. Copy this table:

	All 4 angles are equal	Only opposite angles are equal
All 4 sides are equal		
Only opposite sides are equal		

Enter in each box the name of a quadrilateral that satisfies the two statements that refer to that box.

4. (*a*) What sort of quadrilateral is ABCD?

(*b*) Angle DAB = 124°. Calculate the other three angles.

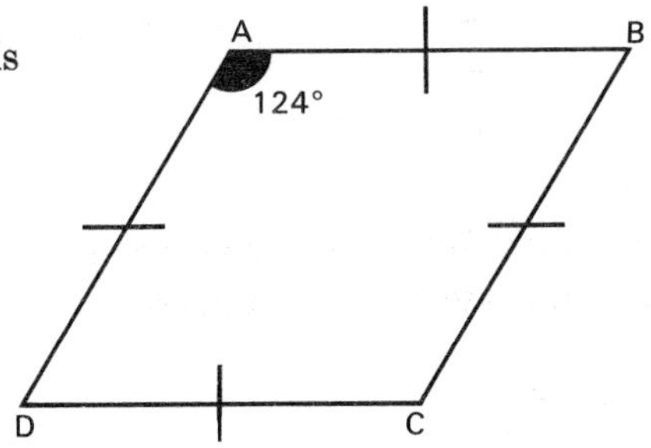

If diagonals BD and AC are drawn and intersect at X and if BD = 9 cm:

(*c*) How long is XB?

(*d*) What is the size of ∠ADB?

(*e*) What is the size of ∠ABD?

(*f*) What is the size of ∠AXD?

Revision Exercise XV

1. Copy and complete the mapping diagram for the function $f(x) = x - 7$ (i.e., $y = x - 7$).

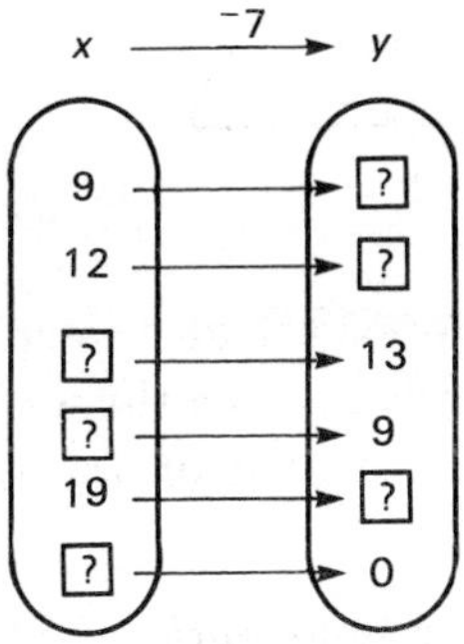

2. If $y = 9x$, find the value of y when:
(*a*) $x = 3$ (*b*) $x = 7$ (*c*) $x = 10$ (*d*) $x = 5$

3. If $y = 2x + 10$, find the value of y when:
(*a*) $x = 4$ (*b*) $x = 8$ (*c*) $x = 0$ (*d*) $x = 5$

4. If $f(x) = 3x - 6$, find the value of:
(*a*) $f(4)$ (*b*) $f(10)$ (*c*) $f(2)$ (*d*) $f(9)$

5. If $y = 3x - 9$, find the value of y when:
(*a*) $x = 3$ (*b*) $x = 0$ (*c*) $x = 2$ (*d*) $x = {}^{-}2$

6. If $f(x) = 2x - 8$, find the value of:
(*a*) $f(4)$ (*b*) $f(0)$ (*c*) $f(3)$ (*d*) $f({}^{-}3)$

7. If $y = x^2$, find the value of y when:
(*a*) $x = 3$ (*b*) $x = 8$ (*c*) $x = {}^{-}5$ (*d*) $x = {}^{-}7$

8. If $f(x) = x^2$, find the value of:
(*a*) $f(2)$ (*b*) $f(5)$ (*c*) $f({}^{-}3)$ (*d*) $f({}^{-}10)$

Revision Exercise XVI

1. Convert from base 2 to base ten:
(*a*) 1001_2 (*b*) $11\,010_2$ (*c*) $111\,010_2$ (*d*) $1\,001\,101_2$

2. Convert from base ten to base 2 (binary):
(*a*) 10_{ten} (*b*) 28_{ten} (*c*) 45_{ten} (*d*) 67_{ten}

3. Convert from base 8 to base ten:
(*a*) 23_8 (*b*) 30_8 (*c*) 61_8 (*d*) 72_8

4. Convert from base ten to base 8:
(*a*) 21_{ten} (*b*) 34_{ten} (*c*) 40_{ten} (*d*) 53_{ten}

5. Convert from hexadecimal to base ten:
(*a*) 18_{hex} (*b*) 20_{hex} (*c*) $2A_{hex}$ (*d*) $4F_{hex}$

6. Convert from base ten to hexadecimal:
(*a*) 18_{ten} (*b*) 34_{ten} (*c*) 47_{ten} (*d*) 59_{ten}

17 Transformation Geometry

Exercise 1

A The diagram shows 8 triangles. For each question write the type of transformation (translation, reflection or rotation) that has been used to map:

1. A onto B
2. A onto E
3. G onto A
4. F onto D
5. C onto F
6. C onto D
7. H onto E
8. E onto H
9. B onto G
10. F onto A

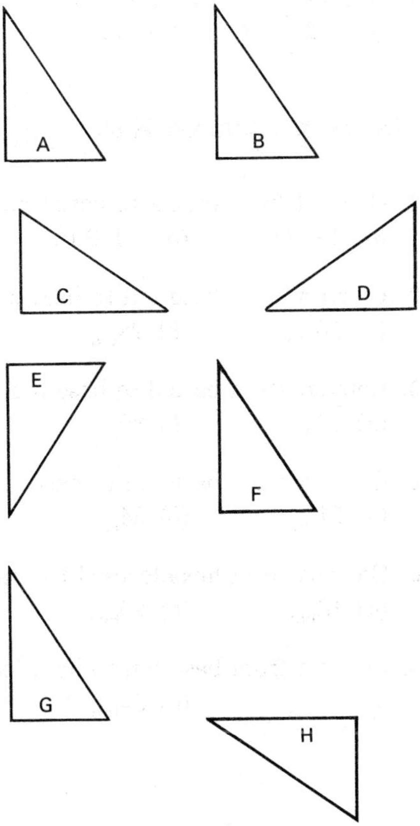

B If the following quadrilaterals were cut in half along the lines shown, what sort of transformation or transformations (there may be more than one answer to a question) would map one half onto the other half?

1. A square

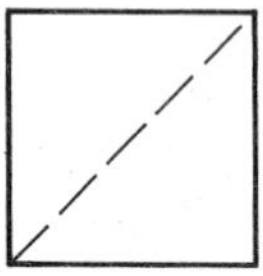

2. A rectangle

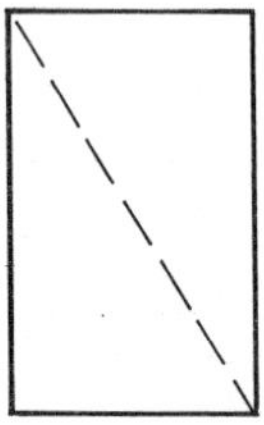

3. A rectangle

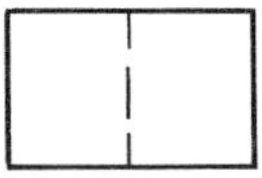

4. A parallelogram

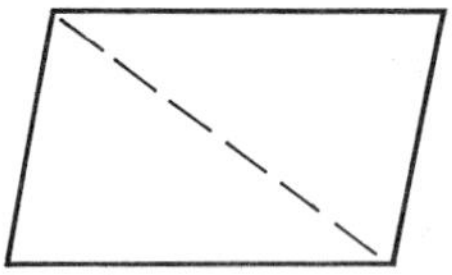

5. An isosceles trapezium

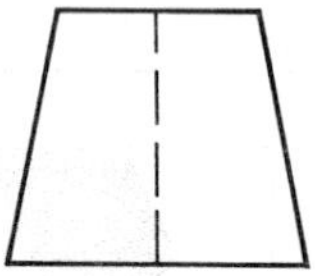

6. A rhombus

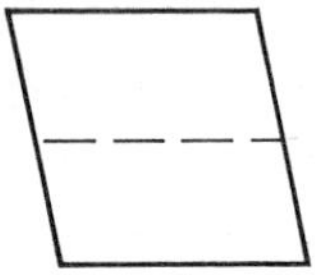

7. A square

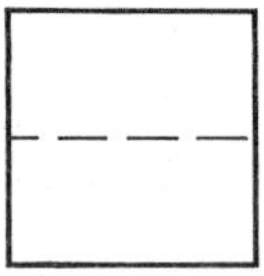

8. A rhombus

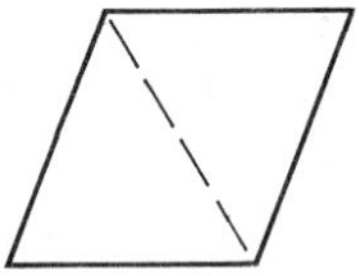

9. A kite

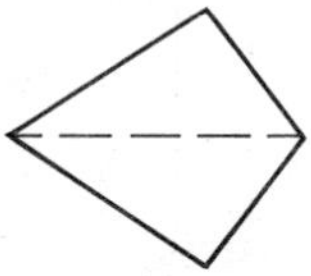

10. A rhombus

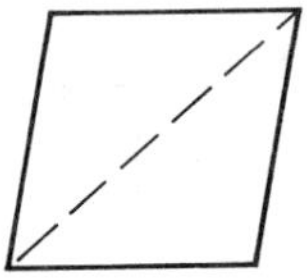

11. A parallelogram

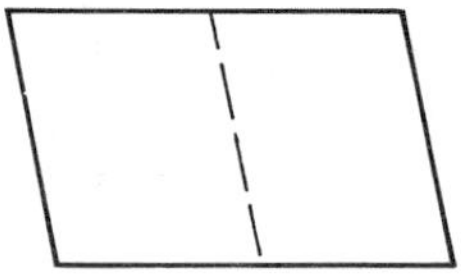

12. A rectangle

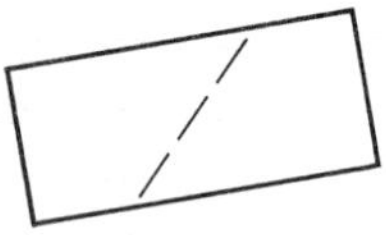

C **1.** For each shape in part B, ignoring the broken lines, write:
(*a*) whether or not it has bilateral symmetry,
(*b*) its order of rotational symmetry.

2. Explain why symmetry can help you with the questions on transformations in part B.

Exercise 2

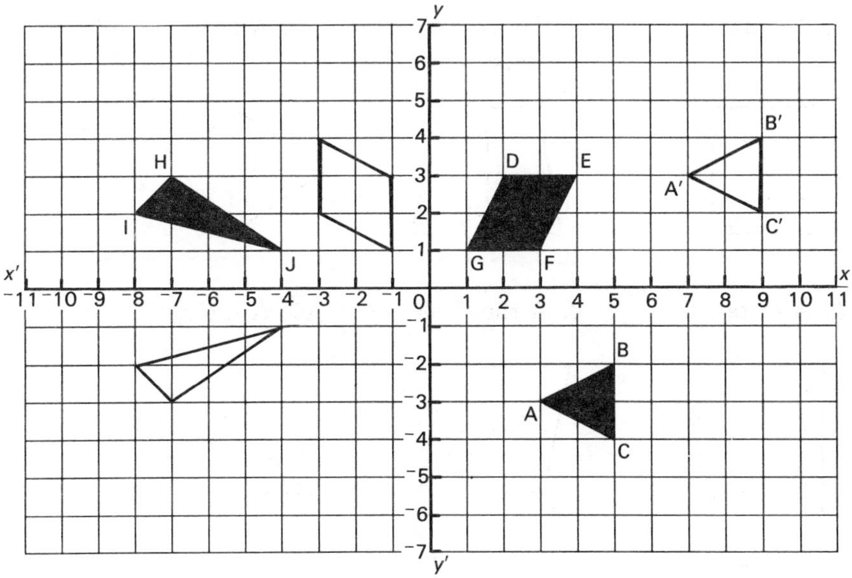

1. $\triangle$ABC and its image under a translation are shown.
   (*a*) What are the co-ordinates of A?
   (*b*) What are the co-ordinates of the image of A?
   (*c*) What are the co-ordinates of the image of C?

2. $\triangle$HIJ has been reflected in the x-axis. Its image is shown.
   (*a*) What are the co-ordinates of H?
   (*b*) What are the co-ordinates of the image of H?
   (*c*) What are the co-ordinates of I?
   (*d*) What are the co-ordinates of the image of I?
   (*e*) What are the co-ordinates of J?
   (*f*) What are the co-ordinates of the image of J?
   (*g*) Why are the x-co-ordinates of any point on $\triangle$HIJ and the image of that point always the same?
   (*h*) Why do the y-co-ordinates of any point on $\triangle$HIJ and the image of that point have the same numerical value but different sign?

3. (*a*) Write the co-ordinates of vertices D, E, F and G.
   (*b*) Write the co-ordinates of the images of D, E, F and G under a rotation through 90° anticlockwise about the origin.

Exercise 3

If you wish to answer the following questions without plotting any points or drawing any shapes you may do so. If you prefer to plot points to help you, then draw a pair of axes as shown but use a scale of 1 cm to 1 unit.

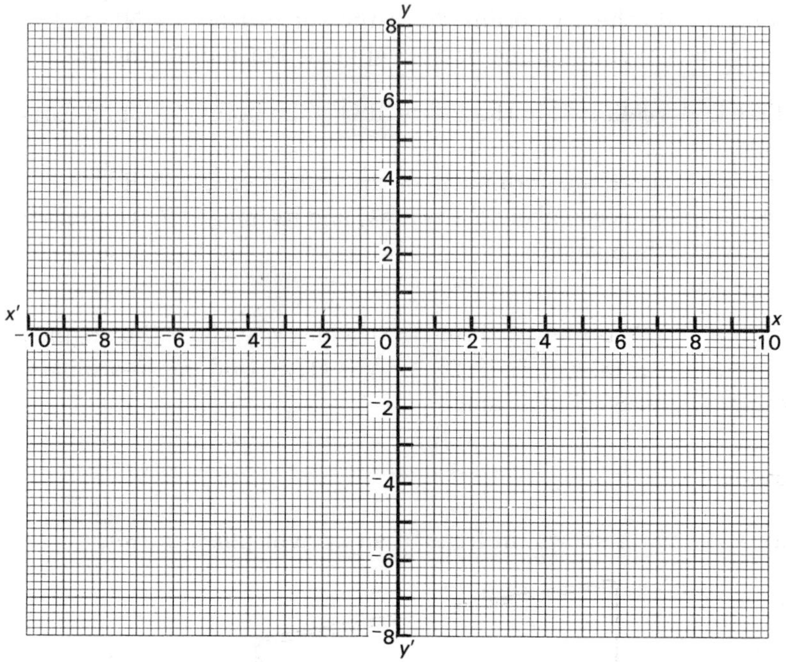

A **1.** If the point A(2, 4) is translated 5 units to the right, parallel to the x-axis, what are the co-ordinates of its image A′?

2. The point B($^-2$, 6) is translated 6 units to the right, parallel to the x-axis. What are the co-ordinates of its image, B′?

3. △CDE where C is ($^-5$, 5), D is ($^-8$, 5) and E is ($^-8$, 3) is translated 6 units downwards, parallel to the y-axis. What are the co-ordinates of the vertices of its image?

4. Square FGHI is translated to F′G′H′I′ such that F(3, 5) moves to F′(6, 7). Find the images of G(5, 5), H(5, 3) and I(3, 3).

B **1.** △JKL is reflected in the x-axis. If J is ($^-4$, 3), K is ($^-2$, 3) and L is ($^-2$, 2), what are the co-ordinates of the vertices of the image of △JKL?

2. $\triangle$MNP, where M is ($^-4$, $^-4$), N is ($^-3$, $^-7$) and P is ($^-1$, $^-6$), is reflected in the y-axis:
   (*a*) What are the co-ordinates of the vertices of the image of $\triangle$MNP?
   (*b*) Why are the y-co-ordinates of the vertices of $\triangle$MNP and its image the same?
   (*c*) Why do the x-co-ordinates of the vertices of $\triangle$MNP and its image have the same numerical value but a different sign?

3. Line QR is reflected in the x-axis. If Q is the point (9, 0) and R the point (7, $^-2$):
   (*a*) What are the co-ordinates of the images of Q and R?
   (*b*) What is special about the point Q and its image? (Give a reason why it happened.)

C Rectangle STUV is rotated through 90° clockwise about the origin, 0. If S is (1, 1), T is (3, 1), U is (3, 2) and V is (1, 2), find the co-ordinates of their images, S′, T′, U′ and V′.

Exercise 4

Place a pencil, as shown, in front of an upright plane mirror.

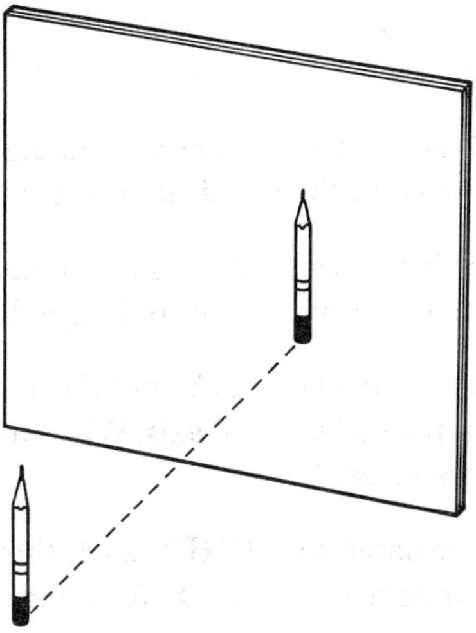

1. (*a*) If the pencil is 16 cm from the mirror, how far is its image from the mirror?
   (*b*) If the pencil is 12 cm from the mirror, how far is its image from the mirror?

2. (*a*) If the pencil is moved closer to the mirror, what happens to its image?
   (*b*) If the pencil is moved further away from the mirror, what happens to its image?

3. (*a*) If the pencil is moved 6 cm closer to the mirror, how far does its image move?
   (*b*) If the pencil is moved 2 cm further away from the mirror, how far does its image move?

4. If a pencil 16 cm from a mirror is moved 4 cm closer to the mirror:
   (*a*) How far did its image move?
   (*b*) How far from the mirror is the pencil now?
   (*c*) How far from the mirror is its image now?

5. Hold a pencil in front of a mirror. Keep the mirror still. Steadily move the pencil towards the mirror. Does the image move faster, slower or at the same speed as the pencil itself?

6. Hold a pencil in front of a mirror. This time, keep the pencil still. Steadily move the mirror towards the pencil and watch the image move. Notice that the image moves towards the mirror *twice as fast* as the mirror moves towards the pencil.

   Explain why. (Consider the distances of the pencil and its image from the mirror as the mirror moves.)

Exercise 5 **M**

I need to move a heavy rectangular table without help and without sliding it across the carpet. To do this, I decide to lift the table so that it stands on one leg and then to rotate it about that corner. The two diagrams show this. The first shows the table being rotated clockwise about corner A. The second shows the table then being rotated anticlockwise about corner B.

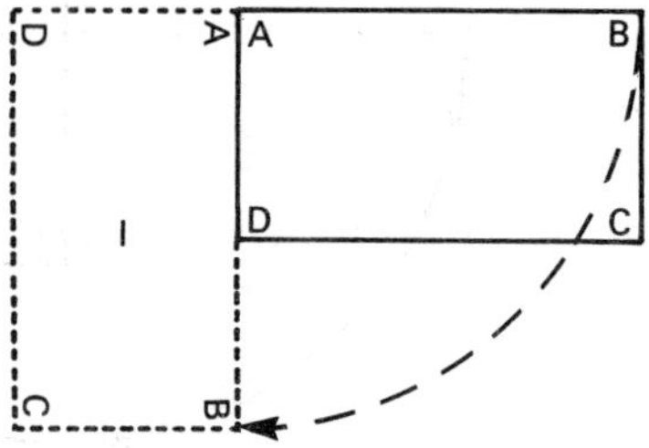

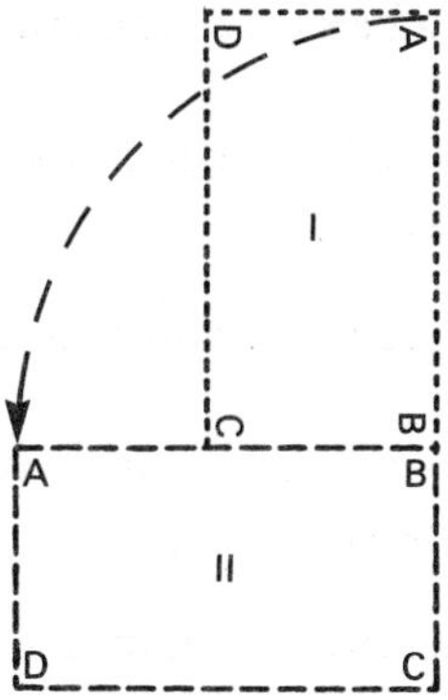

While moving the table, the rotations must only be $\frac{1}{4}$, $\frac{1}{2}$ or $\frac{3}{4}$ turns.

To prevent a lot of drawing a notation is needed (that is, a way of showing the moves). You may invent your own notation but I shall use $\overset{\curvearrowright}{D}$ to stand for a quarter turn clockwise about corner D and $\overset{\curvearrowleft}{D}$ to stand for a quarter turn anticlockwise about D, so the first diagram in Exercise 5 becomes $\overset{\curvearrowright}{A}$ while the second becomes $\overset{\curvearrowleft}{B}$.

The movements shown below can be written as $\overset{\curvearrowleft}{A} + \overset{\curvearrowleft}{B} + \overset{\curvearrowleft}{C} + \overset{\curvearrowleft}{C} + \overset{\curvearrowleft}{D}$.

Note that the movement from II to III is a half turn anticlockwise about C and this is shown as two quarter turns $\overset{\curvearrowleft}{C} + \overset{\curvearrowleft}{C}$. Note also that + means 'followed by'.

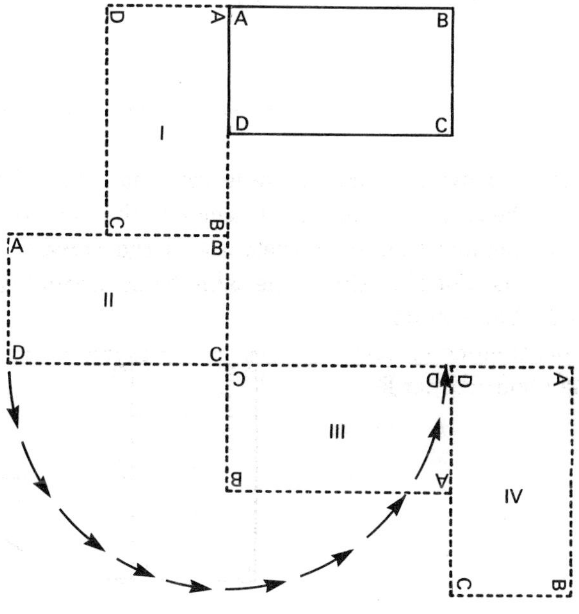

A Write the movements given below using the symbols as explained on the previous page:

1.

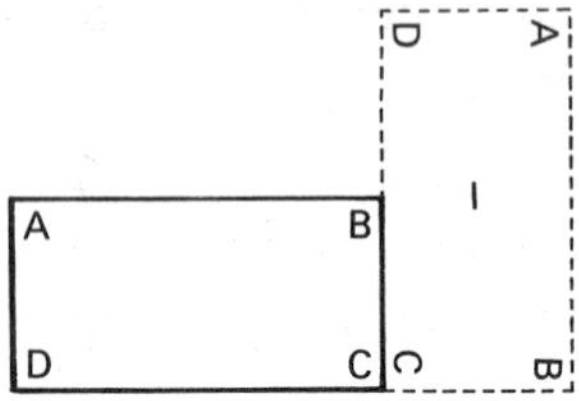

2.

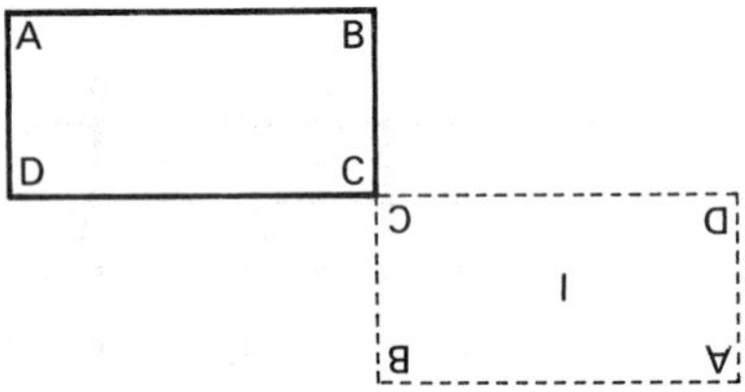

3.

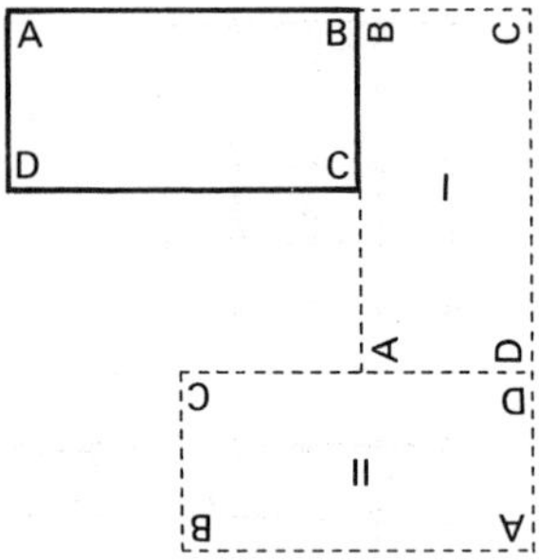

4.

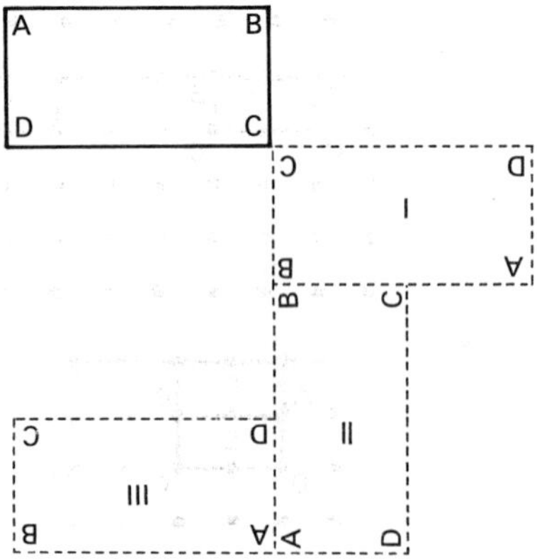

B Move a table measuring 2 m by 1 m using $\frac{1}{4}$, $\frac{1}{2}$ or $\frac{3}{4}$ turns from the starting position, labelled S, to the finishing position, labelled F. (The finishing position is shown dotted.) *Use as few moves as possible.* It would be helpful to cut a rectangle out of paper (or card) to use as a table on a 'board' of squared or dotty paper.

e.g.

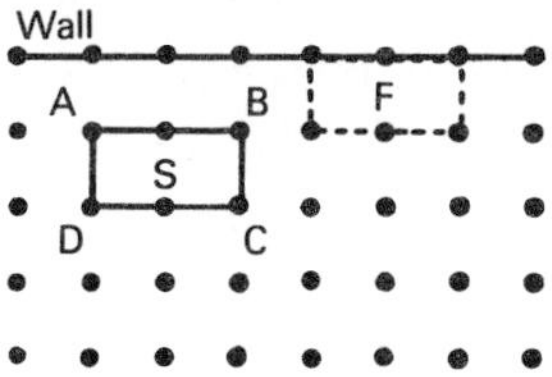

Moves are $\overset{\frown}{C} + \overset{\frown}{C} + \overset{\frown}{C} + \overset{\frown}{A}$.
Note that $\overset{\frown}{C} + \overset{\frown}{A}$ does not work because the table would hit the wall.

1.

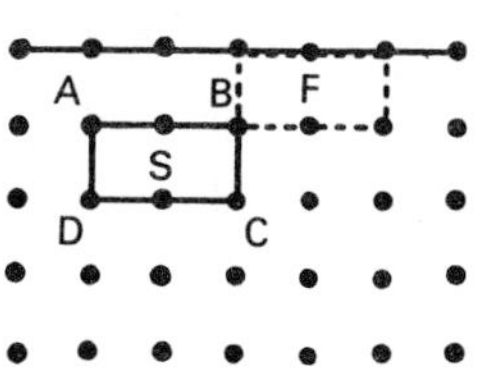

2.

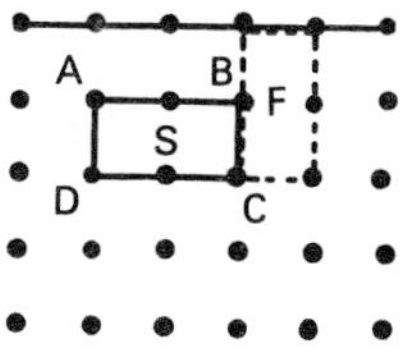

3.

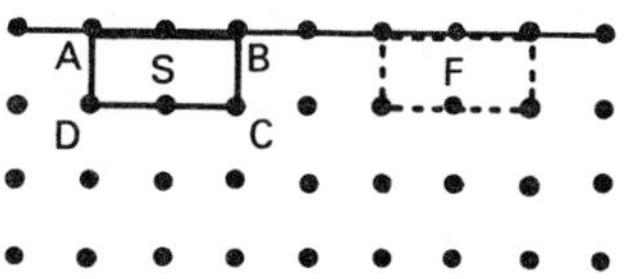

4.

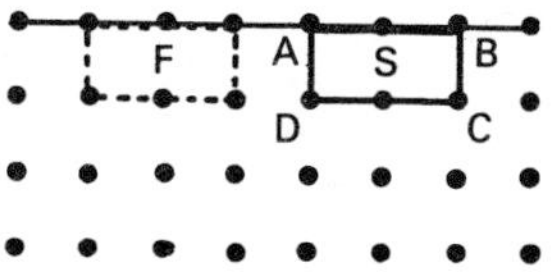

5.

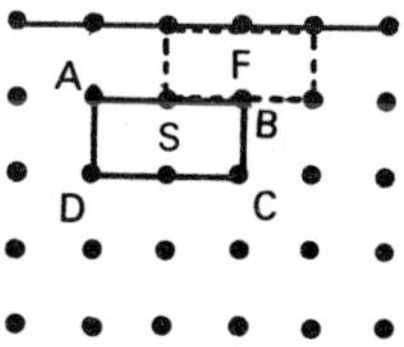

6.

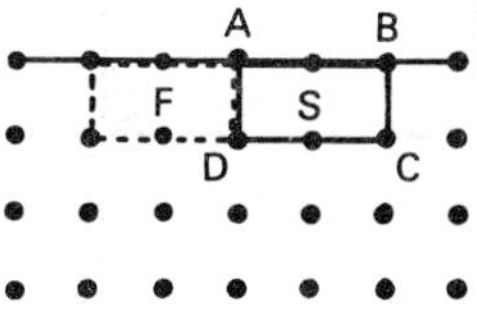

7.

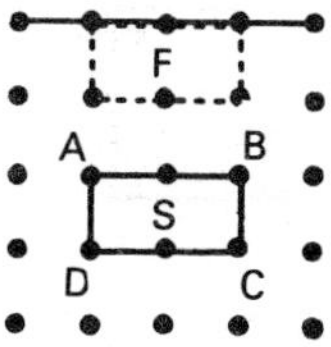

8.

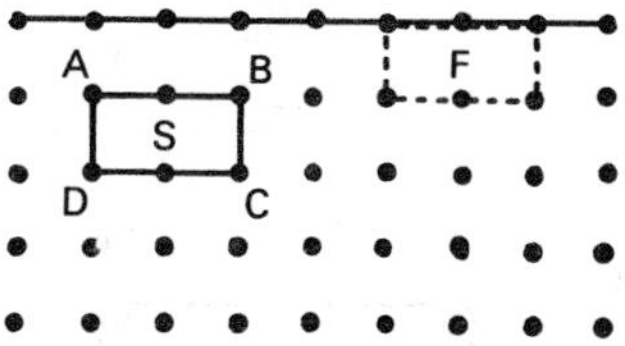

9.

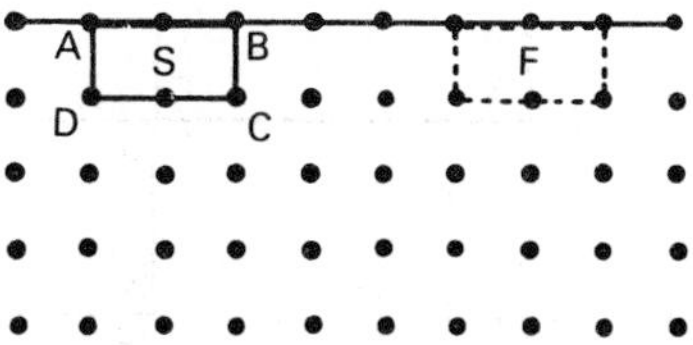

10.

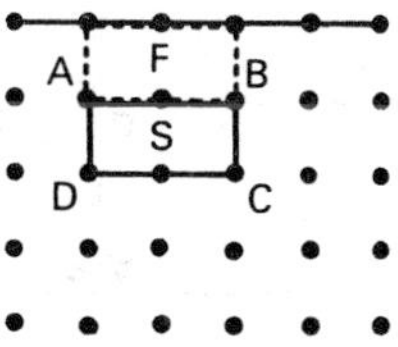

C Repeat part B but start in position F with the table facing the same direction in which it finished in part B, then move to position S. Compare your answers with those to part B.

D Two copies of the starting and finishing positions for part B, question 4 are given here. The starting positions are identical but although the finishing positions occupy the same space, in one, AB is next to the wall, while in the other, CD is next to the wall.

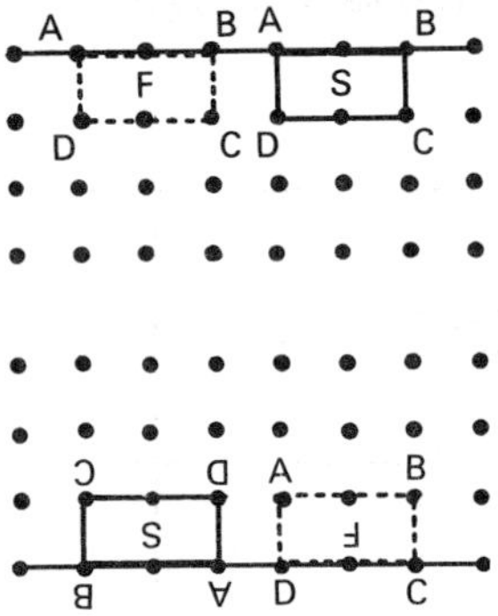

Is it possible from the given starting position, to finish in both of these finishing positions?

E Place your labelled cut-out rectangle on a piece of dotty paper and label the dot which vertex A touches with the letter A. Move the rectangle by rotating as before and label this new dot which vertex A touches, with the letter A. Repeat this, covering most of the paper. What do you notice about the positions of the dots that are labelled with the letter A?

F **1.** From the starting position shown, movement $\widehat{C}$ would cause the table to hit the wall.
Make a diagram and draw the locus of A to show where it would hit the wall during movement $\widehat{C}$.

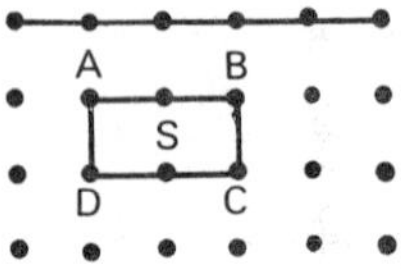

2. Repeat question 1 for the same starting position using movement $\widehat{B}$.

Wallpaper designs and the patterns made by wall tiles illustrate many of the ideas of transformation geometry. Look for them.

Exercise 6 M

1. Here is a tile.
The other tiles have the same design.

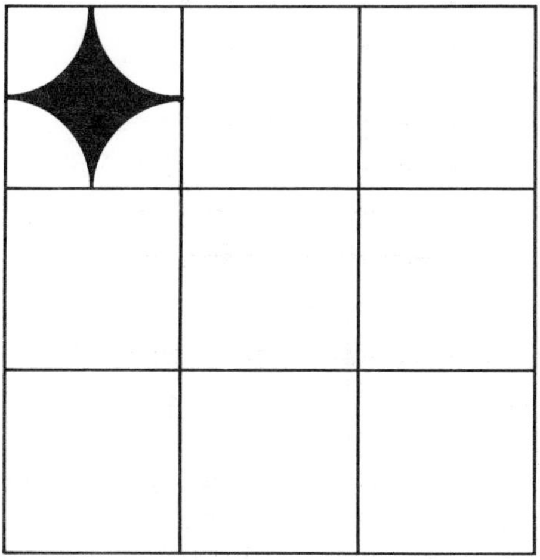

Copy the given diagram and fill in the blank spaces to show all the tiles.

Note how the overall pattern can appear 'different' when several tiles are put together.

2. Copy and complete the wallpaper pattern:

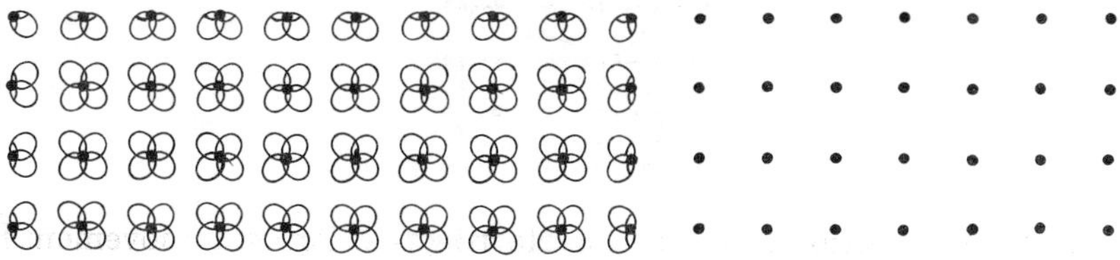

Enlargements

Exercise 7 M

Enlarge these shapes. Use squared paper.

1. Make each side twice as long:

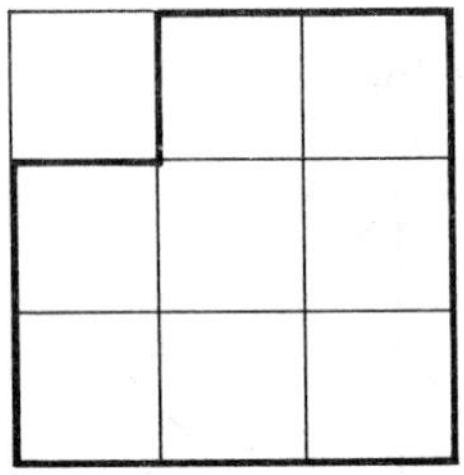

2. Make each side twice as long:

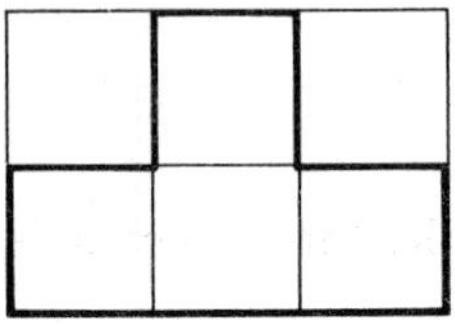

3. Make each side 3 times as long:

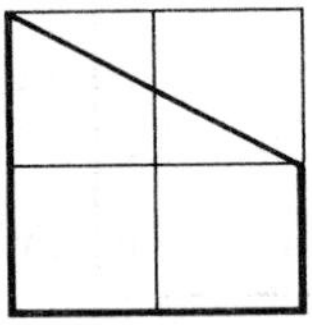

4. Make each side 4 times as long:

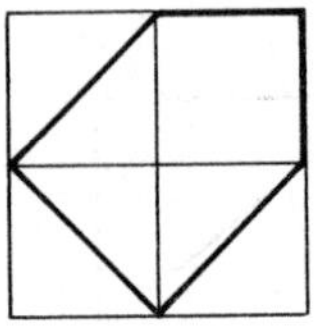

5. Make each side 3 times as long:

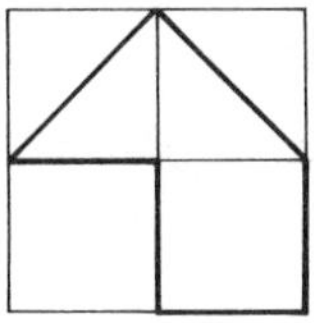

6. Make each side twice as long:

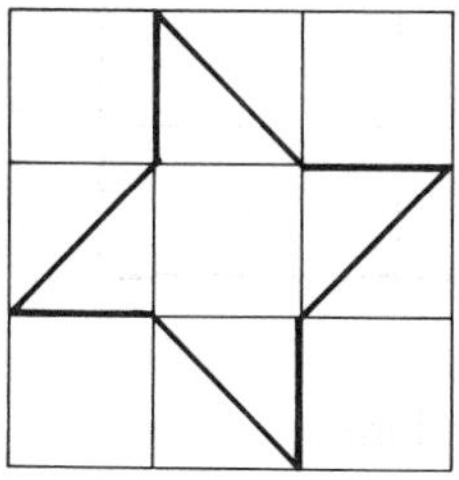

Exercise 8

1. (*a*) Enlarge the rectangle. Make each side twice as long.

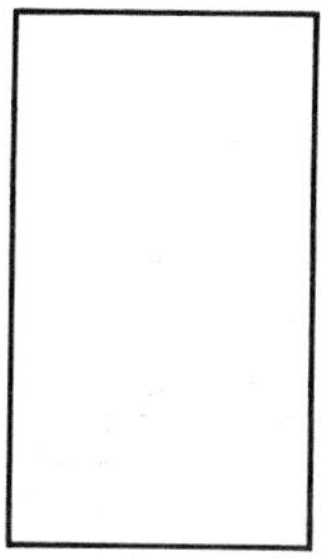

(*b*) How many times as long are the diagonals?

2. Enlarge the triangle. Make each side 3 times as long. (Check that all 3 sides of the enlargement are 3 times as long as the sides of the original triangle.)

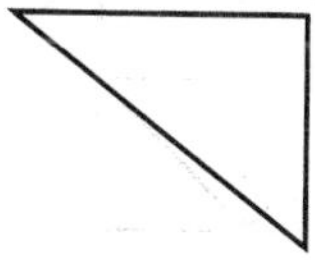

In showing a film, the picture on the film is enlarged as it is focused on a screen. The further the screen is moved from the projector, the bigger the image that is obtained.

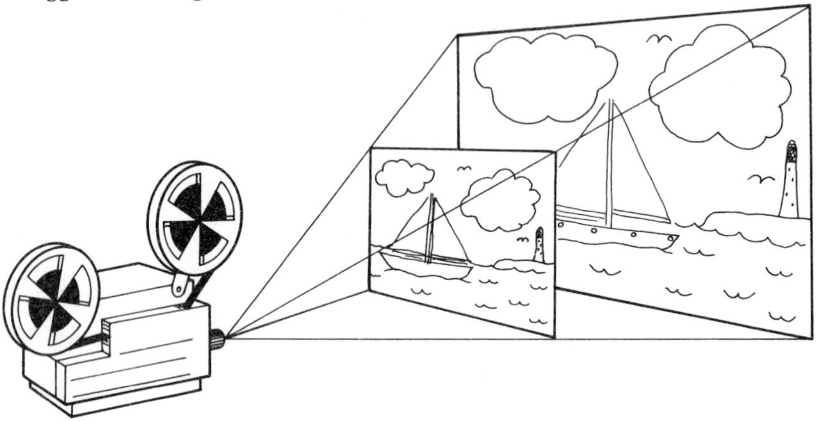

When enlarging a photograph, the further the enlarger is from the baseboard, the larger the enlargement that is obtained.

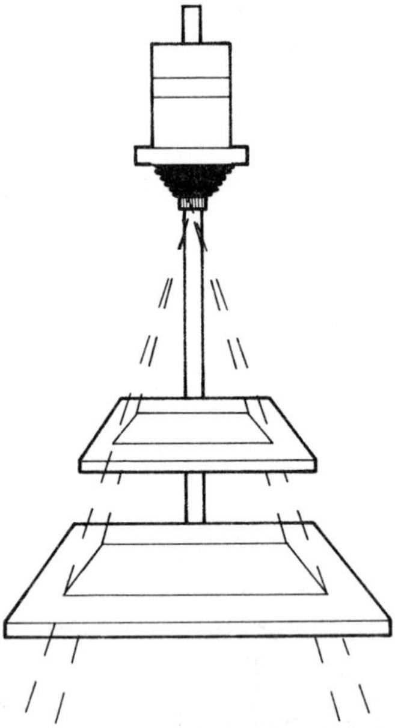

By standing near a wall and shining a torch at it, a spot of light will show on the wall. By moving further away from the wall the spread of light increases. This causes the spot of light on the wall to become larger.

These ideas can help you to draw enlargements.

Exercise 9

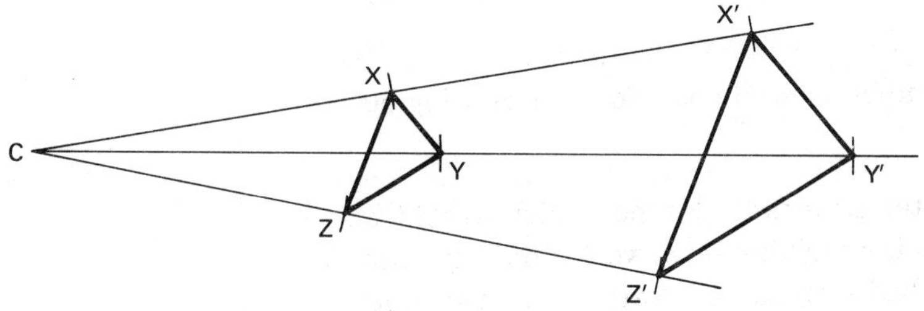

1. Draw a small triangle and label it XYZ.

2. Mark a point C outside the triangle.

3. From C, draw straight lines through vertices X, Y and Z.

4. Set a pair of compasses to length CX, place the point on X and draw an arc to cross the line CX produced. Label the point, X′. (CX′ should be twice as long as CX.) X′ is the image of X.

5. Repeat step 4 for CY to find point Y′ which lies on the line CY produced.

6. Repeat step 4 for CZ to find Z′ on the line CZ produced.

7. Join X′Y′Z′. $\triangle X'Y'Z'$ is an enlargement of $\triangle XYZ$. $\triangle XYZ$ is called the object and $\triangle X'Y'Z'$ the image under the enlargement.

8. (*a*) How many times as big as XY is X′Y′?
   (*b*) How many times as big as YZ is Y′Z′?
   (*c*) How many times as big as ZX is Z′X′?

9. Calculate the ratios:

   (*a*) $\dfrac{X'Y'}{XY}$ (*b*) $\dfrac{Y'Z'}{YZ}$ (*c*) $\dfrac{Z'X'}{ZX}$

Note In an enlargement, if all the lengths of the image are twice as long as the original lengths, we say that the *scale factor* = 2. If all the lengths are 5 times as long, the scale factor = 5, and so on.

Note also that the point from which the lines are drawn (point C in Exercise 9) is called the *centre of enlargement*.

Exercise 10

Throughout this exercise, use the same method of enlargement as in Exercise 9.

1. (*a*) Draw another small triangle. Label it PQR. Enlarge your triangle using a scale factor of 3.

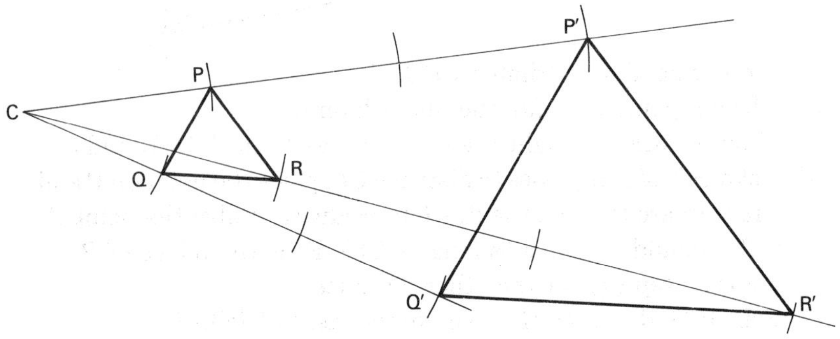

For example, to find P′, the image of P, first set a pair of compasses to length CP. Place the point on P and draw an arc to cross the line CP produced. Move the point of the pair of compasses to this newly marked position and draw another small arc to cross the same line again. This new position is P′.

(*b*) Calculate the ratios $\frac{P'Q'}{PQ}$, $\frac{Q'R'}{QR}$ and $\frac{R'P'}{RP}$.

Write what you notice.

2. Draw a small quadrilateral. Enlarge it using a scale factor of 2.

3. Draw another small quadrilateral. Enlarge it using a scale factor of 3.

Exercise 11

1.

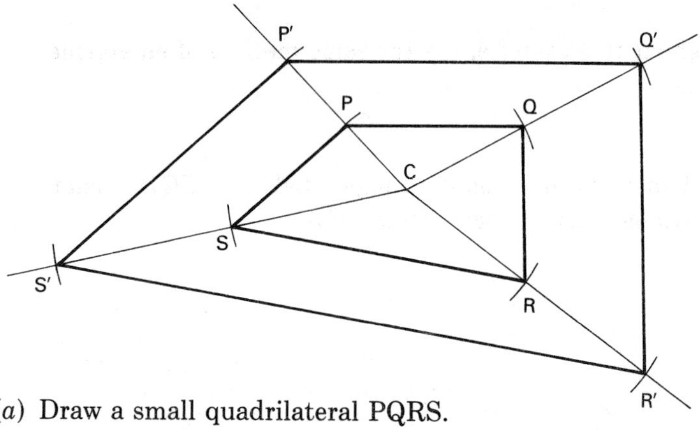

(*a*) Draw a small quadrilateral PQRS.
(*b*) Mark a point C *inside* the quadrilateral.
(*c*) From C, draw straight lines through vertices P, Q, R and S.
(*d*) Set a pair of compasses to distance CP, place the point on P and draw an arc to cross the line CP produced. Label the point P′ (CP′ should be twice as long as CP). P′ is the image of P.
(*e*) Repeat step (*d*) for the other 3 vertices.
(*f*) Join P′Q′R′S′, which is an enlargement of PQRS.
(*g*) What is the scale factor of enlargement?

2. Draw a small triangle. Enlarge it from a point inside the triangle using a scale factor of 2.

3. Draw another small triangle. Enlarge it from a point inside the triangle using a scale factor of 4.

Exercise 12

1. Draw a pair of axes where x ranges from 0 to 90 (that is, $0 \leqslant x \leqslant 90$) and y ranges from 0 to 60 $(0 \leqslant y \leqslant 60)$.

2. Plot these points and join them in the order given. (Use straight lines): (33, 3), (25, 3), (28, 0), (44, 0), (45, 3), (33, 3), (33, 30), (43, 5), (25, 5) and (33, 20).

3. Now enlarge your picture using a scale factor of 2 and using the origin as the centre of enlargement.

4. Compare the co-ordinates of the image with the co-ordinates of the object. Write what you notice.

18 Ratio and Proportion

Ratio

Exercise 1

R

1. How many times as long as 8 m is 24 m?

2. By how many times is 360 g heavier than 90 g?

3. By how many times is 2 h longer than 20 min?

4. Write these ratios in their simplest form:
   (*a*) 12 : 6
   (*b*) 9 : 6
   (*c*) 28 : 21
   (*d*) 11 : 22
   (*e*) 16 : 20
   (*f*) 45 : 36
   (*g*) 30 : 48
   (*h*) 84 : 48

5. Write these ratios in their simplest form:
   (*a*) $3 : 1\frac{1}{2}$ (*b*) $5 : 7\frac{1}{2}$ (*c*) 4.8 : 3.6 (*d*) 1.2 : 0.8

6. Write as ratios in their simplest form:
   (*a*) 20 gal to 16 gal
   (*b*) £1.50 to £1.25
   (*c*) 15 cm to 10 cm
   (*d*) 14 lb to 21 lb

7. Find the missing values that make the ratios the same:
   (*a*) 18 : 12 = [?] : 2 (*b*) 25 : [?] = 5 : 3

8. Write these ratios in the form $m : 1$:
   (*a*) 10 : 4 (*b*) 21 : 2 (*c*) 34 : 5 (*d*) 4.5 : 0.3

9. Write these ratios in the form $1 : m$:
(*a*) $7 : 35$ (*b*) $12 : 27$ (*c*) $14 : 10.5$ (*d*) $55 : 44$

10. Which is better value for money:
(*a*) 200 g for £1.20 or 300 g for £1.78?
(*b*) 4 kg for £3.12 or 5 kg for £3.95?
(*c*) 18 m for £3 or 11.8 m for £2?

Exercise 2

1. A teaspoon holds 5 mℓ. How many teaspoons can be filled from 45 mℓ?

2. There are two medicine bottles. How many times as much medicine as the smaller bottle does the larger one hold if:
(*a*) The larger bottle holds 500 mℓ and the smaller 100 mℓ?
(*b*) The larger bottle holds 450 mℓ and the smaller 150 mℓ?
(*c*) The larger bottle holds 250 mℓ and the smaller 100 mℓ?

3. A mug holds 250 mℓ and a cup 200 mℓ. What is the ratio of the contents of the mug to that of the cup? Give your answer in the form $m : 1$.

4. A car travels at 70 m.p.h., while a van travels at 50 m.p.h. Give the ratio of the speed of the car to that of the van in the form $m : 1$.

5. There are 36 women and 12 men on a coach and no one else. Write in their simplest forms, the ratios of:
(*a*) The number of women to the number of men.
(*b*) The total number of people on the coach to the number of women.

6. 2 lb of oranges are used to make 5 lb of orange marmalade. How many oranges are needed to make 15 lb?

7. If 200 g of plain flour is needed to make 16 biscuits, how much flour should be used for 24 biscuits?

8. If 400 g of mincemeat is used to make 20 mince pies, how many mince pies can be made from:
(*a*) 600 g of mincemeat? (*b*) 780 g of mincemeat?

Exercise 3

1. Draw a small quadrilateral. Label it RSTU.

2. Enlarge the quadrilateral from a point inside it using a scale factor of 3. Label the image R′S′T′U′.

3. Calculate the ratios:

   (*a*) $\frac{R'S'}{RS}$ (*b*) $\frac{S'T'}{ST}$ (*c*) $\frac{T'U'}{TU}$ (*d*) $\frac{U'R'}{UR}$

   Write the ratios in the form $m : 1$.

4. Compare the ratios calculated in question 3 with the scale factor of the enlargement. Write what you notice.

Exercise 4 R

1. A nurse diluted a drug with water in the ratio 1 : 5. If 50 mℓ of the drug was used:
   (*a*) How much water was used?
   (*b*) How much solution was made up altogether?

2. An orange drink is diluted with water in the ratio 1 : 4.
   If 1 ℓ of water is used:
   (*a*) How much orange is used?
   (*b*) How many litres are made up altogether?

3. If 400 components out of 28 000 were faulty, find the ratio of the number of faulty parts to the total number of parts. Give your answer in the form $1 : m$.

4. A model ship is built to a scale of 1 : 200. If the model is 0.6 m long, what is the length of the real ship?

Ratio and Rivers

Most of the water that is near the bed or the banks of a river is slowed down by them. If the volume of water increases at a certain part of a river, the depth will be greater so the extra water will be further from the river bed and will hardly be affected by the bed – so the river will tend to flow faster.

At certain parts of rivers that are likely to flood, new channels must be built or existing channels must be changed – they can be made wider or deeper (by increasing the height of the banks or by lowering the river bed).

Widening or deepening the channels will take the extra water; however, it is also better to move the water away from the flood danger-area as fast as possible. To decide whether it is better to widen or deepen the channel, the ratio, width : average depth can be used (the average being the *mean*). Engineers try to create channels where the ratio, width : average depth = 2 : 1 (that is, they try to make the width twice the depth).

Exercise 5 **M**

Copy and complete the following table for ten different rivers. Give the ratio width : mean depth in the form $m : 1$.

	Width	Mean depth	$\frac{\text{Width}}{\text{Mean depth}}$
1.	24 m	4 m	
2.	84 m	12 m	
3.	108 m	36 m	
4.	15 m	6 m	
5.	527 m	68 m	
6.	30 m	16 m	
7.	420 m	48 m	
8.	189 m	56 m	
9.	1.14 km	75 m	
10.	141 m	48 m	

Ratios, Gears and Bikes

Exercise 6 **M**

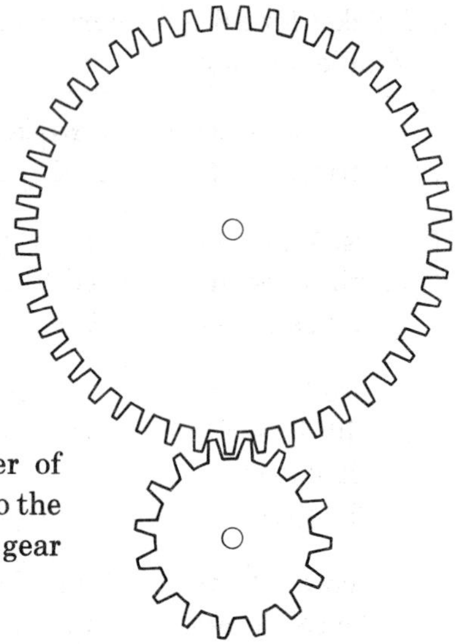

A **1.** If the large gear wheel turns clockwise, which way does the small gear wheel turn?

2. The large wheel has 48 teeth and the small wheel has 16 teeth.

(*a*) If the large wheel makes one full turn, how many full turns does the small wheel turn?

(*b*) Find the ratio of the number of teeth on the large gear wheel to the number of teeth on the small gear wheel.

B Copy and complete the following table for two gear wheels in contact:

	No. of teeth on: large wheel	small wheel	$\frac{\text{No. of teeth on large wheel}}{\text{No. of teeth on small wheel}}$	No. of turns of: large wheel	small wheel
1.	48	24	2 : 1	1	
2.	48	12		1	
3.	40	10		1	
4.	42	21		1	
5.	42	14		1	
6.	39	13		2	
7.	39	26		2	
8.	40	30		3	

Exercise 7

The diagram shows a hand drill. The handle turns the large wheel which in turn drives the small wheel.

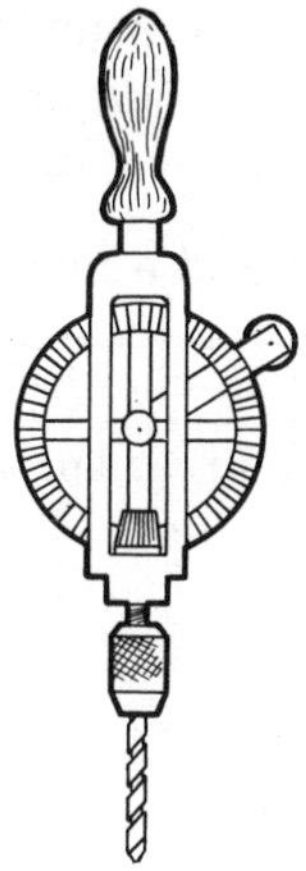

The drill bit makes the same number of turns as the small wheel. If the large wheel has 60 teeth and the small wheel 15 teeth, then:

1. Write the ratio of the number of teeth on the large wheel to the number of teeth on the small wheel.
2. If the large wheel makes one full turn, how many full turns (revolutions or revs) will the small wheel make?
3. When the large wheel makes 8 revs, how many revs will the small wheel make?
4. If the large wheel makes 25 revs, how many revs will the drill bit make?
5. If the large wheel turns at 60 rev/min (60 revolutions per minute, which is 60 full turns in one minute), at how many rev/min does the drill bit turn?
6. If the small wheel makes 40 revs, how many revs will the large wheel make?
7. If in drilling a hole, the bit is turning at 200 rev/min, how fast (in rev/min) must the large wheel be turning?

The gear ratio on a bike depends on the ratio of the number of teeth on the front sprocket (called the chainwheel) to the number of teeth on the rear sprocket. The jockey wheels do not affect the gear ratio. (They take up the slack in the chain at a change of gear.) The rear sprockets are fixed to the hub in the centre of the rear wheel, so one revolution of the rear sprockets means that the rear wheel has also made one full turn. Also, one revolution of the pedals means that the chainwheel has also made one revolution.

If a chainwheel has 52 teeth and a rear sprocket 26 teeth:

$$\text{Ratio} = \frac{\text{no. of teeth on chainwheel}}{\text{no. of teeth on rear sprocket}} = \frac{52}{26} = \frac{2}{1}$$

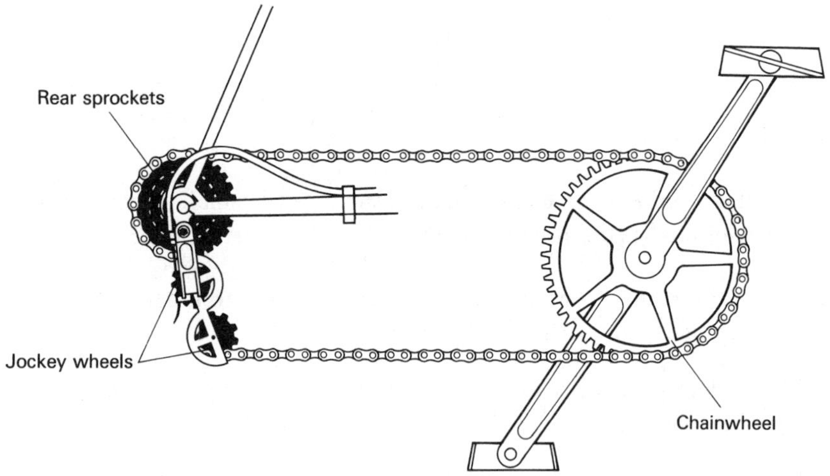

One turn of the chainwheel results in 2 turns of the rear sprocket (which means 2 turns of the rear wheel).
Distance travelled will be 2 × circumference of rear wheel.
The distance travelled for one full turn of the chainwheel is called the gear ratio (when using the metric system).

So we have:

$$\text{Gear ratio} = \frac{\text{no. of teeth on chainwheel}}{\text{no. of teeth on rear sprocket}} \times \begin{array}{l}\text{circumference of}\\ \text{rear wheel}\end{array}$$

(where the circumference is measured in metres).

In imperial units where the diameter of the rear wheel is given in inches:

$$\text{Gear ratio} = \frac{\text{no. of teeth on chainwheel}}{\text{no. of teeth on rear sprocket}} \times \text{diameter of rear wheel}$$

Multiplying this gear ratio by π gives the distance travelled in inches for one revolution of the chainwheel.

Exercise 8 **M**

A 10-gear bicycle has two front chainwheels, one with 52 teeth and the other with 40 teeth. The number of teeth on each of the rear sprockets is 14, 15, 17, 21 and 28.

1. Copy and complete the following table to show the gear ratios in metric if it has a 27-inch wheel (which is 0.6858 m diameter or 2.155 m circumference). Give each gear ratio correct to 2 d.p.

		Rear sprockets				
		14	15	17	21	28
Front chainwheels	52			*6.59		
	40					

$$\text{*Gear ratio} = \frac{52}{17} \times 2.155 = 6.59$$

2. Which rear sprocket gives top gear?

3. Which front chainwheel gives top gear?

4. (*a*) In top gear, how far will the bike travel when the pedals make 60 revolutions?
(*b*) In top gear, how many revolutions of the pedals are needed for the bike to travel 1 km?

5. A good steady pedalling rhythm is 75 rev/min In top gear, pedalling at this rate:
(*a*) How far would you travel in 1 min?
(*b*) How fast would you travel in kilometres per hour?
(*c*) How fast would you travel in m.p.h.? (To change km/h to m.p.h., multiply by 5 then divide by 8.)

Rates

Exercise 9

A These statements are incomplete. Copy and complete them.

1. The car travelled quite fast at 70 miles

2. The car's petrol consumption was 38 miles

3. Mrs Downing's car uses too much petrol. It only gets 6.3 km

4. The cyclist's steady pedalling rhythm was 80 revs

5. We go to school for about 33 h

B Select the correct answer:

1. Milk costs 24 p. Is that:
A. Cheap? B. Expensive? C. A fair price? D. I don't know?

2. Milk costs 48 p. Is that:
A. A better value than in question 1?
B. A poorer value than in question 1?
C. The same value as in question 1?
D. I don't know?

The statements as written in Exercise 9 were meaningless. Each needed two quantities to make sense, but only one has been given.

To answer section B, we need to know how much milk we get for our money before we can decide whether or not it is good value. When both quantities are given we have what is called a *rate*. Miles per hour, pence per pint, etc. are all rates.

The second quantity in a rate is usually given as one unit, so we have:

the number of miles travelled in *one* hour (m.p.h.);
the cost of *one* pint (cost per pint);
the number of miles travelled on *one* gallon (m.p.g.);
the cost of *one* kilogram (cost per kilogram);

and so on.

If steak costs £6.95 per kilogram – then its price per kilogram can also be written as £6.95/kg, which is still read as £6.95 per kilogram; metres per second can be written m/s and the same applies to other rates.

Exercise 10

1. A car travels at 40 m.p.h. How far does it travel in 3 h?
2. A car travels at 75 km/h. How far does it travel in 5 h?
3. If milk costs 24 p a pint, how much do 6 pt cost?
4. If milk costs 46 p/ℓ, what is the cost of 500 mℓ?
5. If a power-drill bit turns at 2400 rev/min, how many revs does it turn in 20 s?
6. If a shop gives a discount of 20 p in the pound, what would be the discount on an article that was selling at £16?
7. A car-hire firm charged 14 p/km on their hire cars. What would be the charge on a journey of 270 km?
8. If carpeting costs £7.75 per square metre (£7.75/m^2), what would be the cost of 12 m^2?
9. If net curtaining costs £4.29 per metre, what would 8 m cost?
10. Elite type on a typewriter uses 12 characters per inch. If I type 9 lines, each 8 in wide, how many characters do I type altogether?

Exercise 11

1. A car uses 4 gal of petrol in travelling 152 miles. What is its petrol consumption in m.p.g.?
2. A car uses 6 ℓ of petrol in travelling 84 km. How many kilometres per litre does the car travel?
3. A box of a dozen pencils costs £2.28. What is the price per pencil?
4. 50 m of electric cable cost £8.50. What is the price per metre?
5. If I obtained 84 French francs for £7, what is the exchange rate per pound?
6. I obtained 21.33 guilders for £9. What is the exchange rate per pound?

7. A cricketer scored 36 runs in 8 overs. Calculate his batting rate in runs per over.

8. Mrs Hardy earned £104.16 for working 28 h. Calculate her earnings rate per hour.

Proportion (Direct Proportion)

If you earn £3 an hour you should be paid £6 for working 2 h, £9 for 3 h, £12 for 4 h and so on.
Your earnings depend on the number of hours worked.

More hours ⟶ more pay
Less hours ⟶ less pay

Hours worked and earnings are said to be in *direct proportion.*

The proportional relationship between the two quantities can be seen from a table.

Hours worked	1	2	3	4	5	6	7	8
Earnings (£)	3	6	9	12	15	18	21	24

$$\frac{1}{3} = \frac{2}{6} = \frac{3}{9} = \frac{4}{12} = \frac{5}{15} = \frac{6}{18} = \frac{7}{21} = \frac{8}{24}$$

Note If you double the hours worked you double the earnings; in fact, whatever number the hours worked are multiplied by, the earnings are multiplied by the same number.

Exercise 12

A For each of the following, write whether it is 'TRUE' or 'FALSE':

1. If 3 cartons of fruit juice cost £1.80, then 6 cartons of the same size (and make) cost £3.60.

2. Henry VIII had 6 wives so Henry IV had 3 wives.

3. A 15-year-old boy takes size 8 in shoes. When he is twice as old he will take size 16.

4. Two friends living near each other travel to school together. If Belinda travelled on her own, the journey would take 25 min. When she travels with Fariyal, the journey must take 50 min.

5. A car travelling at a steady speed travels 120 km in 2 h, so it will travel 480 km in 8 h.

6. Amy, aged 13 years, is 1.57 m tall. When she is 26 years old, she will be 3.14 m tall.

7. In the high jump Joe, aged 15 years, can jump 1.4 m. At the age of 60 years, he will be able to jump 5.6 m.

8. On his own, Tony takes 3 min to sing a song. If 10 people sing the same song together, it will take them 30 min.

B Which of the following are in direct proportion and which are not?

1. The number of pounds exchanged and the amount of foreign currency obtained.

2. The age of a person and how heavy that person is.

3. The number of eggs boiled and the time taken.

4. The distance a person can throw a javelin and that person's age.

5. Distance travelled by a mower while mowing and the number of turns of the roller on the mower.

6. The amount of water in a bath and the time the tap runs (at a steady rate).

7. The number of people in a room and the amount of heat needed to warm the room.

8. The distance between two places on a map and the true distance.

Exercise 13 **M**

The tables give sets of numbers that are in direct proportion. Copy and complete them:

1.

Number of items bought	1	2	3	5	8	10	12
Cost (£)		12		30			

2.

Distance travelled (km)			45	60			150
Petrol used (l)	1	2	3		7	9	

3.

Distance travelled (km)				480	640		800
Time taken (h)	1	2	4	6		9	

4.

Number of pages typed	1	2		5	7		15
Time taken (min)			56		98	140	

Here are 3 methods of solving the same proportion problem. (You need not learn all three.)

Problem 4 books cost £24. Find the cost of 6 books if they all cost the same.

Method 1 (Making a table)

Number of books	4	2	6
Cost of books (£)	£24	£12	£36

So 6 books cost $\underline{\underline{£36}}$

Method 2 (Unitary method)

4 books cost £24

so 1 book costs £6

$\therefore$ 6 books cost $\underline{\underline{£36}}$

Method 3 (Ratio method)

4 books cost £24

so 6 books cost $(\frac{6}{4} \times £24) = \underline{\underline{£36}}$

Reasoning for method 3 is:

We can multiply by $\frac{4}{6}$ or $\frac{6}{4}$ (the ratio of the numbers of books). Since more books cost more money, it is necessary to multiply by $\frac{6}{4}$ (it gives a bigger answer).

Exercise 14

1. If it costs 90 p to post one parcel, what would it cost to post 5 parcels if the parcels were identical?

2. If 2 ℓ of orange juice fills 6 identical glasses, how many of the glasses will 8 ℓ fill?

3. At the daily rate, a hotel charges £72 for 3 days. At the same rate, what would be the charge for 6 days?

4. A ticket for a 6-mile journey costs 42 p. What should it cost for an 18-mile journey?

5. If 15 m of material will make 3 pairs of curtains, how many pairs of curtains of the same size can be made from 45 m?

6. If I use 1.2 m of wood to frame 2 photographs of the same size, what length of wood do I need to frame 6 photographs which are the same size as the other two?

7. If I use 120 mℓ of milk in 4 cups of coffee and use the same amount of milk in each drink, how much milk do I need for:
(*a*) 32 cups?
(*b*) 6 cups?

8. If it costs £20 to insure articles worth £6000, what would it cost, at the same rate, to insure articles worth:
(*a*) £42 000? (*b*) £9000? (*c*) £27 000?

9. If 4 three-pin plugs cost £3.36, what would be the cost of:
(*a*) 6 plugs? (*b*) 7 plugs?

10. 5 miles is the same distance as 8 km. How many kilometres is:
(*a*) 15 miles? (*b*) 35 miles? (*c*) 2.5 miles? (*d*) 9 miles?

11. If 4 cm on a map represents 10 km,
(*a*) What distance is represented by 10 cm?
(*b*) What length represents a distance of 60 km?
(*c*) What length represents a distance of 35 km?
(*d*) What distance is represented by 9 cm?

12. If 450 g of self-raising flour is used to make 2 cherry cakes of the same size:
(*a*) How many grams are needed for 3 cakes?
(*b*) How many kilograms are needed for 8 cakes?
(*c*) How many cakes can be made from 2.25 kg?
(*d*) How many cakes can be made from 3.15 kg?

19 Flow Charts

It is important to do things in the correct order:

e.g. To open the window and *then* to look around outside is correct,

but to look around outside *then* to open the window is not!

Exercise 1

Here are the chapter headings for a story. Put them in a sensible order.

The train
The big fall
The journey begins
The climbing expedition
Hospital
The return journey
The descent
On board ship
The cabin in the mountains

Exercise 2

Write the following statements in the correct order:

1. Open the door.
   Turn the handle.
   Close the door.
   Enter the room.

2. Get washed.
   Get dressed.
   Have breakfast.
   Get out of bed.

3. Put more pressure on the point of the needle than on the pencil.
   Set the pair of compasses to the size of the radius.
   Sweep the pencil in one direction only.
   Place the point of the needle at the required centre.

Exercise 3

The words in each statement have been given in the wrong order. Write each sentence correctly.

1. touches tangent a circle a
2. a to up add triangle of angles 180°
3. sides a with hexagon called polygon six a is
4. four sides rhombus a has equal
5. has cube faces eight a six and vertices
6. rotational but has parallelogram a symmetry symmetry bilateral not

7. angle angle an an which greater a is than right-angle is obtuse

8. number a divided only prime can be itself by one and

9. equal semi-circle angles a in 90°

10. of of polygon exterior sum the the angles 360° equals a

In carrying out a task, a flow chart (or flow diagram) can be used to help you to sort out the order of doing things. Here are two flow charts, the first shows how to use a cassette recorder while the second shows how to find the perimeter of a rectangle.

How to Use a Cassette Recorder

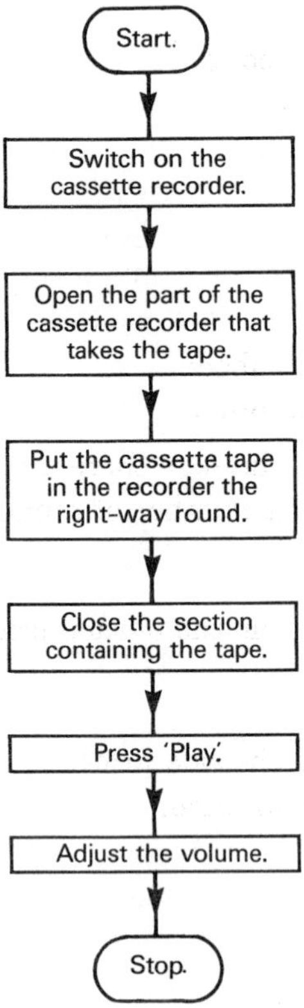

Finding the Perimeter of a Rectangle

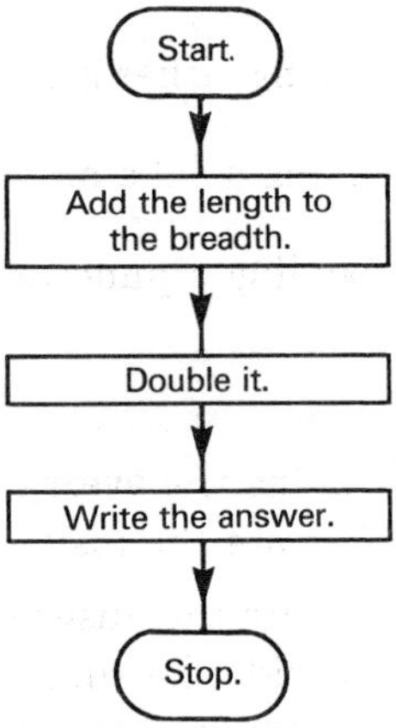

The flow charts clearly show an order (simply follow the arrows). Note the shapes of the boxes used. For *start* and *stop*, a 'running-track' shape is used. *Instructions* are written in rectangular boxes.

Exercise 4

Draw flow charts for the following. Use rectangles for instruction boxes and 'running tracks' for start and stop.

A **1.** Writing and posting a letter.
Here are the instructions (in the wrong order):

Stick a stamp on the envelope; Write the letter; Seal the envelope;
Take out a pen, writing paper and an envelope;
Write the address on the envelope;
Post the letter; Put the letter inside the envelope;
Go to the post-box.

2. Cleaning your teeth.

3. Making either a cup of tea or a mug of coffee.

4. Baking a cake or cooking a meal.

5. Mending a puncture.

B **1.** Finding the average (mean) of some numbers.
Here are the instructions (in the wrong order):

Write the answer; Count how many numbers there are;
Divide the sum of the numbers by the number of numbers;
Calculate the sum of the numbers.

2. Calculating the sale price of an article from the normal price if the percentage discount is 20%.
Use:

Find 20% of the normal price; Write the sale price;
Subtract the discount from the normal price;
Find out what the normal price is.

3. Measuring an angle.

4. Calculating the circumference of a circle.
(Circumference of a circle, $C = \pi d$.)

5. Calculating the area of a circle.
(Area of a circle, $A = \pi r^2$.)

Here are three different flow charts that are supposed to show you how to obtain the correct shade of green from blue and yellow paints:

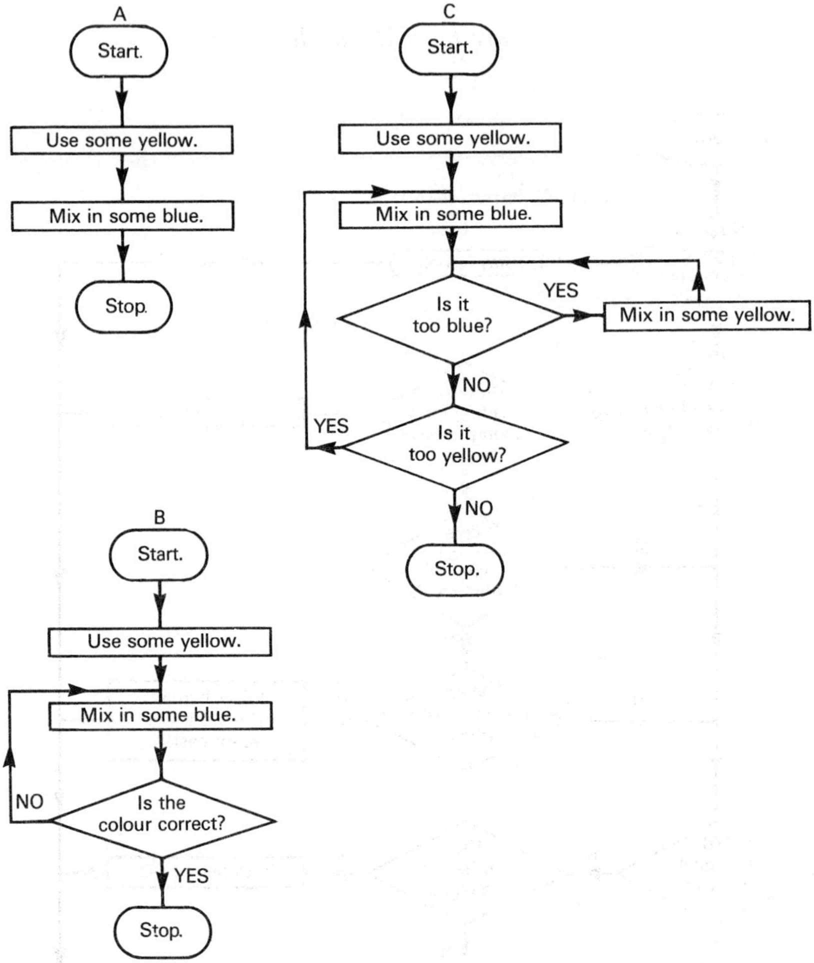

Neither A nor B works! Follow them through to satisfy yourself that you would not get the correct shade of green. Note the new type of box in B. It is called a *decision* box. The answer to a question in a decision box must be either 'YES' or 'NO'. Note that there are 2 paths leaving the decision box, one for 'YES' and the other for 'NO'.

Flow chart C uses two decision boxes. Follow flowchart C through to satisfy yourself that it works.

Exercise 5

The flow chart below gives a possible cure for a headache.

A Cure for a Headache?

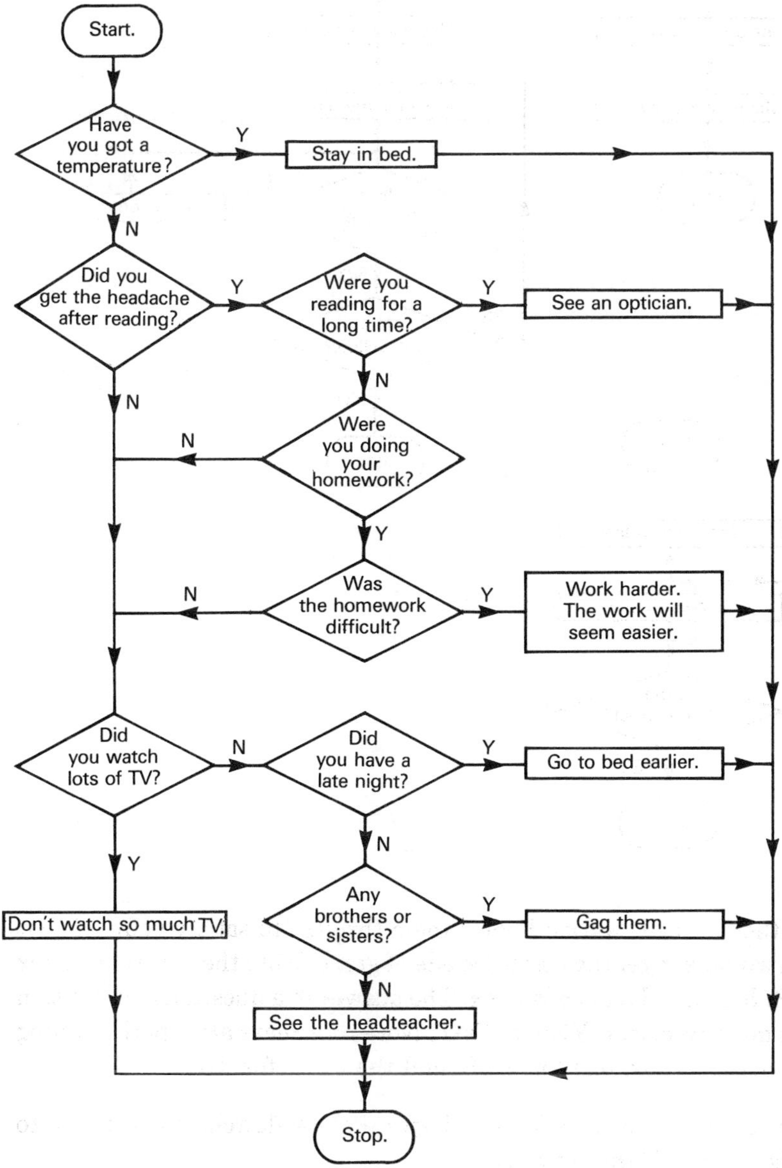

Use the flow chart on the previous page to find the cure needed by the following people.

1. Stuart did not have a temperature. He had not been reading but he watched TV for 5 h.

2. Heidi did not have a temperature. Her headache started after reading for a short time – it wasn't her homework. She only watched TV for 1 h then went to bed early, in fact, earlier than her brothers and sisters.

3. Niamh's temperature was normal. She read for about half an hour before getting the headache – it wasn't homework. She didn't watch television and didn't have a late night. Being an only child, no one disturbed her all evening.

4. Lee didn't have a temperature. His headache started after reading schoolwork – he certainly found his homework difficult.

Exercise 6

A Number Flow Chart

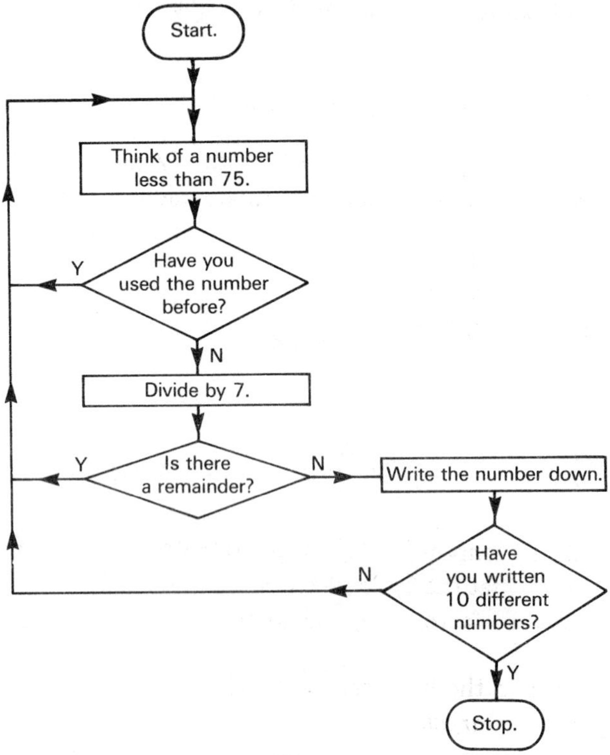

These questions refer to the flow chart opposite.

1. Use the flow chart for the numbers 60, 30, 14, 27, 19, 7, 45, 21, then use some numbers of your own choice.

2. Describe the set of numbers the flow chart helps you to find.

Exercise 7

Which of the following should be written in a *decision* box?

1. Is it cold?

2. Do I turn right or left at the T-junction?

3. Are there more apples than oranges?

4. Does $9 + 7 = 16$?

5. Does $8 \times 7 = 52$?

6. Is $9 > 2$?

7. Am I overweight?

8. Was it black or white?

9. Is the water hot?

10. Should I put the switch up or down?

11. Do you enjoy reading?

12. Is the door open or closed?

13. Shall I ring at 8 o'clock?

14. Do you prefer strawberry or banana milk shake?

15. Did you go to a disco last week?

16. Are you married or single?

17. Is the light on or off?

18. Do the diagonals of a rhombus bisect each other?

Exercise 8 M

An outline of a flow chart is given. Copy it.

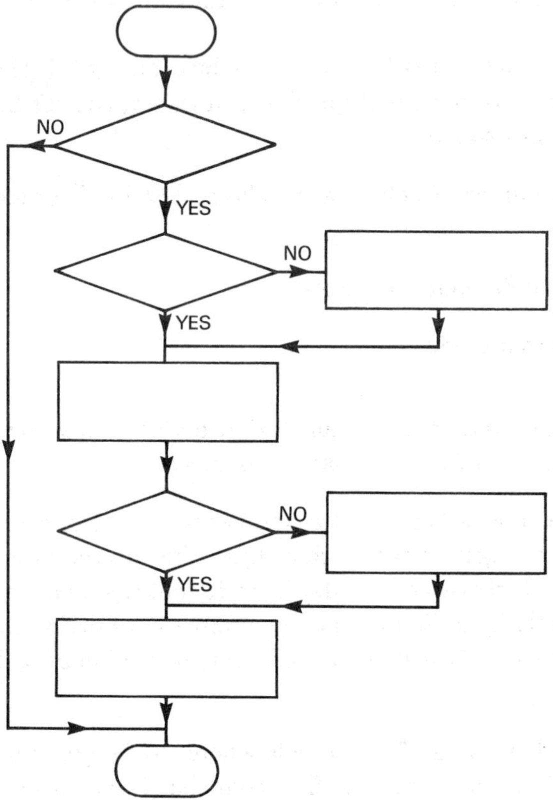

On your copy, write one of the following words, statements or questions in each box so that the flow chart makes sense.

Stop.
Start.
Read the instructions.
Buy some.
Do you have any medicine?
Get one.
Do you have a spoon?
Take the medicine.
Do you have a cough?

Exercise 9

Draw flow charts to show the following:

A **1.** How to catch a bus.
Use the following in your flow chart (they are given in the wrong order):
Start; Stop; Get on the bus; Is there a bus coming?; Is there room to get on?; Go to the bus stop; Wait and watch; Did the bus stop?; Signal the bus to stop.

2. How to boil an egg (including the choice of a hard- or soft-boiled egg).

3. Preparing to do your homework.

4. How to cross a road.

B **1.** How to find numbers less than 50 that divide exactly by 8. (Use the ideas in the flow chart on p. 228.)

2. How to check whether or not a number is exactly divisible by 9. Use the following in your flow chart (given here in the wrong order): Start; Stop; Is there a remainder?; Write that the number does not divide exactly by 9; Write that the number does divide exactly by 9; Find the sum of the digits of the number; Divide by 9; Think of a number.

3. How to find the area of a rectangle where the length and breadth are both less than 10 cm. The flow chart has been started for you.

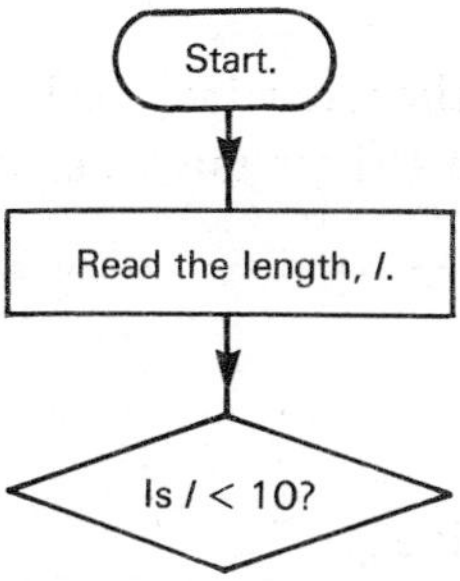

4. How to find the number of pieces of string of any given length that can be cut from one piece of string of length 25 cm.

Functions and Flow Charts

Exercise 10

1. Use flow chart A to find the answer when the starting number is:
   (*a*) 4 (*b*) 7 (*c*) 9

A B C

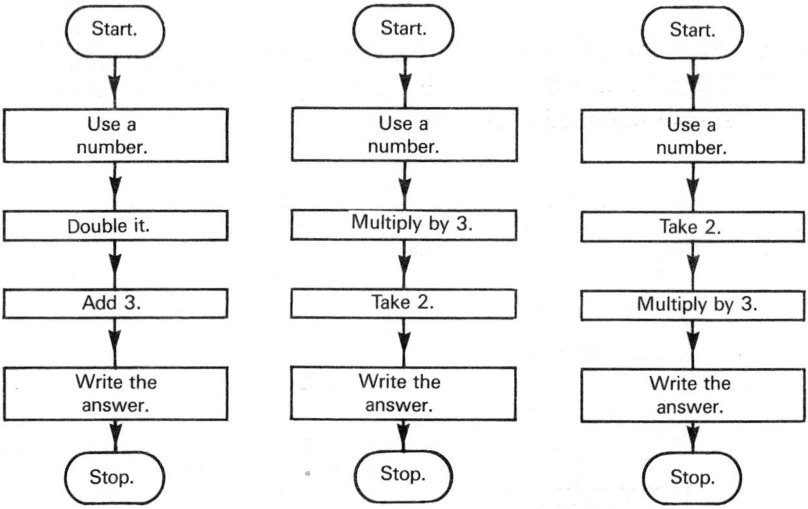

2. Use flow chart B to find the answer when the starting number is:
   (*a*) 2 (*b*) 5 (*c*) 9

3. Use flow chart C to find the answer when the starting number is:
   (*a*) 2 (*b*) 5 (*c*) 9

4. Use $y = 2x + 3$ to find y when:
   (*a*) $x = 4$ (*b*) $x = 7$ (*c*) $x = 9$
   Compare your answers with those to question 1.

5. Which flow chart shows the function $y = 3(x - 2)$?

6. Write the function for the flow chart that has not been used in questions 4 and 5.

Exercise 11

Draw flow charts to show the following functions:

A 1. $y = x + 7$ 3. $y = 4x - 3$ 5. $y = 2(x + 6)$

2. $y = 2x$ 4. $y = \frac{x}{3}$

B 1. $f(x) = x - 4$ 3. $f(x) = 2x + 9$ 5. $f(x) = 3(x + 4)$

2. $f(x) = 3x$ 4. $f(x) = \frac{x}{2}$

Exercise 12

1. (*a*) Work through flow chart A using any number you wish.
   (*b*) Work through flow chart B using as your starting number the answer obtained in part (*a*).

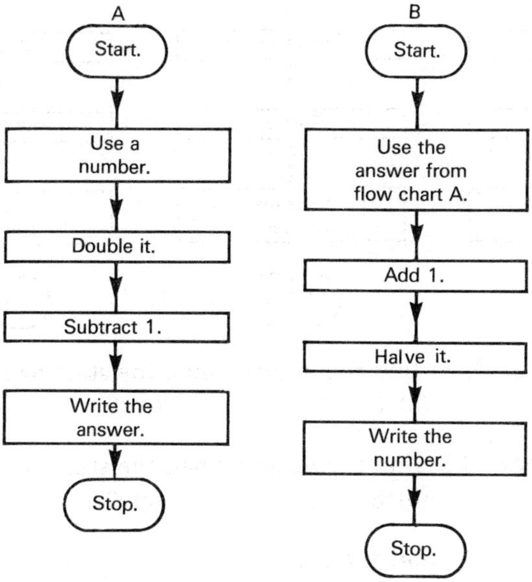

2. Repeat question 1 several times using a different starting number each time.

3. Write what you notice.

Exercise 13

1. Draw flow charts to work the functions in Exercise 11 'backwards'. (The new flow charts show what is called the *inverse function.*)
2. Try to write expressions using x for some of the inverse functions you have found.

20 Simple Equations

Flow charts can be used to solve many simple equations. Consider the equation:

$$2x - 3 = 7$$

The left-hand side (containing the unknown, the letter x in this case) can be shown on a flow chart as for the functions in Chapter 19, pp. 232-3 (see flow chart A below). Alongside the flow chart it is shown how $2x - 3$ is built up by using x for the number. Follow the flow chart through.

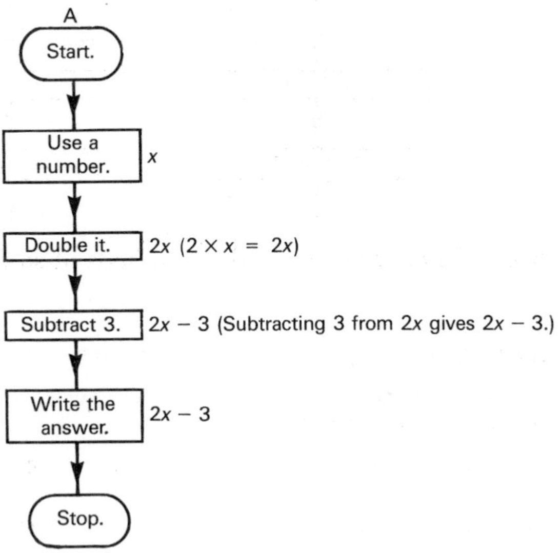

Flow chart B, which was obtained from flow chart A, shows how $2x - 3$ can be broken down bit by bit to obtain x. However, in flow chart B, we start with $2x - 3$ and finish with x. Follow the flow chart through. Now use the number 7 in flow chart B instead of $2x - 3$ since $2x - 3 = 7$ in the question. You should obtain the answer 5. Check your answer by following flow chart A through using the number 5.

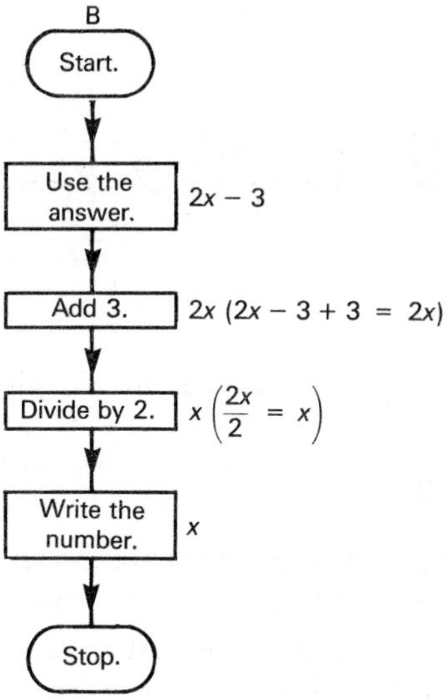

Flow charts A (p. 234) and B can be simplified to:

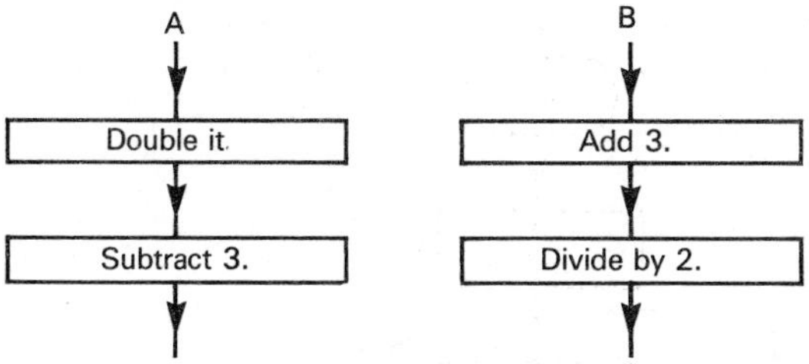

Note There are many other methods of solving simple equations.

Exercise 1 R

Solve these equations:

1. $x + 3 = 11$
2. $x + 10 = 19$
3. $x - 5 = 8$
4. $d - 13 = 2$
5. $g + 17 = 26$
6. $7x = 21$
7. $4x = 40$
8. $5n = 60$
9. $11q = 55$
10. $x \div 2 = 10$
11. $p \div 4 = 12$
12. $\dfrac{x}{5} = 10$

13. $\frac{e}{8} = 4$

14. $2x - 1 = 7$

15. $3x + 5 = 11$

16. $4a + 3 = 15$

17. $3t - 4 = 2$

18. $2k + 9 = 17$

19. $5f - 6 = 34$

20. $\frac{x}{3} = 8$

21. $9l = 108$

22. $2x + 5 = 19$

23. $\frac{c}{6} = 4$

24. $6h - 4 = 14$

25. $\frac{m}{10} = 15$

Exercise 2

Solve these equations:

1. $x + 4 = 6\frac{1}{2}$

2. $x - 3 = 1\frac{3}{4}$

3. $x + 3\frac{1}{2} = 6$

4. $u - 4\frac{1}{2} = 7$

5. $z + 2\frac{1}{4} = 7\frac{1}{4}$

6. $j - 3\frac{2}{3} = 6\frac{1}{3}$

7. $d - 2\frac{3}{4} = 4\frac{3}{4}$

8. $2x = 7$

9. $4v = 10$

10. $3y = 4\frac{1}{2}$

11. $3a = 7.5$

12. $\frac{x}{2} = 0.5$

13. $\frac{n}{3} = 2\frac{1}{3}$

14. $\frac{e}{2} = 5\frac{3}{4}$

15. $2x + 1 = 10$

16. $3w - 5 = 0$

17. $3c + 3 = 13$

18. $4m + 2 = 16$

19. $5q + 2 = 15$

20. $4k - 5 = 8$

Exercise 3

Solve these equations:

1. $x - 9 = {}^{-}5$

2. $x + 7 = 3$

3. $l + 5 = {}^{-}2$

4. $z - 2 = {}^{-}7$

5. $p - 6 = {}^{-}4$

6. $u + 6 = {}^{-}4$

7. $3x = {}^{-}12$

8. $5x = {}^{-}35$

9. $8t = {}^{-}24$

10. ${}^{-}3w = 18$

11. ${}^{-}5y = {}^{-}10$

12. ${}^{-}4a = 20$

13. $\frac{v}{2} = {}^{-}6$

14. $\frac{d}{{}^{-}2} = 4$

15. $\frac{l}{{}^{-}4} = {}^{-}4$

16. $2n + 5 = 3$

17. $3f - 10 = {}^{-}4$

18. $2g - 4 = {}^{-}12$

19. $4k + 7 = {}^{-}9$

20. $5y + 3 = {}^{-}27$

Exercise 4

Find each value of x:

1. $12 - x = 4$

2. $15 - x = 3$

3. $20 - x = 11$

4. $17 - x = 12$

5. $25 - x = 9$

6. $21 - x = 10$

7. $19 - x = 11$

8. $30 - x = 14$

9. $37 - x = 19$

10. $40 - x = 18$

11. $50 - x = 1$

12. $100 - x = 36$

A The line is 4 cm long.

B The line is x cm long.

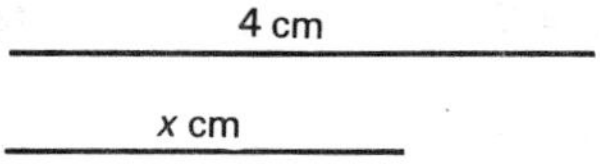

In statement A, the exact length is given, but in statement B, the exact length is not known. x stands for a number that we do not know. (x is unknown.)

This line is d cm long:

This line is 2 cm longer:
So it must be $(d + 2)$ cm long.

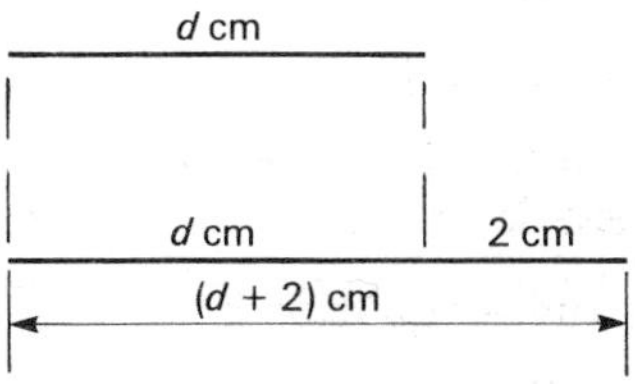

We still do not know the exact lengths but if we are given the length of one of them we can easily find the length of the other.

e.g. If $d = 5$ then the first line is 5 cm long and the second line is $(5 + 2)$ cm or 7 cm long.

Jean earns twice as much as Joe.

If Joe earns £x then Jean earns £$2x$. Check that this is true by substituting any number you like for x. (Avoid using 0 or 1 when substituting as a check; they can cause problems. For example, if $x = 0$ then $2x$, $3x$, $4x$, $5x$ and so on are all equal to 0. When $x = 1$, x^2, x^3, x^4 and so on are all 1.)

The length of a rectangle is 4 cm longer than its breadth.

If the breadth $= b$ cm,

then its length $= (b + 4)$ cm.

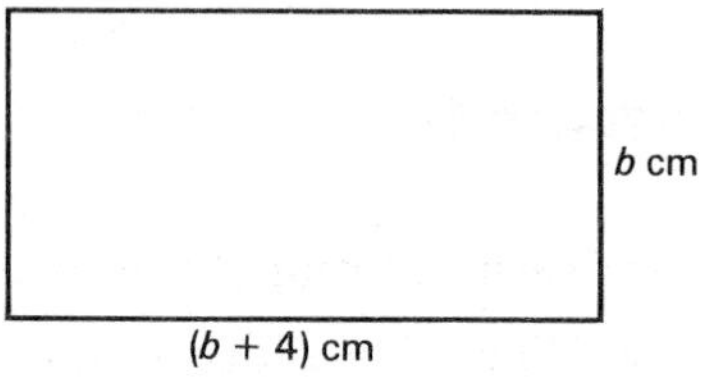

Exercise 5

Write algebraic expressions for the following. If a letter is not given in a question you may choose your own letter.

e.g. 'Think of a number then subtract 8' becomes $n - 8$.

1. I think of a number then add 6.

2. 12 is subtracted from a number m.

3. A number c is multiplied by 8.

4. 25 is added to a number.

5. Janine had £y and spent £15.

6. Ossie is h years old. Russell is twice as old as Ossie.

7. 5 tickets cost £e each. Total cost = [?].

8. Write a number that is one-third of w.

9. I think of a number then multiply it by 9.

10. I think of a number, double it, then subtract 6.

11. The number z is multiplied by 4, then 17 is added.

12. 13 is subtracted from 5 times a number.

13. There are t cups on a shelf. On another shelf there are 3 less than twice as many.

14. Duncan is f years old. Izzat is 3 times as old as Duncan. How old will they be in 7 years' time.

15. The given line is $6r$ m long.
What length is:

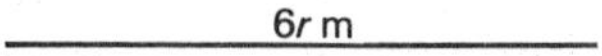

(a) 4 m longer?
(b) 5 m shorter?
(c) twice as long?
(d) half the length?

Exercise 6

R

For each question, form an equation, then solve it:

1. When 5 is added to a number x we get 12. Find the number x.

2. When 11 is added to a number, we get 17. Find the number.

3. I think of a number then subtract 8. If the answer is 4, what is the number?

4. A number, when multiplied by 7, gives 35. Find the number.

5. A number, when divided by 2, gives 18. Find the number.

6. A number, when multiplied by 6, gives 84. Find the number.

7. 4 tickets cost £18 altogether. What is the cost of one ticket if they all cost the same?

8. After using k litres of petrol there are 28 ℓ left. If there were 52 ℓ at the start of the journey, how many litres were used?

9. A piece of wood is t metres long. If 8 pieces of this size have a total length of 60 m, find t.

10. Tina has £18. If after spending £d she has £11 left, find the value of d.

11. The width of a rectangle is 6 cm shorter than its length. If its width is 15 cm, find its length.

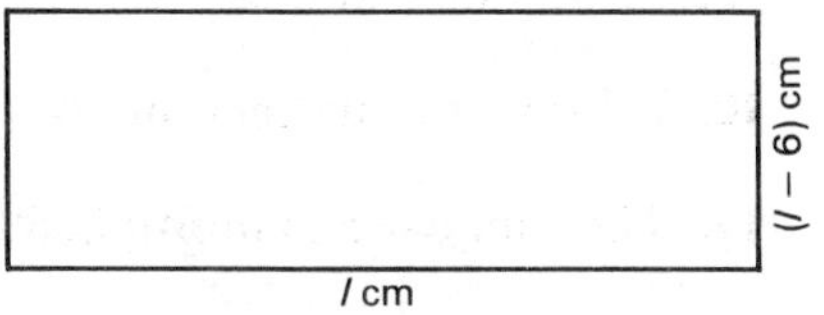

12. A piece of string is u metres long. When it is cut into 4 equal lengths, each piece is 3 m long. How long was the string before it was cut?

Exercise 7

For each question, form an equation, then solve it:

1. When a certain number is doubled then 4 added, the result is 22. Find the number.
2. When 8 is added to 3 times a number the result is 20. Find the number.
3. When 3 is added to double a number the result is 17. Find the number.
4. A number is multiplied by 4 then 6 is added and the result is 30. Find the number.
5. A number is doubled then 9 is subtracted. If the result is 5, find the number.
6. If 2 is subtracted from 5 times a certain number, the result is 13. Find the number.
7. If 7 is subtracted from 6 times a certain number, the result is 23. Find the number.
8. When a certain number is multiplied by 7 then 8 subtracted, the result is 48. Find the number.
9. There are n books in a box. If there were twice as many, a further 6 would be needed to fill the box which holds 40 books when full. How many books are there in the box?
10. There are x oranges in a bowl. If there were twice as many and if 5 of the oranges were eaten there would be 13 left. How many oranges were in the bowl?
11. I have a certain sum of money. If I had 4 times as much, I would have £6 more than I need. If I need £50, how much money have I got?
12. If I had twice as many eggs, I could fill a box and have 8 eggs left over. If a box holds a dozen eggs, how many eggs have I got?
13. Patrick is 4 times as old as his daughter who is now g years old. 12 years ago, Patrick was 36. How old is his daughter now?
14. After travelling at v km/h for 6 h, I still have 45 km of my journey to go. If the total distance I must travel is 345 km, how fast am I travelling?

21 Formulae

Exercise 1

1. The area of a parallelogram can be found by multiplying its base by its perpendicular height. We can write $A = bh$.

   Calculate the area of a house drive that is in the shape of a parallelogram. Its dimensions are given in the sketch.

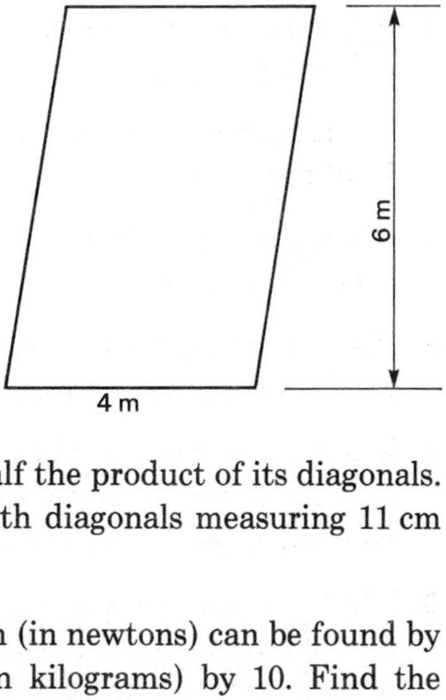

2. The area of a rhombus is equal to half the product of its diagonals. Calculate the area of a rhombus with diagonals measuring 11 cm and 6 cm.

3. (*a*) On Earth, the weight of a person (in newtons) can be found by multiplying a person's mass (in kilograms) by 10. Find the weight of someone with a mass of 54 kg.
   (*b*) If the person in part (*a*) is on the Moon, that person's weight can be found by multiplying the mass by 1.6. Find that person's weight on the Moon.

4. The density of a substance is the ratio of its mass to its volume. This can be written as:

$$\text{Density} = \frac{\text{mass}}{\text{volume}}$$

   Find the density (in kg/m^3) of concrete if $0.2\ m^3$ has a mass of 400 kg.

5. Crown roast of lamb needs to be roasted in an oven at gas mark 4 (180 °C/356 °F) allowing 30 min per pound plus 30 min. For how long should 4 lb of lamb stay in the oven?

6. Inches can be changed into centimetres by multiplying the number of inches by 2.54. Change:
(*a*) 3 in into centimetres, (*b*) 7 in into centimetres.

7. Yards can be converted into metres by multiplying by 0.9144. How many metres are there in:
(*a*) 5 yd? (*b*) 8 yd?

8. If one-way car hire (that is, collecting the car from one place and returning it to a different place) costs £20.50 per day plus a mileage charge of 22 p per mile:
(*a*) What would be the cost of hiring the car for one day and travelling 200 miles?
(*b*) What would be the total cost of hire, if insurance and VAT totalling £14.86 needs to be added to the cost obtained in part (*a*)?

Exercise 2

1. $K = C + 273$ is a formula that can be used to change degrees Celsius into kelvins (the absolute scale). Use the formula to change 69 °C into kelvins.

2. $W = 4n$ gives the wages earned (in pounds) by someone working for n h at £4 an hour. Calculate the earnings of someone who works for 29 h.

3. The formula $A = \frac{S}{n}$ gives each interior angle of a regular polygon with n sides if the sum of the interior angles is S°. For a pentagon, $S = 540°$. Find each interior angle.

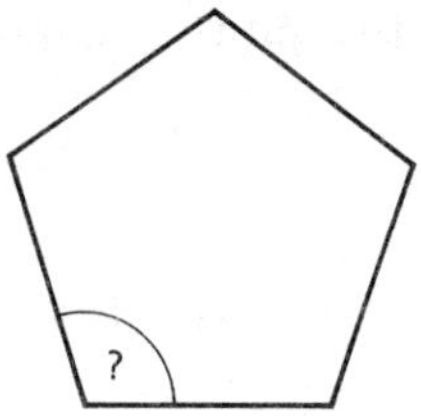

4. The formula $d = 7w$ gives the number of days in w weeks. Use it to find the number of days in 8 weeks.

5. The formula $h = 24d$ gives the number of hours in d days. Use it to find the number of hours in 7 days.

6. The exchange rate is 3 Swiss francs to £1. This can be written as $S = 3L$ where L is the number of pounds and S the number of Swiss francs. Use this formula to find the number of Swiss francs you get for:

(*a*) £7 (*b*) £48 (*c*) £126

7. Average speed can be calculated using the formula:

$$\text{Average speed} = \frac{\text{total distance}}{\text{total time}}$$

Use the formula to find the average speed of:

(*a*) A man who runs 100 m in 10 s.

(*b*) A car that travels 600 m in 30 s (giving the answer in m/s).

8.

$$\begin{matrix}\text{Work done} \\ \text{(in joules)}\end{matrix} = \begin{matrix}\text{force used} \\ \text{(in newtons)}\end{matrix} \times \begin{matrix}\text{distance moved} \\ \text{(in metres)}\end{matrix}$$

Find the work done in moving a box of mass 35 kg to a height of 4 m.

(*Note* The force used = the weight = 10 × the mass = 350 N)

9. Here are three formulae that can be used when roasting beef (in all three formulae, T stands for the number of minutes the beef should be in the oven when the oven is at gas mark 5, 190 °C):

$T = 27\,M + 27$, where M is the mass in pounds

$T = 60\,M + 27$, where M is the mass in kilograms

$T = 6\,M + 27$, where M is the number of 100 g in the mass of the meat (*e.g.* if the beef weighs 650 g then $M = 6.5$)

Use the above formulae to find the cooking time of:

(*a*) 2 kg of beef,

(*b*) 3 lb of beef,

(*c*) 1 lb of beef,

(*d*) 800 g of beef,

(*e*) 450 g of beef.

10. $A = \pi dh$ gives the area of a label that wraps around a tin, as shown, without overlapping itself. d is the diameter of the bottom of the tin, h is its height.
Calculate the area of a label on a tin where the diameter is 75 mm and the height 108 mm.
Use $\pi = 3.14$.

11. Pressure exerted can be calculated using the formula:

$$\text{Pressure} = \frac{\text{force}}{\text{area}}$$

Calculate the pressure exerted on the ground by a man of mass 64 kg if he stands on one leg, given that the area of the part of his foot that touches the ground is $0.016\ \text{m}^2$.
Note A mass of 64 kg creates a force of 640 N and the unit of pressure will be N/m^2.

12. If the man in question 11 stands on a plank of mass 6 kg (weight 60 N) the total force becomes 700 N. This weight is spread out over the area of the bottom of the plank which is $0.4\ \text{m}^2$. Calculate the pressure on the ground.

13.

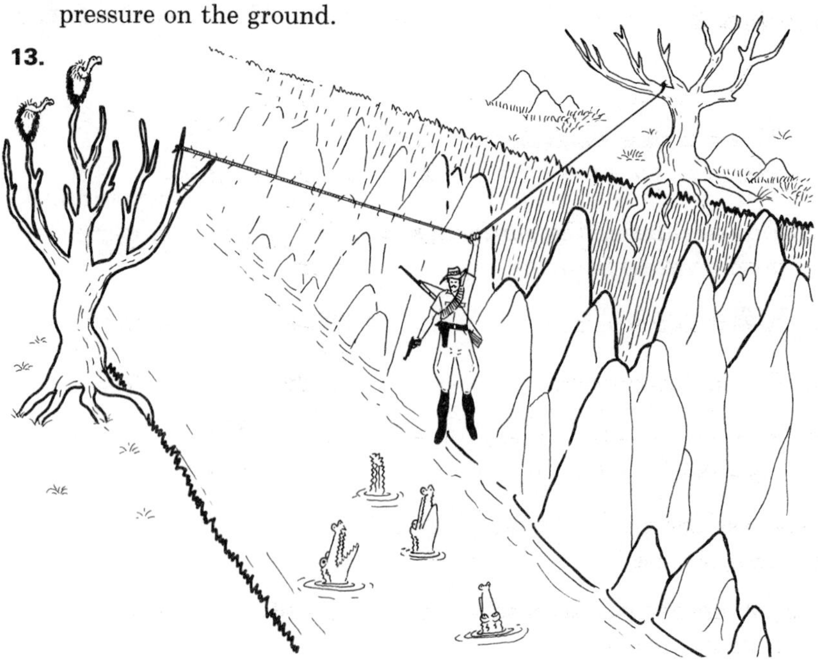

In the formula:

$$P = \frac{WL}{4S}$$

P is the pull on each tree when someone weighing W N hangs from the centre of a rope of length L m. S m is the distance by which the rope sags. Calculate force P when the rope is 12 m long and sags by 1 m when someone of mass 68 kg (weight, $W = 680$ N) hangs in the middle.

14. $d = \sqrt{\frac{3h}{2}}$ gives the approximate distance in miles that someone can see when h ft above sea-level. Use the formula to find the distance in miles (to 3 significant figures) that can be seen from a height above sea-level of:

(*a*) 270 ft (*b*) 100 ft (*c*) 2000 ft

15. $d = \sqrt{12.6\,h}$ gives the approximate distance d in kilometres that can be seen from a point h m above sea-level. Find in kilometres (to 3 s.f.) the distance that can be seen from a height of:

(*a*) 100 m (*b*) 3000 m (*c*) 850 m

Exercise 3

	Example	
A Ask someone to:		
1. Throw 2 dice (away from you so that you can not see the result.)	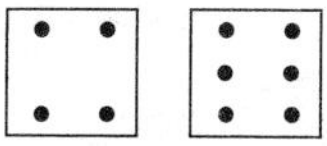	
2. Choose either of the numbers and multiply it by 5.	 $\times 5$	$= 20$
3. Add 8 to the result.	$20 + 8$	$= 28$
4. Double this answer.	2×28	$= 56$
5. Add the number shown on the other die.	$56 +$ 	$= 62$
B Now ask the person to tell you the number obtained.	62	
All you need to do now is to subtract 16 from this result.	$62 - 16$	$= 46$

The digits in your answer will be the 2 numbers shown on the dice.

4 6

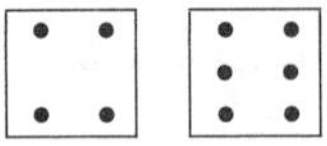

C *Challenge* Try to work out why this puzzle works.

Hint Let the 2 numbers shown on the dice be m and n, then follow through the given steps using m and n.

Exercise 4

A Ask someone to:

Example:

1. Throw 3 dice (away from you so that you cannot see the result).

2. Select any one of the numbers and multiply it by 5.

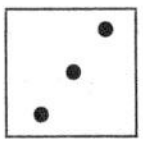 × 5 = 15

3. Add 2 to the result. 15 + 2 = 17

4. Multiply the answer by 2. 17 × 2 = 34

5. Add any one of the other numbers on the dice. 34 + 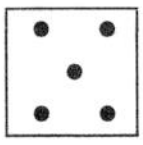 = 39

6. Double your answer. 39 × 2 = 78

7. Subtract 5. 78 − 5 = 73

8. Multiply by 5. 73 × 5 = 365

9. Add the number shown on the last die. 365 + 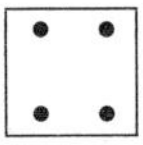 = 369

B Ask the person to tell you the number obtained. 369

All you need to do is to subtract 15 from this result and the digits in your answer will be the numbers shown on the dice. 369 − 15 = 354

3 5 4

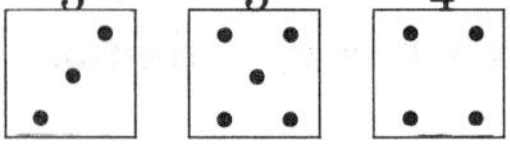

C *Challenge* Try to work out why this puzzle works.

Transformation of Formulae

Exercise 5

e.g.

(a)	(b)	(c)
$x + 6 = 9$, find x.	$x + 6 = d$, find x.	$x + c = d$, find x.
$x + 6 - 6 = 9 - 6$	$x + 6 - 6 = d - 6$	$x + c - c = d - c$
$\underline{\underline{x = 3}}$	$\underline{\underline{x = d - 6}}$	$\underline{\underline{x = d - c}}$

The simplified flow charts for the above are:

(a) (b) (c)

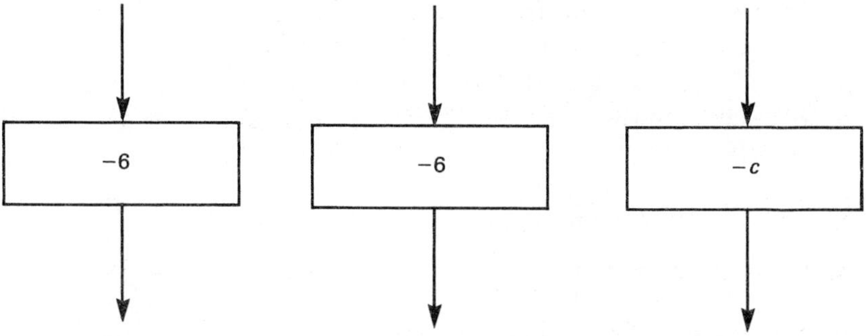

A

1. (a) $x + 4 = 7$, find x.
(b) $x + 4 = m$, find x.
(c) $x + a = m$, find x.

2. (a) $y + 3 = 14$, find y.
(b) $y + 3 = k$, find y.
(c) $y + p = k$, find y.

3. (a) $z - 2 = 7$, find z.
(b) $z - 2 = h$, find z.
(c) $z - f = h$, find z.

4. (a) $b + 9 = 21$, find b.
(b) $b + t = 21$, find b.
(c) $b + t = e$, find b.

5. (a) $c - 1 = 2$, find c.
(b) $c - n = 2$, find c.
(c) $c - n = u$, find c.

6. (a) $d - 11 = 13$, find d.
(b) $d - q = 13$, find d.
(c) $d - q = r$, find d.

7. (a) $12 = t + 1$, find t.
(b) $12 = t + u$, find t.
(c) $s = t + u$, find t.

8. (a) $9 = w - 4$, find w.
(b) $v = w - 4$, find w.
(c) $v = w - x$, find w.

9. (a) $g - 10 = 6$, find g.
(b) $g - 10 = l$, find g.
(c) $g - t = l$, find g.

10. (a) $18 = 6 + f$, find f.
(b) $18 = g + f$, find f.
(c) $h = g + f$, find f.

B Make x the subject of the formula (that is, find x in terms of the other letters):

1. $x + 7 = c$	**7.** $x - p = 10$	**13.** $n = x - 6$
2. $x + 12 = r$	**8.** $x - t = 18$	**14.** $6 = x - e$
3. $x - 8 = v$	**9.** $14 + x = c$	**15.** $u = x - s$
4. $x - 3 = y$	**10.** $f + x = 7$	**16.** $w = x + 17$
5. $x + a = b$	**11.** $x - g = h$	**17.** $4 = l + x$
6. $x + d = 15$	**12.** $m + x = k$	**18.** $q = x + r$

Exercise 6

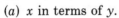

1. $K = C + 273$ gives K (kelvins) in terms of C (degrees Celsius). Rewrite the formula to give C in terms of K.

2. Since angles on a straight line add up to 180°, $x + y = 180$.
Rewrite the formula to give:
(*a*) x in terms of y.
(*b*) y in terms of x.

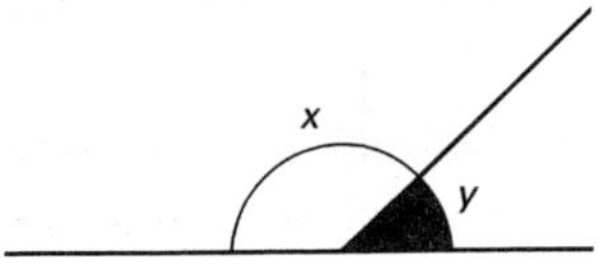

3. Angles a and b given in the diagram add up to 90°. We can write:

$$a + b = 90$$

Transform the formula to give:
(*a*) a in terms of b.
(*b*) b in terms of a.

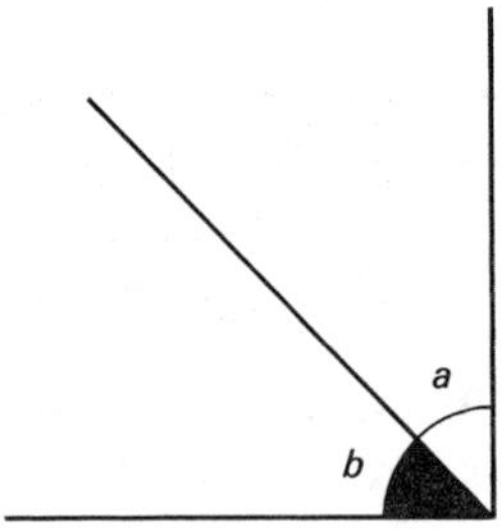

4. If you invest £P and receive £A after 1 year, your interest £I is the difference between A and P.
We can write:

$$A - P = I$$

Rewrite the formula to give A in terms of P and I.

5. If 2 resistors, r_1 and r_2 are connected in series, the total resistance in the circuit, R, is the sum of the 2 resistances.
So $R = r_1 + r_2$
Rewrite this to give r_1 in terms of R and r_2.

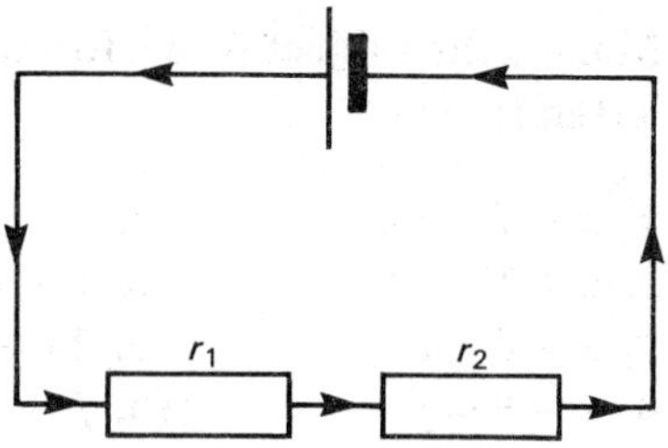

6. A lorry weighs e t when empty and f t when full. If the mass of its load is l t then:

$$e + l = f$$

Write l in terms of e and f.

7. Net pay = gross pay − deductions. Rewrite this to give the gross pay in terms of the net pay and the deductions.

8. Gross wage = basic wage + overtime. Rewrite this to give:
(*a*) Overtime in terms of the gross wage and basic wage.
(*b*) Basic wage in terms of the gross wage and overtime.

9. Normal price − discount = sale price. Rewrite this to give the normal price in terms of the sale price and the discount. Use your rewritten formula to find the normal price of goods bought for £32.76 in a sale if there was £8.95 discount.

10. HP price = deposit + balance. Rewrite this to give the balance in terms of the HP price and the deposit. Use the rewritten formula to find how much there is to pay on an article costing £495.95, if a deposit of £149 has been paid.

Exercise 7

A **1.** (*a*) $2x = 10$, find x.
(*b*) $2x = c$, find x.
(*c*) $ax = c$, find x.

2. (*a*) $3p = 6$, find p.
(*b*) $3p = t$, find p.
(*c*) $bp = t$, find p.

3. (*a*) $5k = 50$, find k.
(*b*) $uk = 50$, find k.
(*c*) $uk = n$, find k.

4. (*a*) $8d = 72$, find d.
(*b*) $ad = 72$, find d.
(*c*) $ad = h$, find d.

5. (*a*) $9w = 45$, find w.
(*b*) $9w = z$, find w.
(*c*) $kw = z$, find w.

6. Find t:

(*a*) $\frac{t}{2} = 4$ (*b*) $\frac{t}{2} = e$ (*c*) $\frac{t}{v} = e$

7. Find m:

(*a*) $\frac{m}{3} = 9$ (*b*) $\frac{m}{r} = 9$ (*c*) $\frac{m}{r} = f$

8. Find l:

(*a*) $\frac{l}{9} = 6$ (*b*) $\frac{l}{9} = h$ (*c*) $\frac{l}{s} = h$

9. Find f:

(*a*) $\frac{f}{6} = 7$ (*b*) $\frac{f}{c} = 7$ (*c*) $\frac{f}{c} = y$

10. (*a*) $4y = 8$, find y.
(*b*) $xy = 8$, find y.
(*c*) $xy = 8$, find x.

B Make t the subject of the formula:

1. $4t = u$

2. $5t = a$

3. $pt = 6$

4. $mt = g$

5. $te = h$

6. $\frac{t}{4} = b$

7. $\frac{t}{x} = 9$

8. $j = 2t$

9. $7 = at$

10. $s = kt$

11. $d = tw$

12. $ty = 8$

13. $\frac{t}{v} = z$

14. $n = \frac{t}{e}$

15. $ct = q$

16. $tp = f$

17. $m = td$

18. $rt = w$

19. $b = xt$

20. $\frac{t}{l} = h$

21. $g = \frac{t}{u}$

Exercise 8

1. $P = 4l$ gives the perimeter of a square in terms of the length of its sides. Rewrite the formula to give l in terms of P.

2. $d = 2r$ gives the diameter of a circle in terms of its radius. Write a formula that gives r in terms of d.

3. $A = lb$ gives the area of a rectangle in terms of its length and breadth. Transform the formula to give:
   (*a*) l in terms of A and b.
   (*b*) b in terms of A and l.

4. The circumference of a circle $C = \pi d$, where d is the diameter. Make d the subject of the formula.

5. $m = \dfrac{s}{60}$ gives the number of minutes in s seconds. Write the formula giving s in terms of m.

6. Ohm's law gives:

$$\frac{V}{I} = R$$

   where V is the voltage, I the current and R the resistance. Write the formula giving V in terms of I and R.

7. $D = \dfrac{m}{V}$ gives the density D of a substance of mass m and volume V.
   (*a*) Make m the subject of the formula.
   (*b*) Use your formula to find the mass of 0.5 m^3 of marble if its density is 2700 kg/m^3.

8. Wages earned = hours worked × hourly rate
   (*a*) Make hours worked the subject of the formula.
   (*b*) Calculate the hours worked by someone who earned £174 at a rate of £6 an hour.
   (*c*) Calculate the hours worked by someone who earned £131.58 at a rate of £3.87 an hour.

9. (*a*) Transform the formula:

$$\text{Average speed} = \frac{\text{distance}}{\text{time}}$$

making distance the subject.

(*b*) Use your formula to find the distance travelled in 4 h by a car travelling at an average speed of 65 km/h.

10. $V = Ah$ gives the volume of a cuboid with base area A and perpendicular height h.

(*a*) Rewrite the formula giving A in terms of V and h.

(*b*) Rewrite the formula giving h in terms of V and A.

(*c*) Find the volume of a box with base area 120 cm^2 and perpendicular height 6 cm.

(*d*) Find the perpendicular height of a box with base area 750 cm^2 and volume 15 000 cm^3.

(*e*) Find the base area of a box with volume 0.27 m^3 and perpendicular height 0.3 m.

22 Co-ordinates and Graphs

Co-ordinates

Exercise 1

For *each* question in this exercise draw a pair of axes as shown.

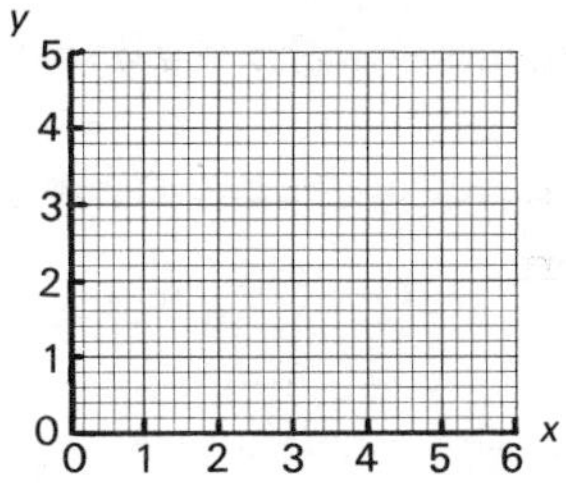

The squares in the given diagram represent 1 cm squares.

1. Plot the points (1, 1) and (3, 5). Join them with a straight line then write the co-ordinates of the mid-point of that straight line.

2. Plot and join the points A(0, 5) and B(4, 2) using a straight line. How long is AB?

3. Plot the points C(1, 4), D(1, 2) and E(5, 2). Join them in that order using straight lines. Find and plot a point F such that CDEF is a rectangle. Write the co-ordinates of F.

4. Plot the points G(2, 1), H(3, 4) and I(6, 1). Join them to form a triangle. Find the area of the triangle.

5. Plot the points S(0, 2), T(2, 4), U(6, 4), V(4, 2) and join them to form a parallelogram. Find the area of the parallelogram.

6. Plot the points W(0, 5), X(4, 4), Y(6, 0) and Z(0, 0). Join them to form a quadrilateral. Find the area of the quadrilateral.

Exercise 2

For *each* question in this exercise draw a pair of axes as shown. The squares in the diagram represent 1 cm squares.

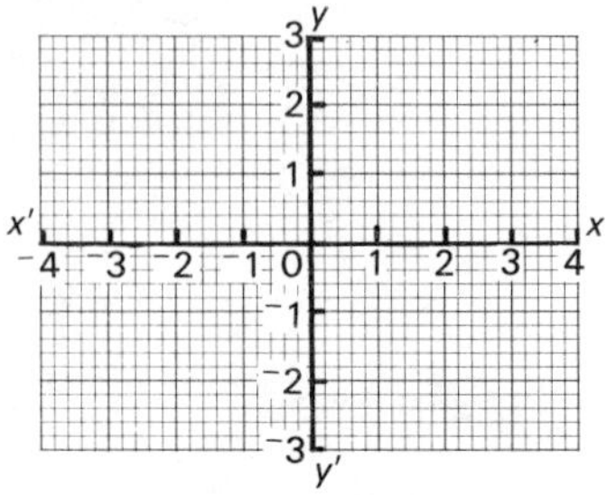

1. (*a*) Plot the points J(0, 1), K(3, 2), L(4, 1) and M(3, 0), then join them to form a quadrilateral.
   (*b*) Write the name of the quadrilateral.
   (*c*) Reflect the quadrilateral in the *y*-axis, then label the image J′K′L′M′.
   (*d*) Write the co-ordinates of J′, K′, L′ and M′.

2. (*a*) Plot the points P(0, 1), Q(⁻2, 1), R(⁻2, ⁻1) and S(1, ⁻1), then join them to form a quadrilateral.
   (*b*) Write the name of the quadrilateral.
   (*c*) Plot the points P′(0, 2) and Q′(⁻4, 2). Complete quadrilateral P′Q′R′S′ so that it is an enlargement of PQRS where each side of the enlargement is twice as long as each side of the original quadrilateral.
   (*d*) Write the co-ordinates of R′ and S′.
   (*e*) Compare co-ordinates, P′ with P, Q′ with Q, R′ with R and S′ with S. Write what you notice.

Exercise 3 Graphs from Given Data

Plot graphs from the given data. Use either a straight line or a smooth curve.

1. A bath is being emptied at the rate of 8 ℓ/min. The following table shows the number of litres of water in the bath at each minute.

Time (min)	1	2	3	4	5	6	7	8	9
Quantity of water (ℓ)	68	60	52	44	36	28	20	12	4

(*a*) Draw a pair of axes as shown, time should range from 0 min to 10 min while quantity of water should range from 0 *l* to 80 *l*.

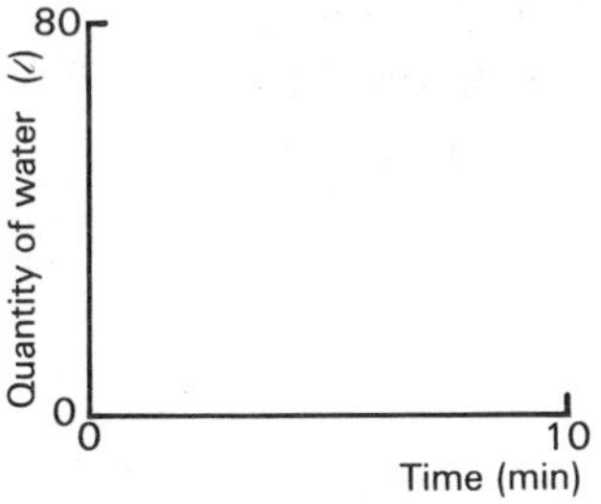

(*b*) Plot a graph from the table opposite.

Use the graph to help you to find:

(*c*) How much water there was in the bath to start with.

(*d*) How much water remains in the bath after $5\frac{1}{2}$ min.

(*e*) How long it takes to empty the bath.

2. The table shows the height of a falling stone measured every second as it falls from the top of a cliff.

Time of fall (s)	0	1	2	3	4
Height of stone (m)	80	75	60	35	0

(*a*) Draw a graph. Use a scale of 5 cm to 1 s on the horizontal axis and 1 cm to 5 m for the height on the vertical axis.

(*b*) How high is the cliff?

(*c*) After how many seconds does the stone hit the ground?

Straight-line Graphs

Exercise 4

On graph paper, draw a pair of axes as shown. Use a scale of 1 cm to 1 unit on each axis.

Answer the following questions on the one piece of graph paper using the same axes.

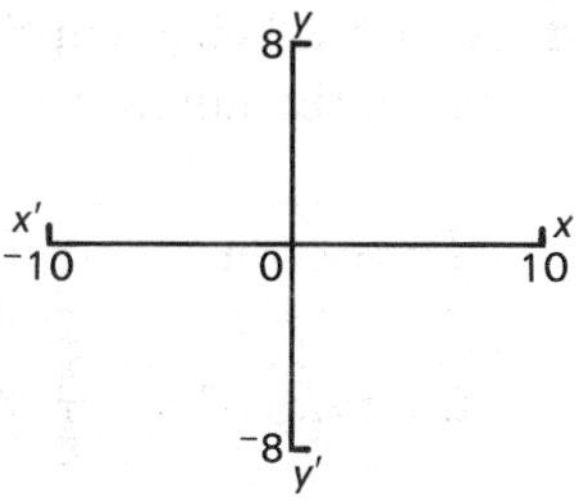

1. (*a*) The points (2, 6), (2, 1), (2, 4), (2, 0), (2, 8), (2, $^-3$), (2, $^-8$) are all related in some way. Plot them and find three more points that satisfy the same relationship.
   (*b*) Join the points in part (a) and label the graph $x = 2$.

2. (*a*) The points (0, 4), (3, 4), ($^-4$, 4), (10, 4), ($^-10$, 4), (7, 4) are all related in some way. Plot them and find three more points that satisfy the same relationship.
   (*b*) Join the points in part (a) and label the graph $y = 4$.

3. Draw and label the graphs:

(*a*) $x = 7$	(*d*) $x = {}^-2$	(*g*) $y = 2$	(*j*) $y = {}^-3$
(*b*) $x = 5$	(*e*) $x = {}^-8$	(*h*) $y = 5$	(*k*) $y = {}^-1$
(*c*) $x = 9$	(*f*) $x = 3.5$	(*i*) $y = {}^-6$	(*l*) $y = 6\frac{1}{2}$

Exercise 5

Draw a pair of axes as shown in the diagram.
Use a scale of 1 cm to 1 unit on the *x*-axis and 1 cm to 5 units on the *y*-axis.

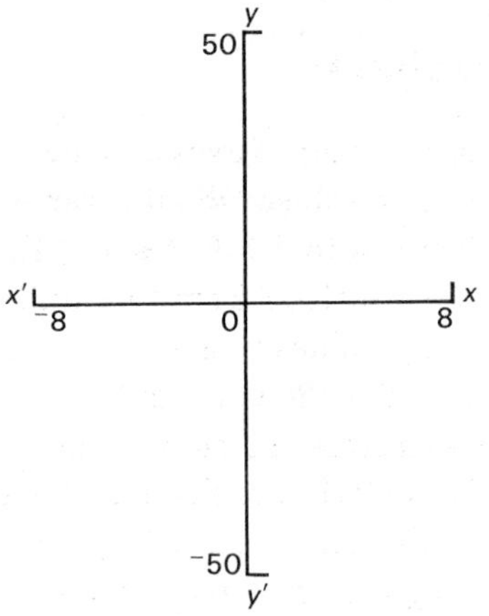

The *x*-values should range from $^-8$ to $^+8$ ($^-8 \leqslant x \leqslant 8$) and the *y*-values should range from $^-50$ to $^+50$ ($^-50 \leqslant y \leqslant 50$).
Draw all the graphs for this exercise on one piece of graph paper, using the one pair of axes.

1. (*a*) The points (2, 4), (4, 8), (5, 10), (8, 16), ($^-2$, $^-4$), ($^-5$, $^-10$) and ($^-8$, $^-16$) are all related in some way. Plot them and find three more points that satisfy the same relationship.
   (*b*) Join the points plotted in part (a), then label the graph $y = 2x$.

2. Draw the graphs:
   (*a*) $y = 5x$ (*b*) $y = 7x$ (*c*) $y = 3x$ (*d*) $y = 8x$

3. The graph of $y = 2x$ has gradient 2. Write the gradients of the graphs of:
(*a*) $y = 5x$ (*b*) $y = 7x$ (*c*) $y = 3x$ (*d*) $y = 8x$

(*Note* The gradient tells you how steep the line is.)

4. Without drawing any graphs, list the following equations in an order such that if graphs were plotted, the steepest would be first:

$y = 9x$, $y = 4x$, $y = 6x$, $y = x$, $y = \frac{1}{2}x$,

$y = 7x$, $y = 5x$, $y = \frac{7}{2}x$, $y = 10x$, $y = 8x$

In the term $4x$, 4 is called the *coefficient* of x.
In $3x - 2$, the coefficient of x is 3.
In $7x + 5$, the coefficient of x is 7.

Note If an equation of a graph is written in the form:
y = something in terms of x
then the coefficient of x tells you the gradient of the graph.

Exercise 6

Draw a pair of axes as shown. The x-values should range from $^-4$ to $^+4$ ($^-4 \leqslant x \leqslant 4$). Use a scale of 2 cm to 1 unit. The y-values range from $^-20$ to $^+20$ ($^-20 \leqslant y \leqslant 20$). Use a scale of 1 cm to 2 units. Draw all the graphs in this exercise on the one piece of graph paper using the same pair of axes.

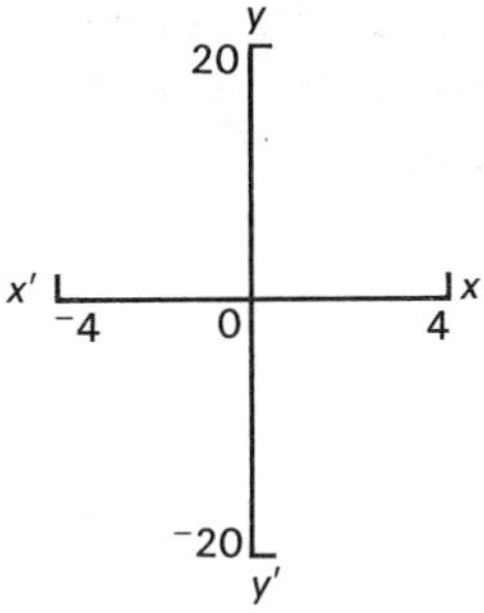

1. Consider the equation $y = 3x + 5$.
When $x = 2$, $y = 11$. Plot the point (2, 11).
When $x = 4$, $y = 17$. Plot the point (4, 17).
When $x = {}^-3$, $y = {}^-4$. Plot the point ($^-3$, $^-4$).
Draw the graph of $y = 3x + 5$.

2. Draw the graph of $y = 3x$.

3. Draw the graph of $y = 3x - 7$.

4. Note that the three graphs you have drawn are all parallel. They have the same slope (their gradients are equal). What is the gradient of each of these graphs?

5. The equations of several graphs are given. For each one, write its gradient.

(*a*) $y = 4x$	(*e*) $y = 10x$	(*i*) $y = 3x + 7$
(*b*) $y = 6x$	(*f*) $y = 10x + 8$	(*j*) $y = 6x - 9$
(*c*) $y = 2x + 1$	(*g*) $y = 10x - 3$	(*k*) $y = 9x - 5$
(*d*) $y = 5x - 3$	(*h*) $y = 5x + 2$	(*l*) $y = x + 6$

Exercise 7

A Draw another pair of axes as for Exercise 6. Draw these graphs on one piece of graph paper using the same pair of axes:

1. $y = 2x + 1$	**6.** $y = 2x - 3$	**11.** $y = 2x$
2. $y = 2x + 2$	**7.** $y = 2x - 7$	**12.** $y = 2x + 9$
3. $y = 2x + 3$	**8.** $y = 2x - 6$	**13.** $y = 2x - 2$
4. $y = 2x + 4$	**9.** $y = 2x - 5$	**14.** $y = 2x - 10$
5. $y = 2x + 7$	**10.** $y = 2x - 1$	**15.** $y = 2x + 10$

B Note that all the graphs in part A are parallel. Note also that each of them crosses the y-axis at a different point. For each graph, find the point at which it crosses the y-axis and look carefully at its equation. Write what you notice.

C **1.** Look at the graph $y = 3x + 5$ drawn in Exercise 6. At what point does this graph cross the y-axis?

2. Look at the graph of $y = 3x - 7$ drawn in Exercise 6. At what point does this graph cross the y-axis?

D For each of the given graphs, write the point at which it crosses the y-axis:

1. $y = 3x + 6$	**5.** $y = x - 9$	**9.** $y = 4x - 6$
2. $y = 3x - 2$	**6.** $y = 3x - 9$	**10.** $y = 7x - 3$
3. $y = 4x + 1$	**7.** $y = 5x + 2$	**11.** $y = 7x + 3$
4. $y = x + 7$	**8.** $y = 6x - 1$	**12.** $y = 5x + 8$

Exercise 8 M

A **1.** (*a*) Draw a pair of axes as shown on p. 259. Use a scale of 2 cm to 1 unit on the x-axis and 2 cm to 5 units on the y-axis.

(*b*) Draw the graph of $y = 4x$.

2. On your copy of the graph, plot the points:

   (4, 16), (2, 8), (1, 4), ($^-1$, $^-4$) and ($^-3$, $^-12$)

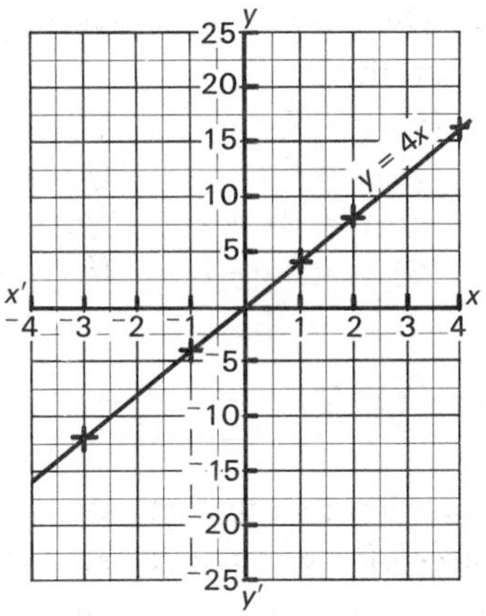

3. Translate each of the five plotted points 5 units 'upwards', parallel to the y-axis. Mark their images.

4. Join these newly plotted points with a straight line.

5. What is the equation of this new straight line?

B 1. Translate the five original points (that were plotted in part A, question 2) 10 units 'downwards' parallel to the y-axis, then join them with a straight line.

2. What is the equation of this new straight line?

C Copy and complete this table:

	Original equation	Translation	Equation of new line
1.	$y = 4x$	3 units upwards	$y = 4x +$?
2.	$y = 4x$	7 units downwards	$y = 4x -$?
3.	$y = 4x$	2 units downwards	$y =$
4.	$y = 4x$	8 units upwards	$y =$
5.	$y = 3x$	1 unit upwards	$y =$
6.	$y = 2x$	4 units downwards	$y =$
7.	$y = 5x$	9 units downwards	$y =$
8.	$y = x$	6 units upwards	$y =$

D Using the same pair of axes as for part A, draw the graphs:
(*a*) $y = 4x + 2$ (*b*) $y = 4x - 5$ (*c*) $y = 4x + 9$

Exercise 9

Draw a pair of axes as in Exercise 6 (p. 257).
Draw the graphs of $y = 4x - 3$ and $y = 2x + 1$ using that one pair of axes.
Write the co-ordinates of the point of intersection of the two graphs.

Exercise 10 M

1. Copy and complete the following table for the function $y = x^2$:

x	$^-8$	$^-7$	$^-6$	$^-5$	$^-4$	$^-3$	$^-2$	$^-1$	$^-0.5$	0	0.5	1	2	3	4	5	6	7	8
$y = x^2$	64	49				9					0.25	1		9				49	

2. (*a*) Copy and complete the following table for the function $y = 2x^2$:

x	$^-7$	$^-6$	$^-5$	$^-4$	$^-3$	$^-2$	$^-1$	$^-0.5$	0	0.5	1	2	3	4	5	6	7
x^2	49		25		9					0.25	1		9				49
$y = 2x^2$	98				18		2			0.5	2		18				98

(*b*) Draw a pair of axes as shown. The x-values should range from $^-7$ to $^+7$. (Use a scale of 1 cm to 1 unit.) The y-values should range from 0 to 100. (Use a scale of 1 cm to 5 units.)

(*c*) Draw a graph of $y = 2x^2$, using the table in part (a) to help you. (The graph should be a smooth curve so do not use a ruler!)

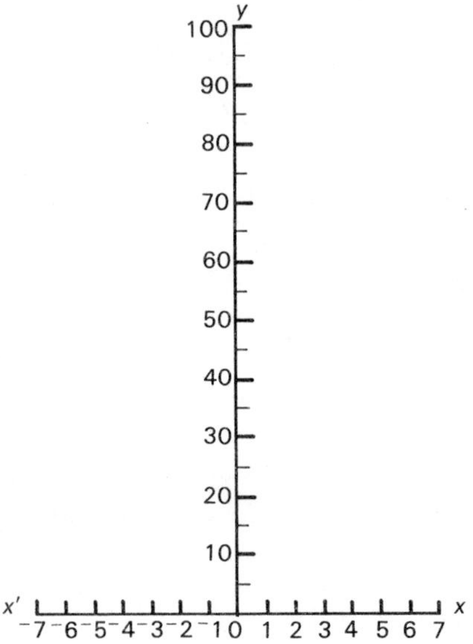

3. (*a*) Draw a table for the function $y = 3x^2$. Make out the table as in question 2 but let the x-values range from $^-8$ to $^+8$.

(*b*) Draw a pair of axes as shown. The x-values should range from $^-8$ to $^+8$. (Use a scale of 1 cm to 1 unit.) The y-values should range from 0 to 200. (Use a scale of 1 cm to 10 units.)

(*c*) Draw a graph of $y = 3x^2$.

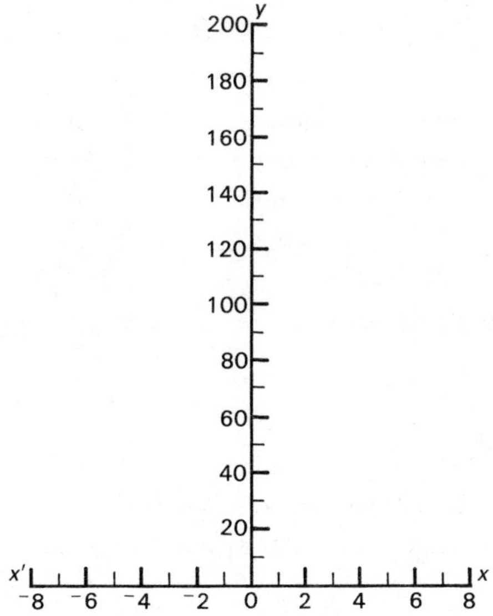

Revision Exercises XVII to XXII

Revision Exercise XVII

1. Here are two tiles. The other tiles have the same design. Draw the given diagram (choose your own size) and fill in the blank spaces to show all the tiles.

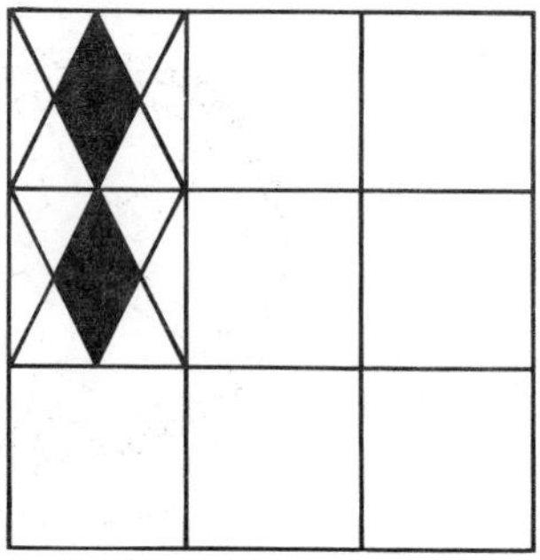

2. Make an accurate copy of the triangle below and the position of C. Enlarge the triangle using a scale factor of 3, where C is the centre of enlargement.

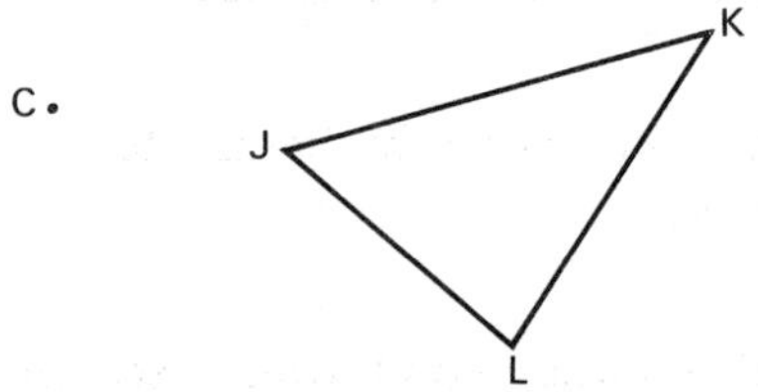

3. Make another copy of $\triangle$JKL. This time, mark a point C inside then enlarge the triangle using a scale factor of 4.

Revision Exercise XVIII

1. Simplify the ratio 15 : 25.

2. Write the ratio 18 : 8 in the form m : 1.

3. Which is better value for money:

   3 ℓ for 75 p or 7 ℓ for £1.68?

4. A bus travels at 80 km/h while a car travels at 112 km/h. Write the ratio of the speed of the car to that of the bus in the form $m : 1$.

5. A model aircraft is built to a scale of 1 : 72. If the model's wingspan measures 20 cm, what is the wingspan of the real aeroplane?

6. (*a*) Two wheels are joined by a chain as shown. If the large wheel turns anticlockwise, which way does the small wheel turn?

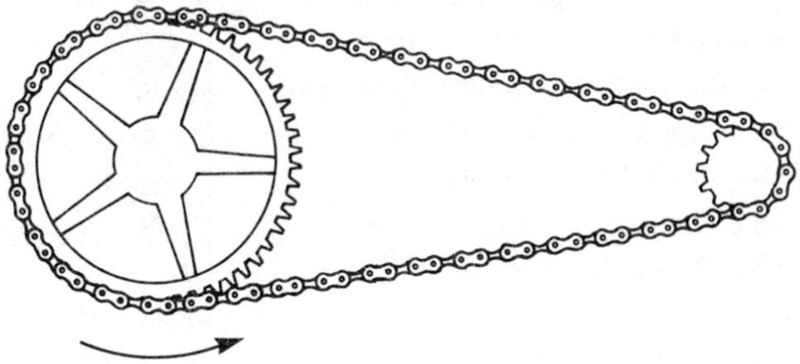

(*b*) The large wheel has 52 teeth and the small wheel has 13 teeth, so if the large wheel makes 8 revolutions – how many revolutions will the small wheel make?

7. A typist can type 240 words in 5 min. How many words can be typed per minute?

8. If discount is 25 p in the pound, what discount would I get on an article costing £10?

9. Copy and complete the table if the quantities are in direct proportion:

Height of object (m)	0.5	1	1.5	2	3			10
Length of shadow (m)					6	12	16	

10. A shop sells foreign stamps where each packet costs the same. If 2 packets cost 56 p, find the cost of:
(*a*) 4 packets, (*b*) 3 packets, (*c*) 11 packets.

Revision Exercise XIX

1. Draw a flow chart to explain what you do when you wash your hair.
2. Draw a flow chart to show how to find the third angle of a triangle when two angles are given.
3. Use the flow chart 'Choosing a Holiday' (opposite) to help with the following:
   (a) Vanessa would like to do both outdoor and indoor activities but she doesn't like water sports. Which centre would be her choice?
   (b) Alf likes less energetic indoor and outdoor activities, including 'peaceful' water sports. Which outdoor activities will he do at the centre of his choice?
   (c) Martin wants to stay indoors. He quite enjoys energetic activities. Which centre would be his choice?
   (d) Sonia likes outdoor activities, water sports in particular. Which water sports will she be able to do at the centre of her choice?
4. Draw a flow chart to show how to make chips.
5. Draw flow charts to show the functions:
   (a) $y = 2x + 1$ (b) $f(x) = 3x - 4$
6. Draw flow charts to work the functions in question 5 'backwards'.

Revision Exercise XX

A Solve these equations:

1. $x + 7 = 15$
2. $x - 9 = 9$
3. $x + 13 = 21$
4. $x - 15 = 7$
5. $3x = 39$
6. $\frac{x}{7} = 9$
7. $2x + 7 = 25$
8. $3x - 1 = 14$
9. $15 - x = 6$
10. $12 - x = 7$
11. $x + 2 = 5\frac{1}{2}$
12. $x + 2\frac{1}{2} = 9$
13. $x - 1 = 4\frac{1}{3}$
14. $x - 1\frac{1}{2} = 8\frac{1}{2}$
15. $2x = 13$
16. $\frac{x}{2} = 4\frac{1}{2}$
17. $4x + 1 = 12$
18. $2x - 4 = 7$
19. $8 - x = 2\frac{1}{2}$
20. $10 - x = 1\frac{2}{3}$

Choosing a Holiday

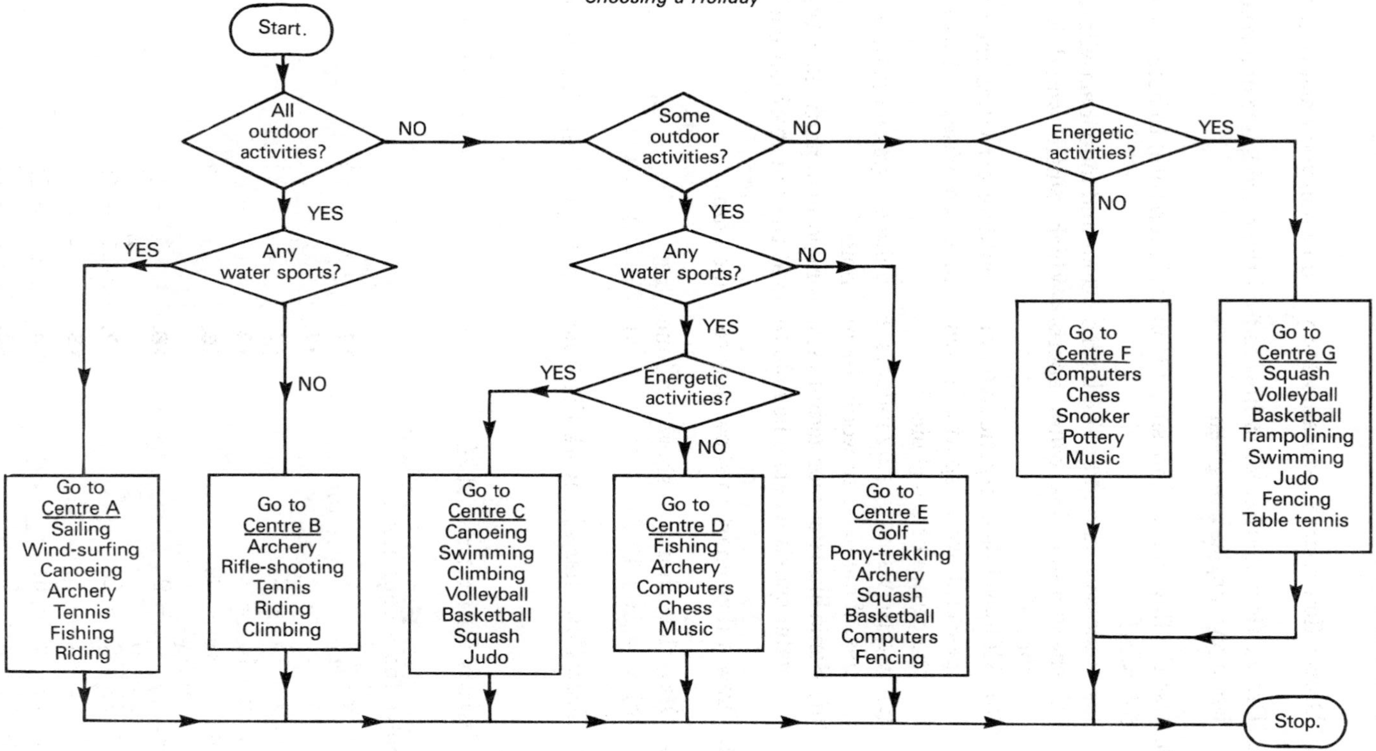

21. $x + 8 = 5$

22. $x - 7 = {}^{-}2$

23. $x - 4 = {}^{-}10$

24. $x + 3 = {}^{-}4$

25. $4x = {}^{-}20$

26. $\frac{x}{3} = {}^{-}4$

27. $3x + 11 = 2$

28. $2x - 5 = {}^{-}9$

29. $4x - 7 = {}^{-}3$

30. $5x + 9 = {}^{-}1$

B Use simple equations to help with these problems:

1. The ages of Raymond and his mum, when added, total 51 years. If Raymond is 13 years old, how old is his mum?

2. Christine has f m of material. After using 3 m she has 8 m left. Find f.

3. Five people pay £x each for tickets. If their payments totalled £30, how much did each pay?

4. There were several passengers on a 53-seater coach. If there were twice as many people there would be 7 too many people for the coach. How many passengers are there on the coach?

5. If I had 3 boxes, each containing the same number of tins, 28 more tins would make 100 tins altogether. How many tins are there in each box?

Revision Exercise XXI

1. If the exchange rate is 11 Norwegian kroner to the pound, then to work out the number of kroner you obtain for your pounds, you need to multiply by 11. Find the number of kroner obtained for:
   (*a*) £9, (*b*) £30, (*c*) £75.

2. HP price − cash price = credit charge

   Rewrite this formula to give the HP price in terms of the cash price and the credit charge.
   Use the rearranged formula to find the HP price of an article that sells for £199.95 cash, if the credit charge is £27.99.

3. The following formulae all give the cooking times of roast pork if it is rolled. T is the total number of minutes the pork should be in the oven at mark 5.

$T = 32M + 35$ where M is in pounds.
$T = 70M + 35$ where M is in kilograms.
$T = 7M + 35$ where M is the number of 100 g in the mass of the pork.

Use the formulae to find the cooking time of:
(*a*) 2 kg of pork
(*b*) 4 lb of pork
(*c*) 900 g of pork
(*d*) 350 g of pork

4. If the mass of an empty jar is e grams, the mass of the jar containing jam, f grams and the mass of the jam, j grams, then $f = e + j$.
(*a*) Rewrite the formula to give e in terms of f and j.
(*b*) Rewrite the formula to give j in terms of f and e.
(*c*) Use the formula to find e if $j = 454$ g and $f = 680$ g.

5. The perimeter of an equilateral triangle with sides of length l units is given by formula $P = 3l$.
(*a*) Make l the subject of the formula.
(*b*) Find each side of an equilateral triangle having a perimeter of 29.1 cm.

6. (*a*) Given that: Watts = amps × volts

Rewrite the formula giving amps in terms of watts and volts.
(*b*) The power of an electric kettle/jug is 2.1 kW (that is, 2100 W). If it works at 240 V find the current (in amps) that it carries.

7. $\text{Pressure} = \dfrac{\text{force}}{\text{area}}$

Using only the initial letters $P = \dfrac{F}{A}$:

(*a*) Rewrite this formula giving F in terms of P and A.
(*b*) Calculate the force (in newtons) when the pressure is 90 N/m^2 and the area is 4 m^2.

Revision Exercise XXII

1. Draw a pair of axes such that x ranges from 0 to 6 and y from 0 to 5 ($0 \leqslant x \leqslant 6$ and $0 \leqslant y \leqslant 5$). Use 1 cm per unit.
Plot the points R(0, 4), S(6, 4), T(1, 1) then join them to form a triangle. Find the area of the triangle.

2. Draw another pair of axes as for question 1. Plot the points D(2, 2) and E(4, 1) and join them with a straight line. Find and plot two more points, F and G such that DEFG is a square.
Write the co-ordinates of F and G.

3. The table gives the voltage and current for a certain wire:

Voltage, V (V)	0	1	2	3	4	5	6	7	8
Current, I (A)	0	0.2	0.4	0.6	0.8	1.0	1.2	1.4	1.6

Draw a graph of I against V. Put V on the horizontal axis and use a scale of 2 cm to 1 V. For the current, use a scale of 1 cm to 0.1 A.

4. Write the gradient of each of the graphs of the following functions:
(*a*) $y = 8x$
(*b*) $y = 3x - 8$
(*c*) $y = 5x + 1$
(*d*) $y = x$
(*e*) $y = \frac{1}{2}x$
(*f*) $y = x + 7$
(*g*) $y = 6x + 4$
(*h*) $y = 7x - 8$
(*i*) $y = 4x + 5$
(*j*) $y = 4x - 5$
(*k*) $y = 8x + 2$
(*l*) $y = 6x - 3$

5. For each of the functions in question 4, give the point at which its graph crosses the y-axis.

6. Draw a pair of axes as shown. Use a scale of 1 cm to 1 unit on the x-axis and 2 cm to 5 units on the y-axis.

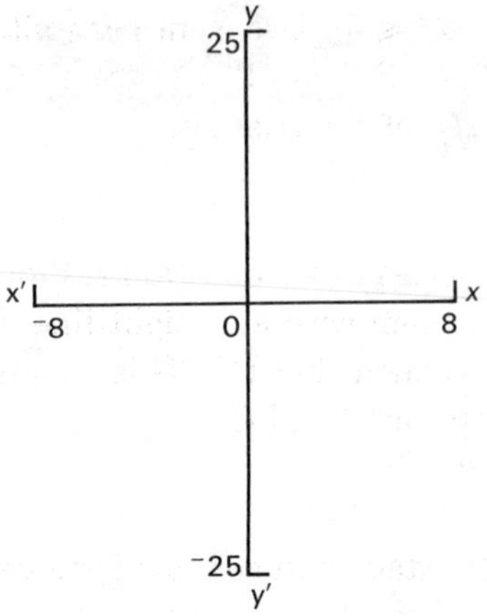

Draw the graphs of $y = 3x - 2$ and $y = x + 6$.
Write the co-ordinates of the point of intersection of the two graphs.

23 Scale Drawings

Points of the Compass

Exercise 1 M

1. Copy the given diagram. The direction of North is marked. Complete your copy to show S, E, W, NE, SW, NW and SE.

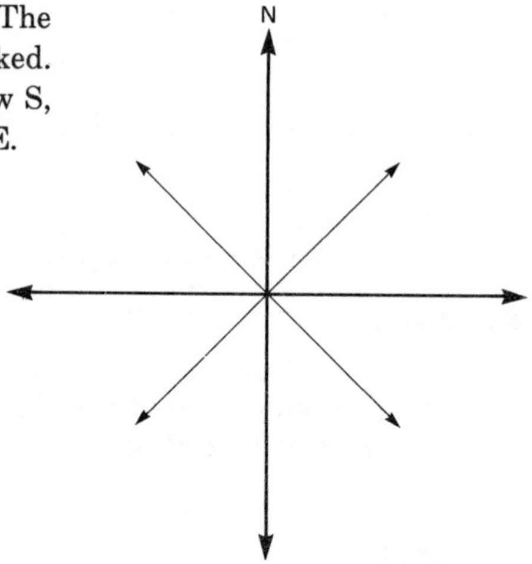

2. By turning clockwise, how many degrees are there from North to:

(*a*) E?
(*b*) W?
(*c*) S?
(*d*) NE?
(*e*) SE?
(*f*) NW?
(*g*) SW?

3. How many degrees are there from:

(*a*) W to SW turning clockwise?
(*b*) W to SW turning anticlockwise?
(*c*) NE to E turning clockwise?
(*d*) NE to SW turning anticlockwise?
(*e*) NW to S turning anticlockwise?
(*f*) SE to E turning clockwise?
(*g*) S to SE turning anticlockwise?
(*h*) W to NW turning clockwise?

Scale Drawings

Consider the scale 1 : 4.

Using this scale,	1 cm	represents	4	cm,
so	10 cm	represents	40	cm,
and	100 cm	represents	400	cm,
that is,	1 m	represents	4	m.

1 : 4 can mean	1 cm	represents	4	cm,
or	1 m	represents	4	m,
or	1 km	represents	4	km,
or	1 mm	represents	4	mm,
or	1 in	represents	4	in,
or	1 ft	represents	4	ft.

Any unit can be used, 1 : 4 simply means $\frac{1}{4}$ of full size.

Exercise 2

1. The map shows the positions of two ships, one at A and the other at B. The port is labelled P.

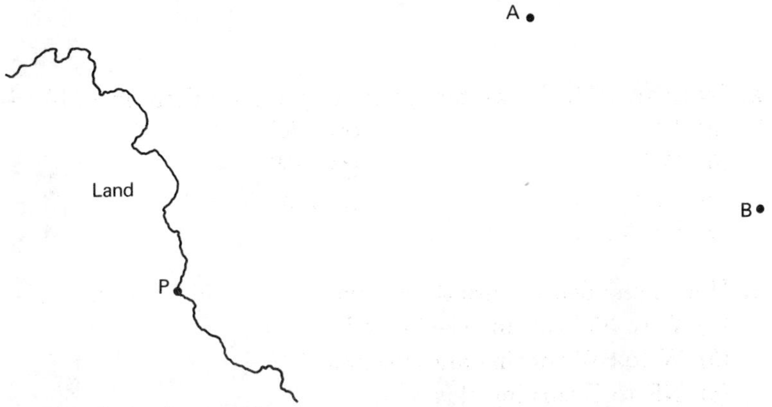

Scale: 1 cm to 2 km

(*a*) How far is ship A from port?
(*b*) How far is ship B from port?
(*c*) What distance apart are the two ships?

2. Give the height of each of the spacecraft drawn below:

A Atlas $1\frac{1}{2}$-stage rocket that launched the first manned orbital flight by the USA in February 1962.

B Titan II. A 2-stage launch vehicle used from March 1965 onwards with Gemini spacecraft that carried a crew of two.

C A $2\frac{1}{2}$-stage A-2 rocket that launched a Soyuz spacecraft in the American–Russian space link-up in 1975.

D The Ariane 3-stage rocket used for the launching of European satellites.

E A space shuttle (first used in April 1981). It takes off mounted on a fuel tank and on two booster rockets. These are dropped after take-off and the winged shuttle enters orbit, then returns to the ground landing like an ordinary aircraft.

F The 3-stage Saturn V was used to launch the spacecraft in 1969 that carried Neil Armstrong, Edwin Aldrin and Michael Collins to the Moon. Armstrong followed by Aldrin were the first men to walk on the Moon while Collins remained in the spacecraft which was orbiting above.

Scale: 1:1000 (1 cm to 10 m)

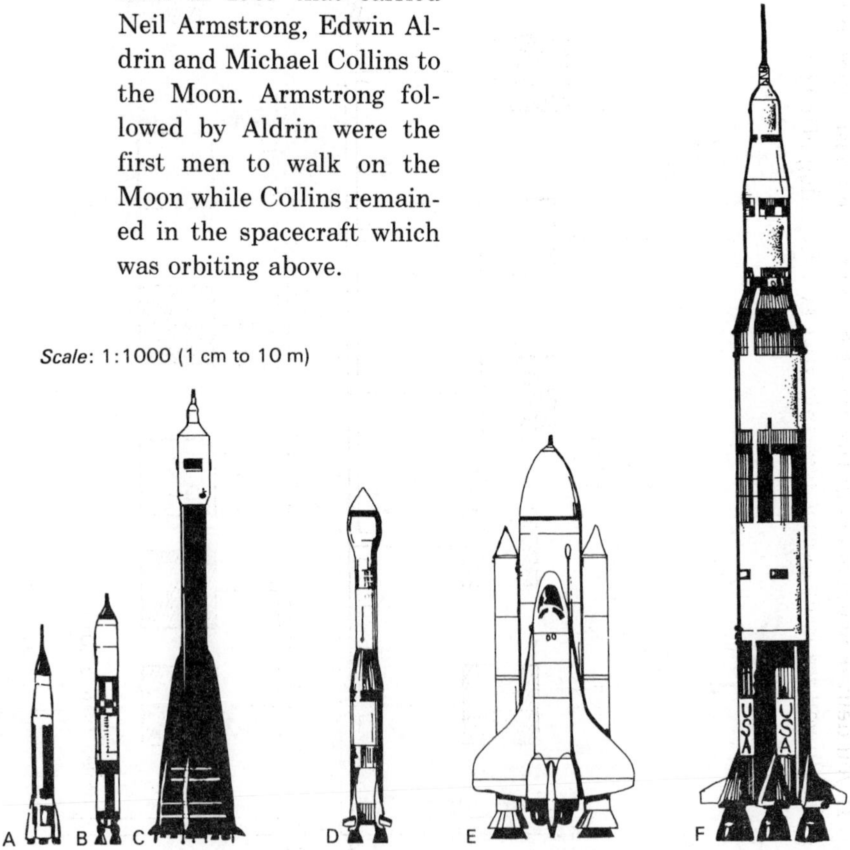

3. *A Newspaper Round*

If you deliver newspapers in the street below to the houses that are shaded and you follow the route shown, how far do you walk altogether (starting at A and finishing at B)?

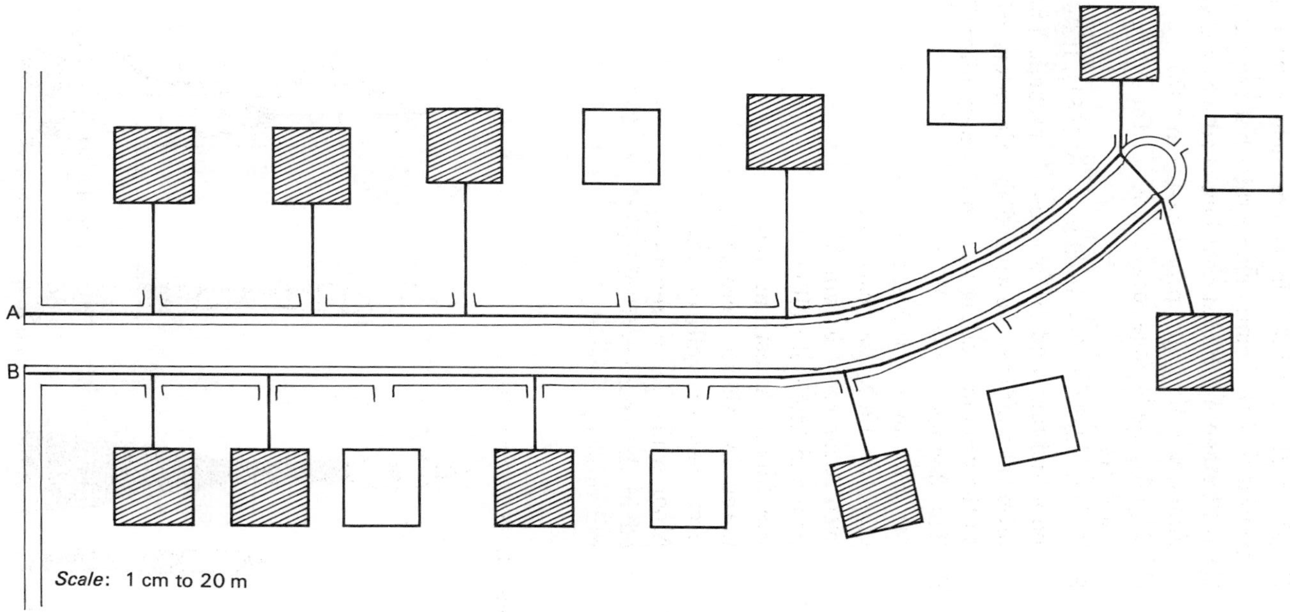

Exercise 3

1. (*a*) Make a scale drawing of a rectangular garden that is 24 m long and 10 m wide. Use a scale of 1 cm to 4 m.
   (*b*) How long is a diagonal of the garden?
   (*c*) Calculate its area.

2. A firm erects garages. They state that you need to mark the corner positions to show the final position of the garage. They also suggest that you measure both diagonals as a check for accuracy.

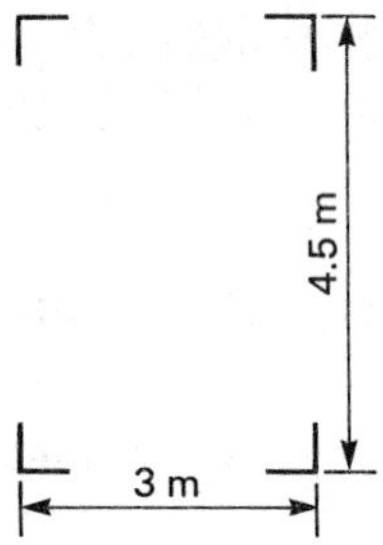

   Assume you order a garage measuring 4.5 m by 3 m. Draw a rectangle using a scale of 1 : 50 (1 cm to 0.5 m) to show its plan. What should the diagonals measure?

3. A ladder leans against a wall and makes an angle of 63° with the ground. The foot of the ladder is 2.5 m from the wall.

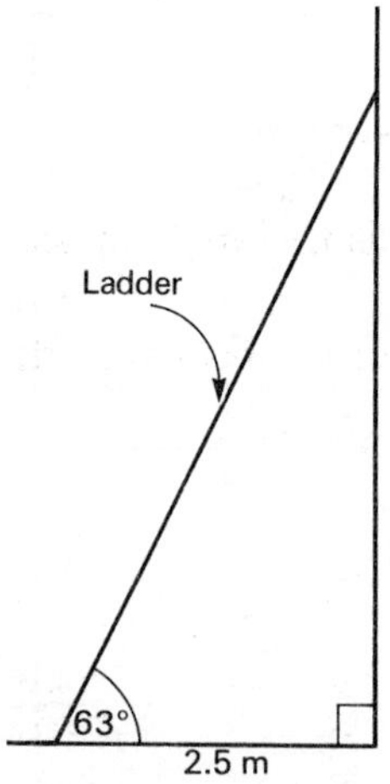

   (*a*) Make a scale drawing. Use a scale of 1 : 50 (1 cm to 50 cm).
   (*b*) How long is the ladder?
   (*c*) How high up the wall does it reach?

4. One end of a garden shed is shown in the sketch. Various measurements are given.

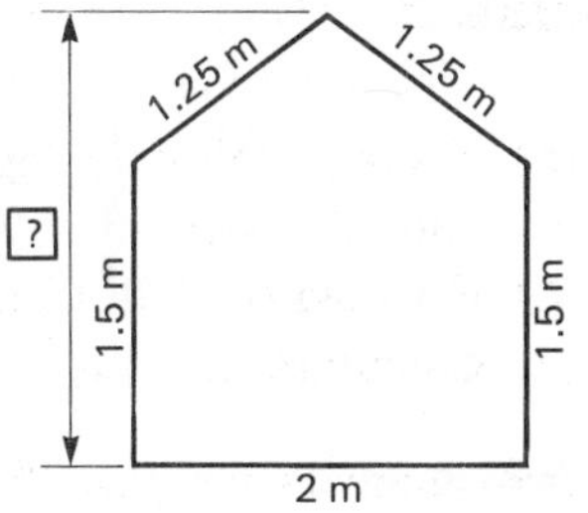

(*a*) Make a scale drawing of the shed using a scale of 1 : 25 (that is 1 cm to 25 cm or 4 cm to 1 m).
(*b*) Find the height of the shed from your scale drawing.
(*c*) Calculate the area of that end of the shed.

Angles of Elevation and Depression

The *angle of elevation* is the angle measured *upwards* from the horizontal to an object.
The angle of elevation of the top of the building from the man is 10°.

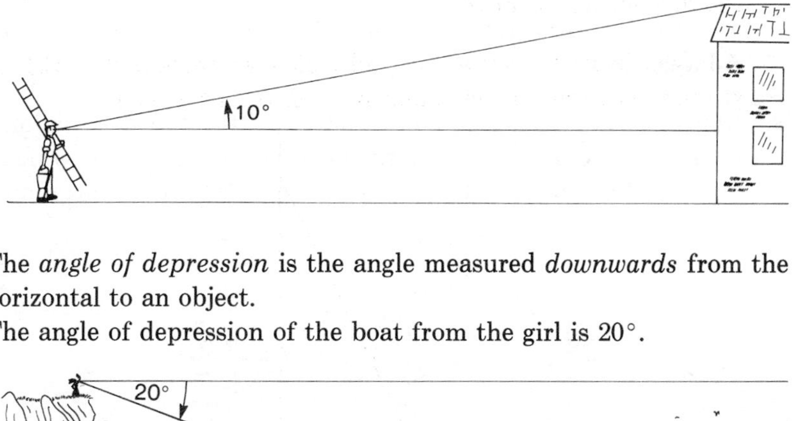

The *angle of depression* is the angle measured *downwards* from the horizontal to an object.
The angle of depression of the boat from the girl is 20°.

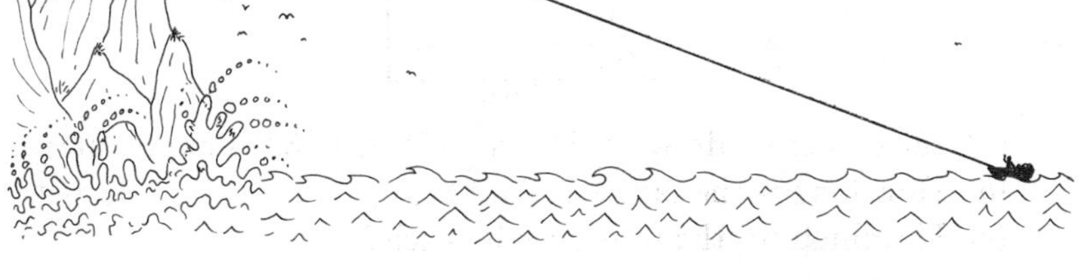

Remember that both of these angles are measured from the horizontal.
'Elevate' means 'to raise or lift'
'the angle of elevation' is 'the turn upwards'.
'Depress' means 'to push down or lower'
'the angle of depression' is 'the turn downwards'.

Exercise 4

1. The angle of elevation of the top of an English Elm from a point on the ground 60 m from the tree is 25°.

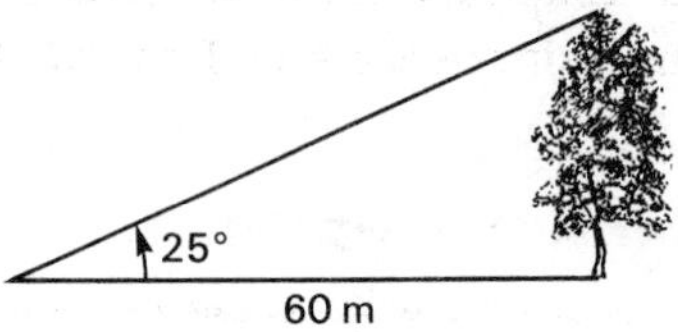

Make a scale drawing using a scale of 1 cm to 10 m and find the height of the tree.

2. The angle of elevation of the top of a building measured from a point on the level ground, 40 m from the building is 32°. Make a scale drawing using a scale of 1 cm to 5 m and find the height of the building.

3. Brian measured the angle of elevation of the top of a building to be 31°. The measurement was taken at eye level from a point 30 m from the building. Brian's eye level is 1.5 m from the ground.

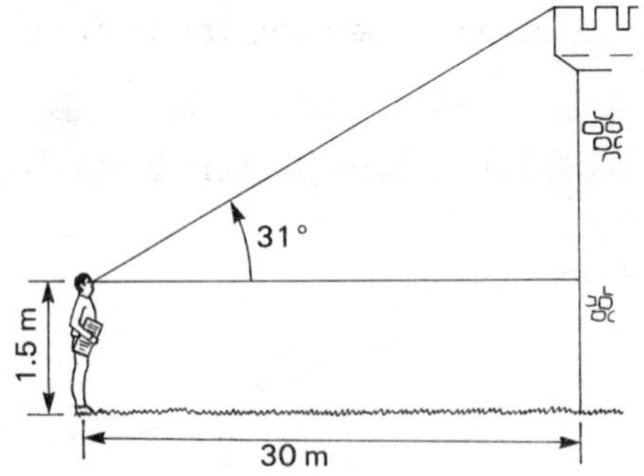

Make a scale drawing using a scale of 1 cm to 3 m and find the height of the building.

4. The angle of depression of a boat at sea taken from a point 24 m above sea level was 15°.

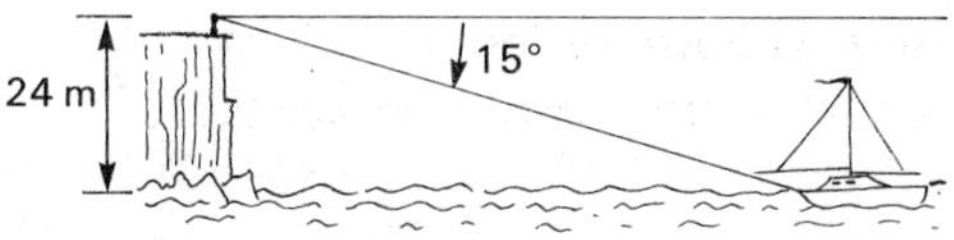

Make a scale drawing using a scale of 1 cm to 10 m. How far is the boat out to sea?

5. A certain landmark on level ground is 100 m from a tower. The angle of depression of that landmark from the top of the tower is 42°. Make a scale drawing using a scale of 1 cm to 20 m and find the height of the tower.

Exercise 5

1. A ship sailed 4 km due east followed by 5 km due south. Make a scale drawing using a scale of 1 : 100 000 (that is, 1 cm to 1 km). How far would the ship have sailed if it had sailed a direct route?

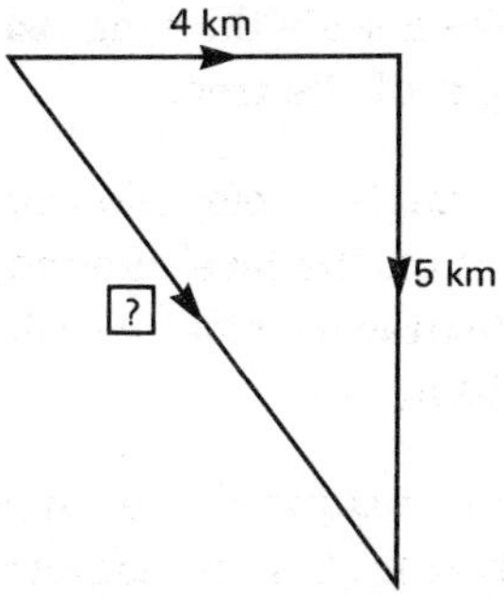

2. A ship sailed 12 km due north. It then changed direction and sailed 16 km due east. Make a scale drawing using a scale of 1 cm to 2 km and find the direct distance between the starting and finishing points.

3. An aeroplane flew 160 km due west. It then changed course and flew 110 km north-west.

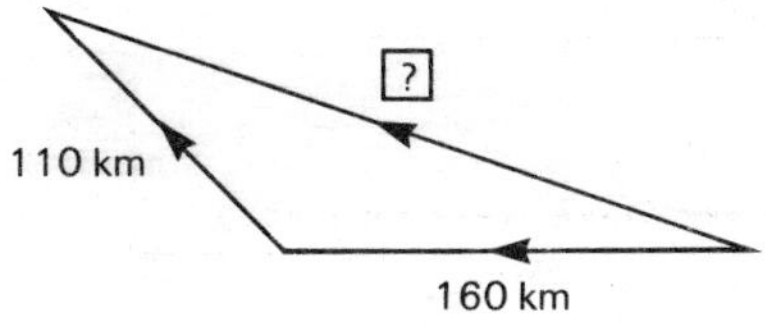

Use a scale of 1 cm to 20 km to make a scale drawing. How far would the aeroplane have flown if it flew directly from its starting point to its finishing point?

4. An aeroplane flew 175 km due north. It then changed course to fly 225 km south-west. Use a scale of 1 cm to 25 km to make a scale drawing. Use your scale drawing to find the direct distance. Note that 2 mm stands for 5 km.

5. Use a scale of 1 cm to 10 km to make a scale drawing to help you to find the direct distance from the starting port to the finishing port if a ship sails 80 km due south, then turns to sail 50 km north–east followed by 25 km due east.

24 Similarity

Exercise 1

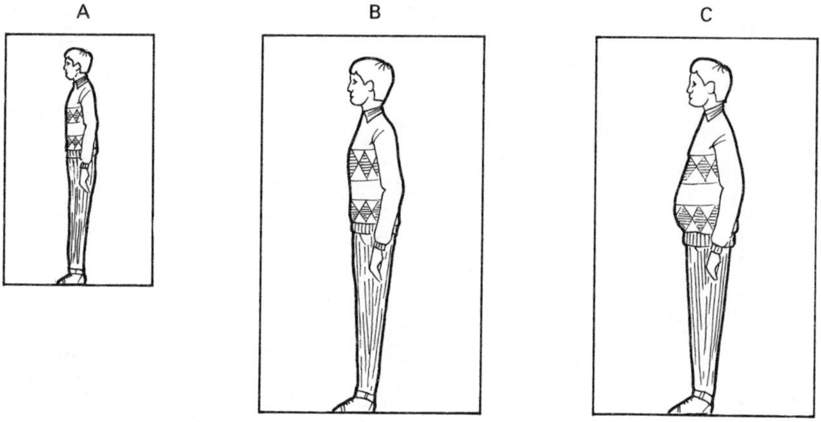

B is an enlargement of A.
Explain why C can not be an enlargement of A.

Figures or solids that have the same shape but have different sizes are *similar* to each other.

If a shape is enlarged (or reduced) the shape and its enlargement (or reduction) are similar.

A scale drawing and the original are similar.

A map of an area and the real area itself are similar.

A scale model and the original are similar.

Exercise 2

For each question, write which two of the three given shapes are similar:

1.

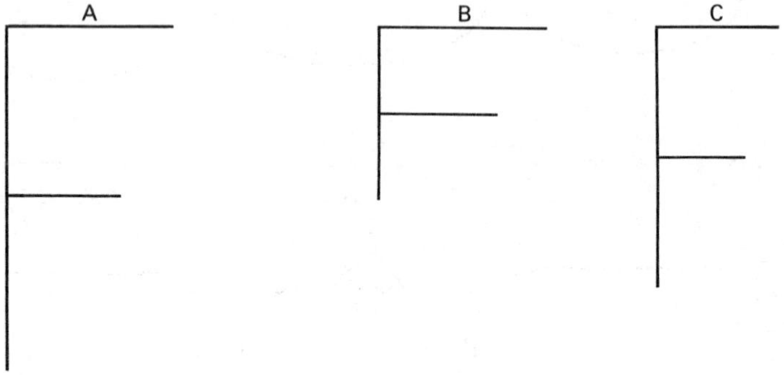

2.

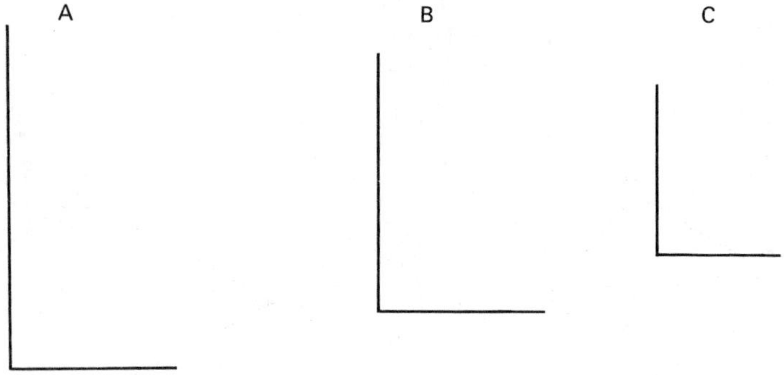

3.

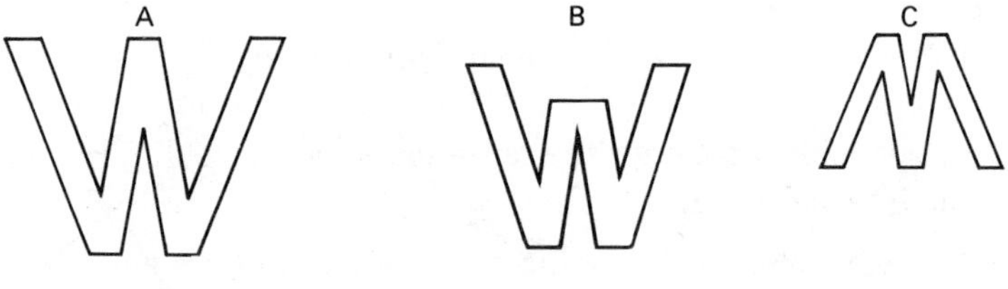

4.

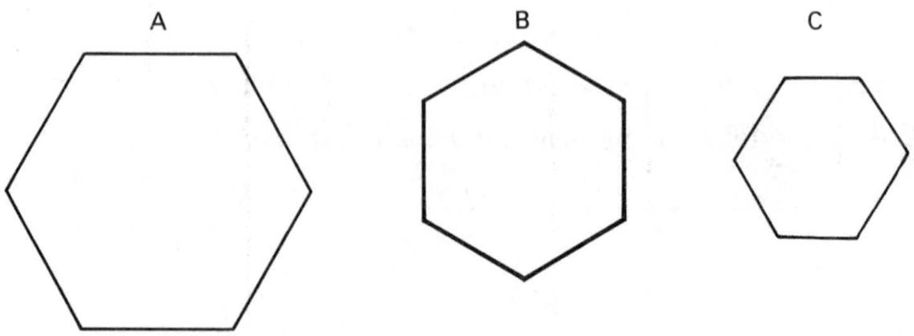

5.

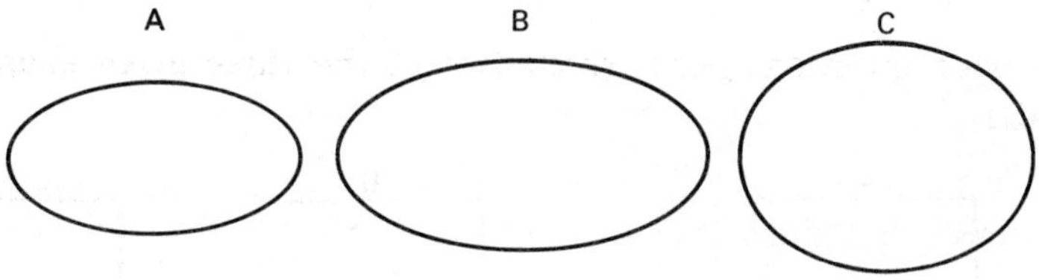

6.

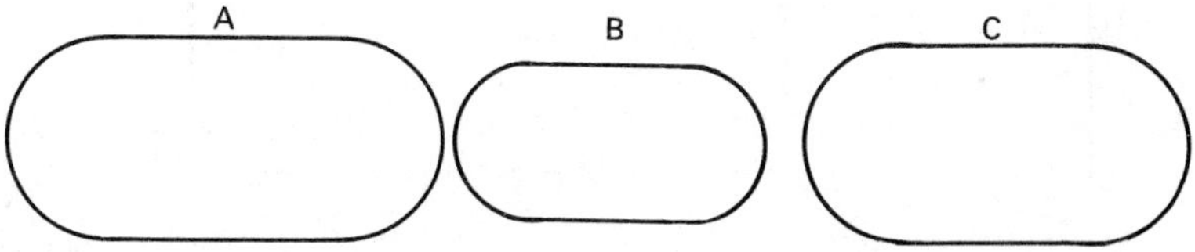

7.

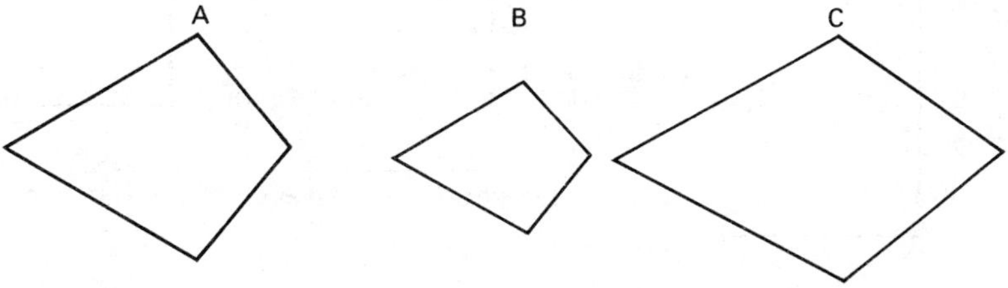

8.

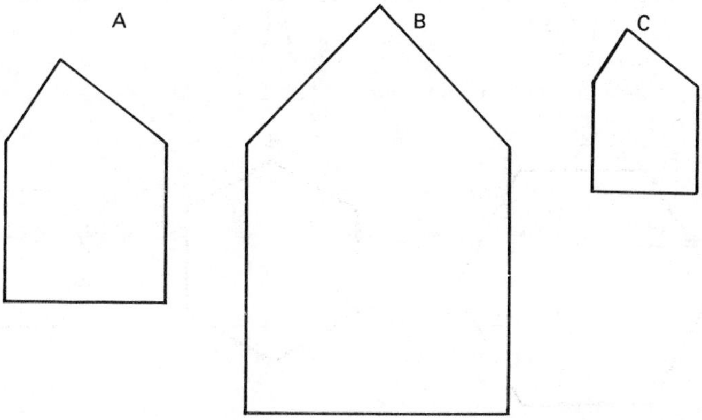

Exercise 3

For each question, write whether or not the two shapes you construct are similar:

1. Draw two rectangles, one with sides measuring 6 cm by 3 cm and the other with sides of 5 cm and 2 cm.

2. Draw two rectangles, one with sides measuring 80 mm by 50 mm and the other with sides of 40 mm and 25 mm.

3. Draw two triangles, one with sides measuring 4 cm, 3 cm and 2.5 cm, the other with sides measuring 8 cm, 6 cm and 5 cm.

4. Draw two triangles, one with sides measuring 5 cm, 4 cm and 4 cm and the other with sides of 7 cm, 6 cm and 6 cm.

5. Draw two squares, one with sides of 5 cm and the other with sides of 3 cm.

Exercise 4

Throughout this exercise, draw as many shapes as you need to help you:

1. For any rectangle, if the length and breadth are doubled, how many times bigger is the diagonal?

2. For any rectangle, if the length and breadth are drawn three times bigger, how many times bigger is the diagonal?

3. If the sides of a square are doubled, how does this affect the lengths of its diagonals?

4. If the sides of a square are made four times as long, how does this affect the lengths of its diagonals?

Exercise 5

Investigate the following:

1. Are all circles similar?
2. Are all squares similar?

3. Are all rectangles similar?
4. Are all parallelograms similar?
5. Are all rhombuses similar?
6. Are all kites similar?
7. Are all trapezia similar?
8. Are all hexagons similar?
9. Are all isosceles triangles similar?
10. Are all equilateral triangles similar?
11. Are all regular pentagons similar?
12. Are all cubes similar?
13. Are all cylinders similar?
14. Are all square-based pyramids similar?
15. Are all spheres similar?

Exercise 6 M

A Copy and complete the following table:

	Model		Real	
	length	width	length	width
e.g. 1	4 cm	3 cm	2 m	1.5 m
e.g. 2	40 mm	10 mm	60 cm	15 cm
1.	8 cm	5 cm	16 cm	?
2.	9 cm	6 cm	45 cm	?
3.	12 cm	8 cm	?	24 cm
4.	7 cm	5 cm	?	20 m
5.	15 cm	7 cm	4.5 m	?
6.	60 mm	36 mm	?	9 m
7.	?	4 cm	56 cm	32 cm
8.	14 cm	?	2.8 m	1.8 m

B **1.** How long is the enlarged picture?

(*a*)

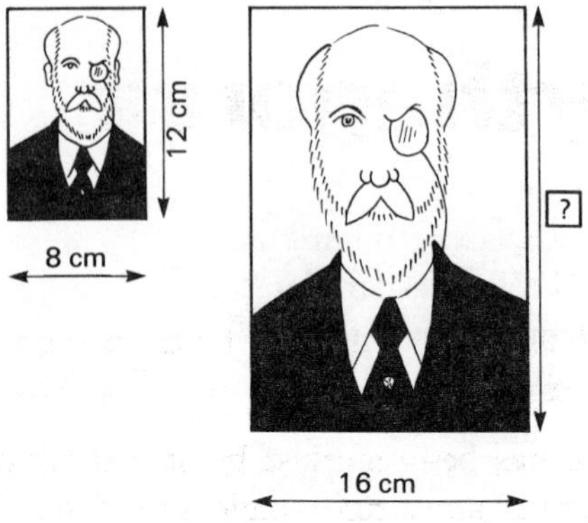

(*b*)

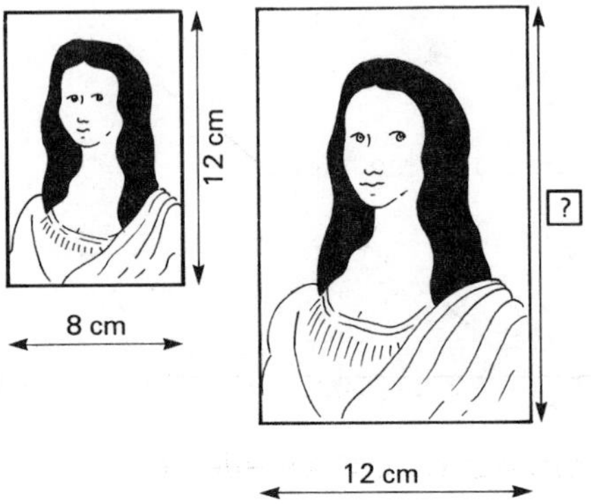

2. A doll's house is 1.2 m long and 0.8 m wide. If it is a model of a real house that is 12 m long, how wide is the real house?

3. A plan of a house measures 28 cm by 12 cm. If the width of the real house is 6 m and its length is bigger than its width, find its real length.

4. A model boat is 25 cm long and 8 cm wide. The real boat is 1.6 m wide. How long is the real boat?

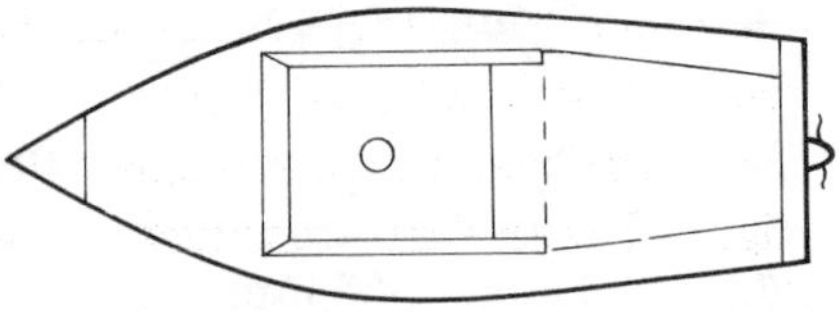

5. A model car is 9 cm long and 3.4 cm wide. The real car is 4.5 m long and 1.4 m high. Find:

(*a*) the width of the real car,

(*b*) the height of the model car.

25 Pythagoras

Landscape gardeners and builders need to make right-angles. One method that is often used is to ***3,4,5*** it.

For example, if a line has been marked by stretching a cord out as shown (AB in the diagram) and a right-angle is needed at B, then these steps can be followed:

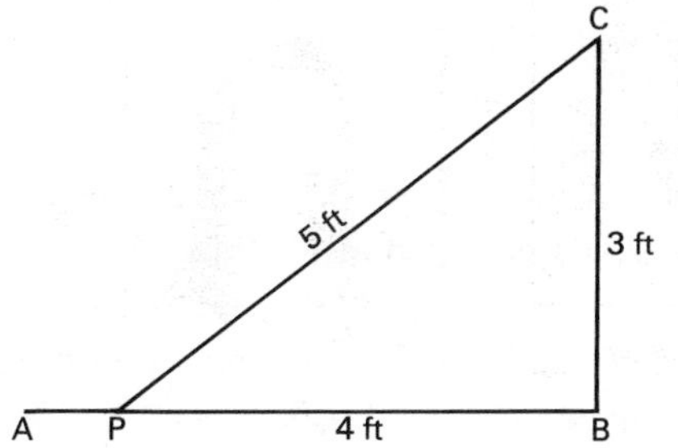

1. Mark a point on AB, 4 ft from B (labelled P).

2. Measure a distance of 3 ft from B with one tape and 5 ft from P with another tape and swing the two tapes together to find point C.

Angle PBC will be a right-angle. (*Note* Any units can be used; they do not need to be feet.)

The method above was used by the Ancient Egyptians thousands of years ago. To mark out their lands, buildings and pyramids, Egyptian 'rope-stretchers' used a piece of knotted rope. The positions of the knots enabled a 3,4,5-triangle to be formed when the rope was pulled tight. The triangle obtained was a right-angled triangle.

The Chinese, before 1100 BC, also knew the 3,4,5-relationship and that a right-angled triangle could be formed. It was also known in India and was mentioned in the Sulvasūtras, the sacred poems of the Brahmans. (The word *Sulvasūtras* is sometimes interpreted to mean rope-stretching.)

Exercise 1 A Challenge

In India, the Hindus discovered other number triples or *triads* (3 numbers) that would give a right-angled triangle in the same way as the 3,4,5-triad.

Try to find some of these other triads.

Exercise 2 Another Challenge

Consider the 3,4,5-triad.

$$3^2 = 9, \quad 4^2 = 16 \quad \text{and} \quad 5^2 = 25.$$

Since $9 + 16 = 25$,
we can write $3^2 + 4^2 = 5^2$.

If we write a triad as (a, b, c), where a, b and c are natural numbers, try to find some triads other than $(3, 4, 5)$ where $a^2 + b^2 = c^2$.

Such triads where $a^2 + b^2 = c^2$ are called *Pythagorean triads*, named after the Greek mathematician *Pythagoras** (*c.* 540 BC).

Hint For this exercise it may be helpful to list the squares of numbers from 1^2 to 30^2.

Exercise 3

Here are two formulae that can be used to find Pythagorean triads:

A $(n, \frac{1}{2}(n^2 - 1), \frac{1}{2}(n^2 + 1))$ where n is odd and greater than 1. This formula was discovered by Pythagoras. For example, when $n = 7$:

$$\tfrac{1}{2}(n^2 - 1) = \tfrac{1}{2}(7^2 - 1) = \tfrac{1}{2}(49 - 1) = \tfrac{1}{2} \times 48 = 24$$

$$\tfrac{1}{2}(n^2 + 1) = \tfrac{1}{2}(7^2 + 1) = \tfrac{1}{2}(49 + 1) = \tfrac{1}{2} \times 50 = 25$$

So $(7, 24, 25)$ is a Pythagorean triad.
Use the formula to find some more Pythagorean triads.

* See appendix 3, p. 377.

B $((l^2 - k^2), 2kl, (l^2 + k^2))$ gives Pythagorean triads when k and l are natural numbers and when $l > k$.
For example, when $l = 4$ and $k = 1$:

$$l^2 - k^2 = 4^2 - 1^2 = 16 - 1 = 15$$

$$2kl = 2 \times 1 \times 4 = 8$$

$$l^2 + k^2 = 4^2 + 1^2 = 16 + 1 = 17$$

So (8, 15, 17) is a Pythagorean triad.

Note It is usual to write the triads with the numbers in order, smallest first.

1. Use the formula to find some more Pythagorean triads.

2. (*a*) Does the formula give the same Pythagorean triads as the formula in part A?
   (*b*) Does the formula give some triads that cannot be obtained by using the formula given in part A?
   (*c*) Does the formula in part A give more Pythagorean triads than the formula in part B?

C Two computer programs for finding Pythagorean triads are listed in appendix 3, pp. 379-80. Run them.

Exercise 4

A The Pythagorean triad (3, 4, 5) contains one even number (the number 4).

Can you find any Pythagorean triads where all three numbers are odd? If so, list them. If you do not think there are any Pythagorean triads having all three numbers odd, then give a reason why not.

B Consider several Pythagorean triads and for each one, find the product of the three numbers.

Is your answer always a multiple of 60?

e.g. $3 \times 4 \times 5 = 60$, a multiple of 60.

In general, if (a, b, c) is a Pythagorean triad, is $a \times b \times c$ always a multiple of 60?

Exercise 5 **M**

A **1.** In the diagram below, squares have been drawn on each side of a right-angled triangle ABC. Calculate the area of each square.

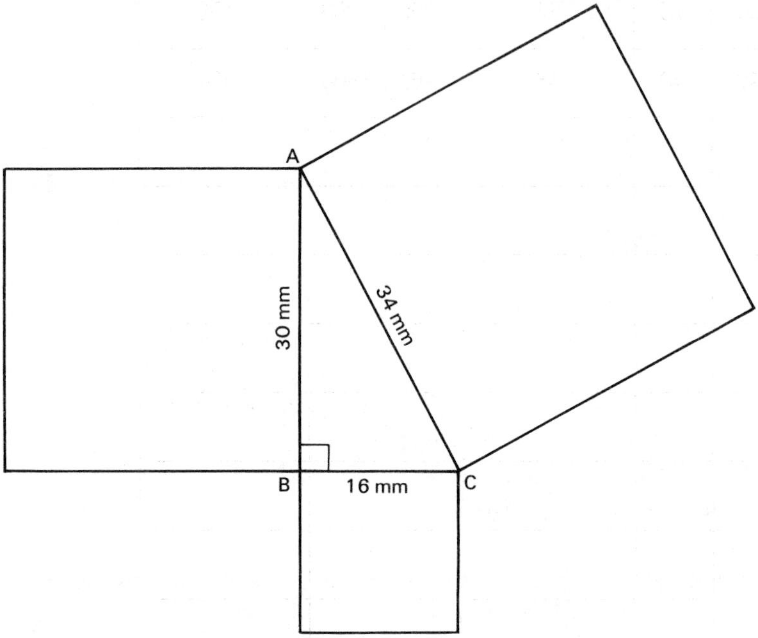

2. Construct a right-angled triangle with sides of 40 mm, 42 mm and 58 mm. Label the triangle ABC as in question 1, where AB = 42 mm, BC = 40 mm and AC = 58 mm.

Calculate the areas of the squares that can be drawn on the sides of this triangle.

B Draw eight more right-angled triangles (all different). Label each one ABC where *B* is the right-angle. Measure and note the lengths of their sides. Calculate and note the areas of the squares that can be drawn on the sides of the right-angled triangles.

C **1.** Copy and complete the table (opposite) for the triangles in parts A and B (work with 4 s.f.). (The values for the two triangles from part A have already been entered in the table.)

Note In any right-angled triangle, the side opposite the right-angle is called the *hypotenuse*.

Length of:			Area of square on:		
AB	BC	hypotenuse AC	AB	BC	hypotenuse AC
30	16	34	900	256	1156
42	40	58	1764	1600	3364

2. For each triangle add the areas of the squares on the two small sides, and compare your answer with the area of the square on the hypotenuse.

Write what you notice.

From your work so far in this chapter, you should have discovered that:

> For any right-angled triangle the area of the square on the hypotenuse is equal to the sum of the areas of the squares on the other two sides.

The above is called the theorem of Pythagoras. Pythagoras was given the credit for proving it although it was probably someone else who first proved it.

Since then, hundreds of proofs have been suggested for the theorem. In the next exercise, the theorem is proved by cutting up paper.

Exercise 6

1. On a piece of paper, draw any right-angled triangle with different-size sides – then cut it out.

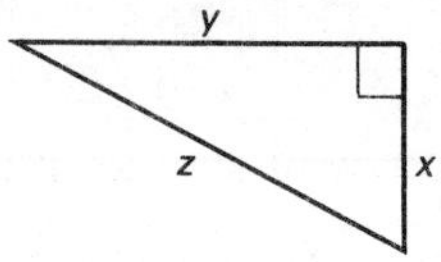

2. Make three more triangles exactly the same as the first, and cut them out also.

3. Draw three squares, each one having sides the same length as one of the sides of your right-angled triangle (that is, sides x cm, y cm and z cm).

4. Using the four triangles and the largest square (area z^2), place them together as in the diagram on the left below. They make an even larger square with side $(x + y)$ cm. Copy the diagram.

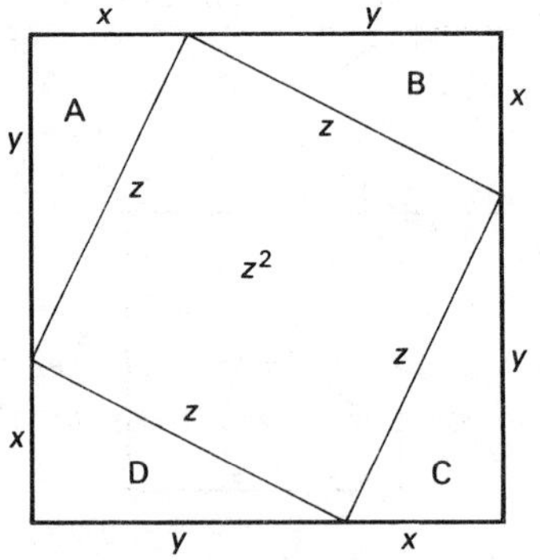

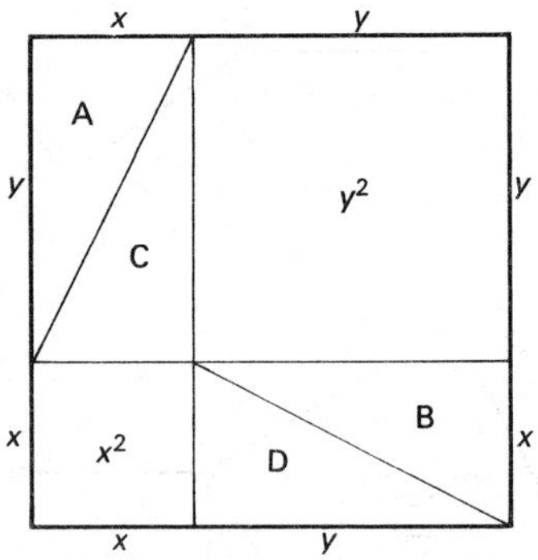

5. Using the four triangles and the two smaller squares (areas x^2 and y^2) place them together as in the diagram on the right above to make another square where each side = $(x + y)$ cm. Copy the diagram.

The two large squares you have made have the same-size sides, $(x + y)$ cm, and therefore have the same area.

Removing the four triangles, A, B, C and D from the first diagram leaves z^2. Removing the four triangles from the second diagram leaves x^2 and y^2.

So $z^2 = x^2 + y^2$

Now z^2 is the area of the square on the hypotenuse of the right-angled triangle and x^2 and y^2 are the areas of the squares on the other two sides.

Therefore we have, for any right-angled triangle:

The area of the square on the hypotenuse is equal to the sum of the areas of the squares on the other two sides.

Exercise 7

For each question, the areas of two squares are given. Find the area of the third square:

1.

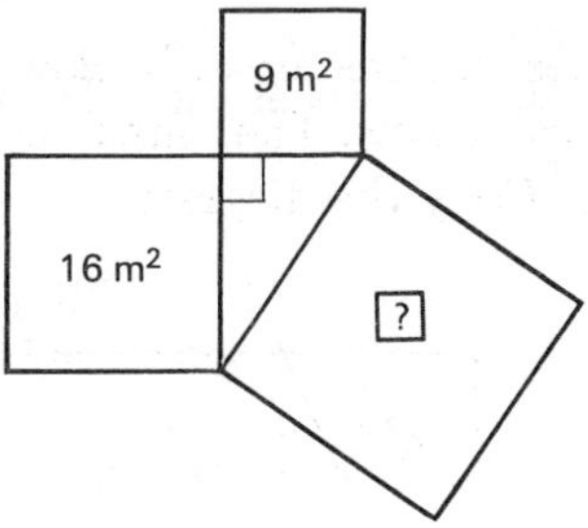

2.

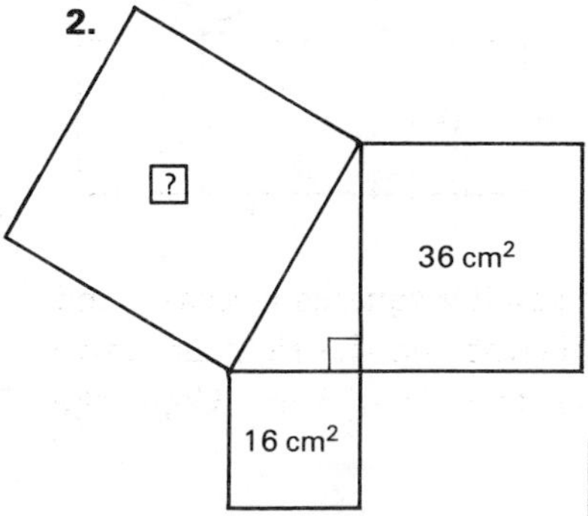

3.

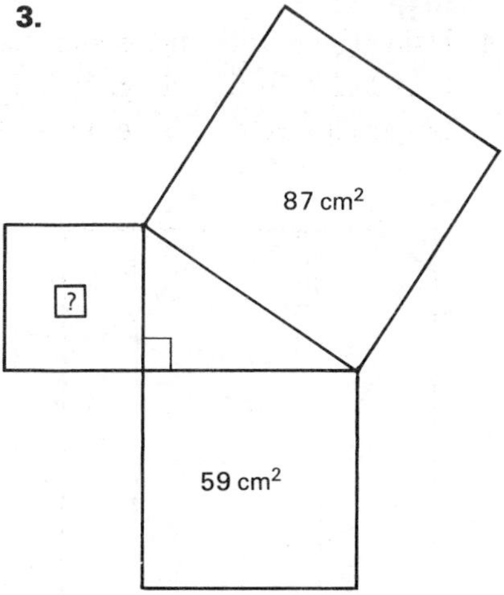

4.

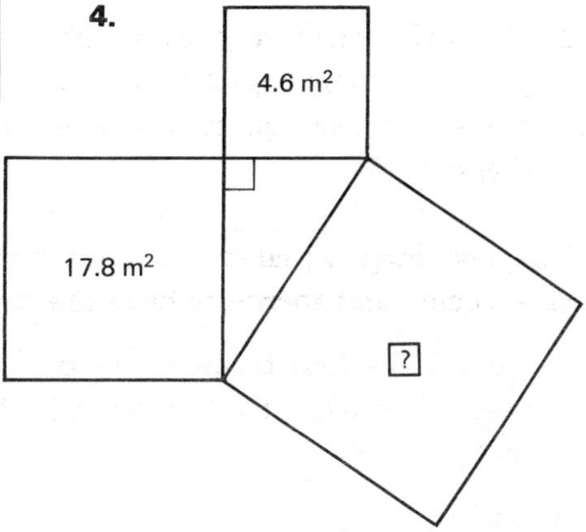

5.

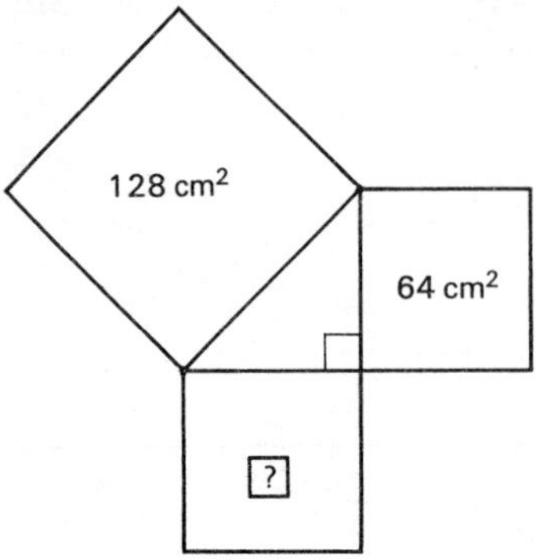

6.

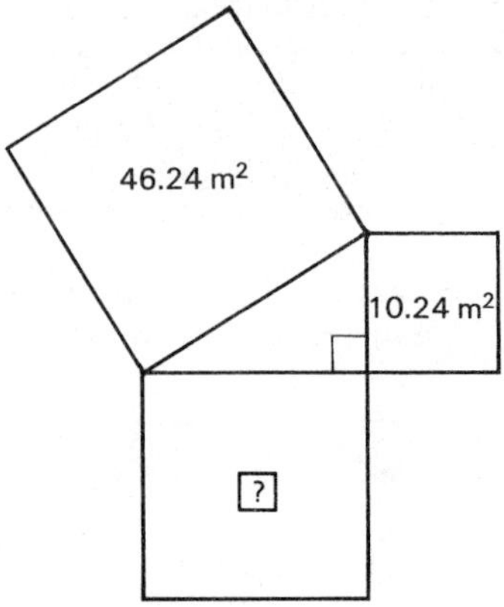

Exercise 8

Calculate the areas of the squares and the lengths of the sides of the triangles as shown by the question marks:

1.

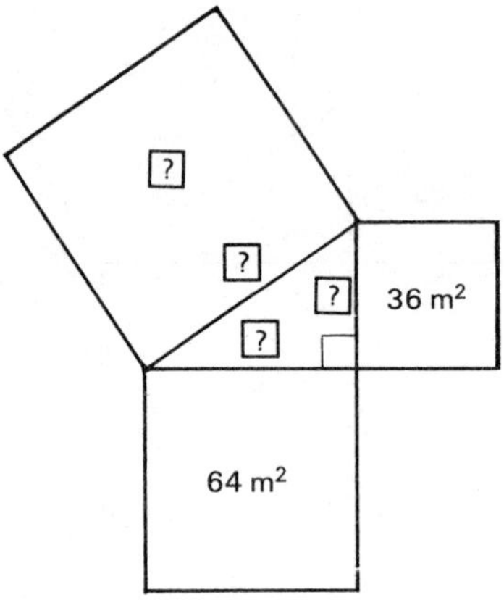

3.

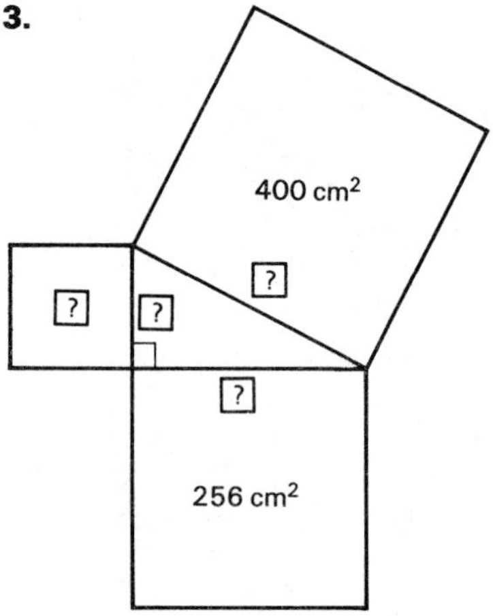

2.

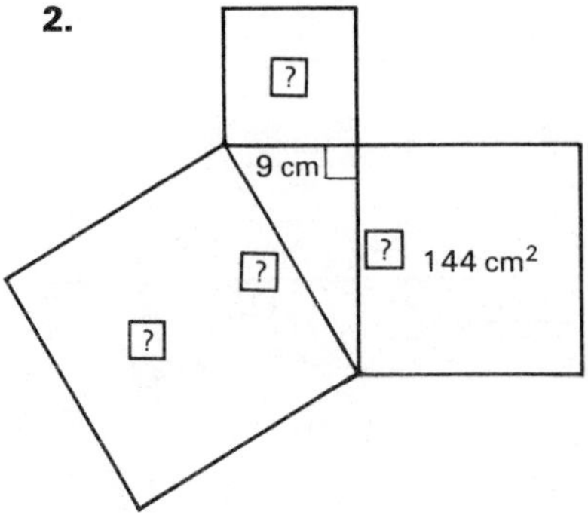

4.

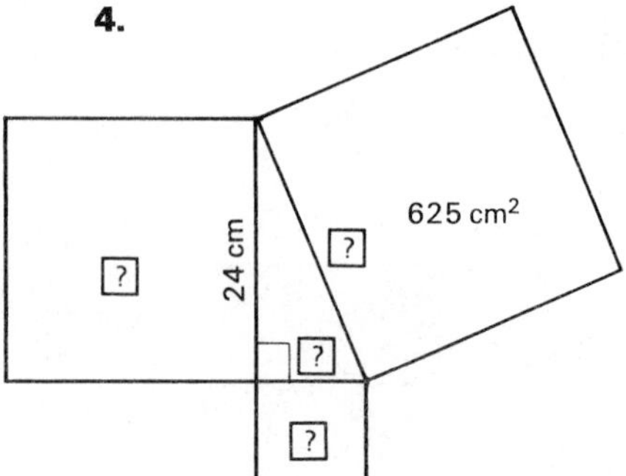

5.

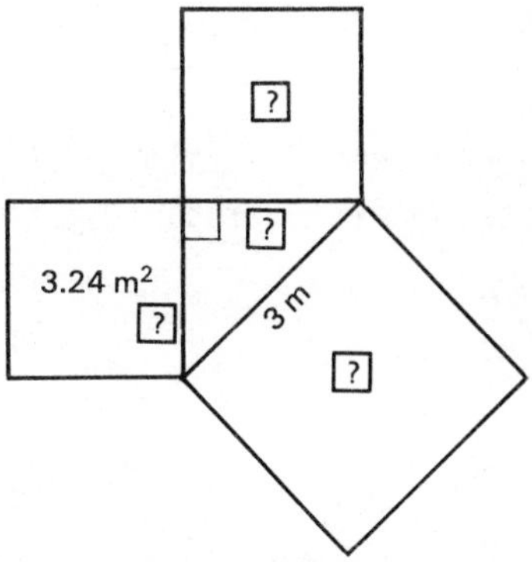

6.

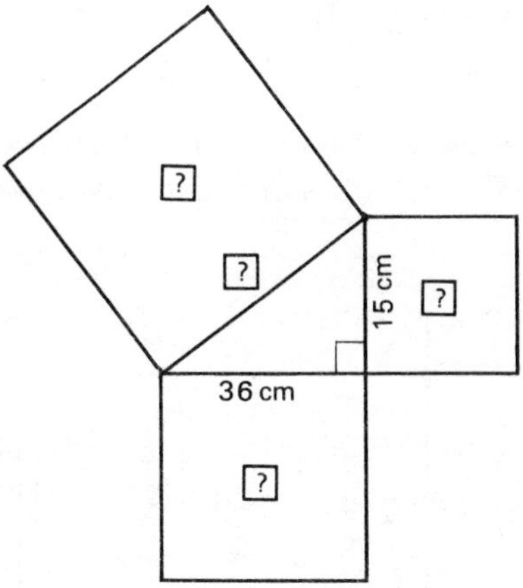

Exercise 9

1. In right-angled triangle ABC, AB = 5 cm and BC = 12 cm. Find:

(*a*) The area of the square on side AB.
(*b*) The area of the square on side BC.
(*c*) The area of the square on side AC.
(*d*) The length of side AC.

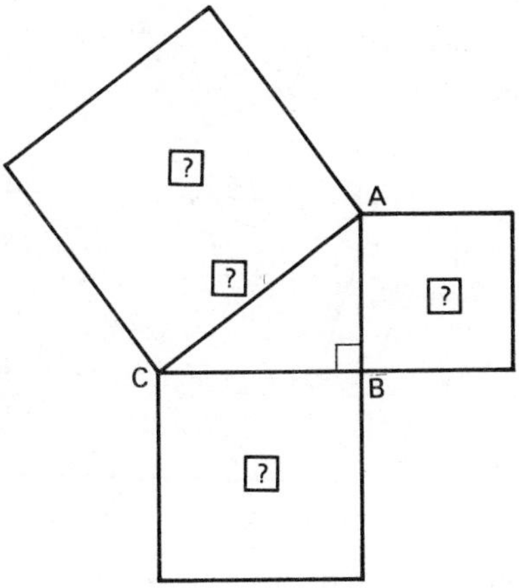

2. Repeat question 1 for a right-angled triangle ABC where AB = 15 cm and BC = 20 cm.

3. Repeat question 1 for a right-angled triangle ABC in which AB = 11 cm and BC = 60 cm.

4. Repeat question 1 for a right-angled triangle ABC in which AB = 2.5 m and BC = 6 m.

5. For a right-angled triangle ABC find the length of hypotenuse AC when AB = 20 cm and BC = 48 cm.

Exercise 10

Sketch the following triangles and calculate the missing lengths. Where necessary, give answers correct to three significant figures:

1.

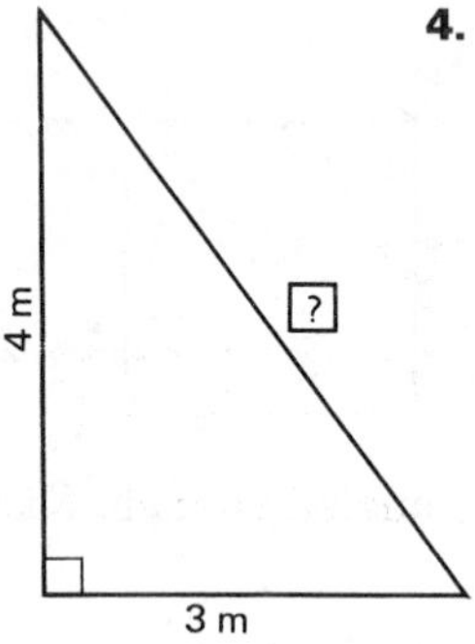

2.

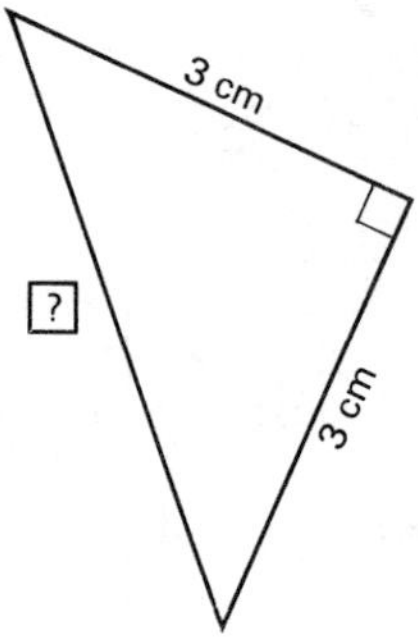

3.

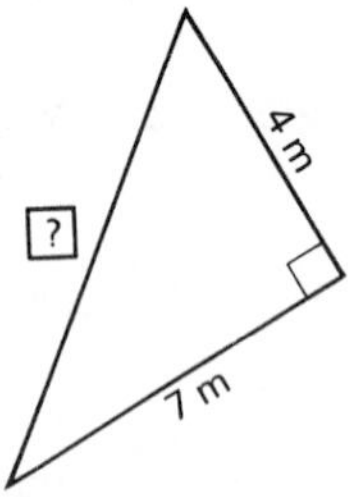

4.

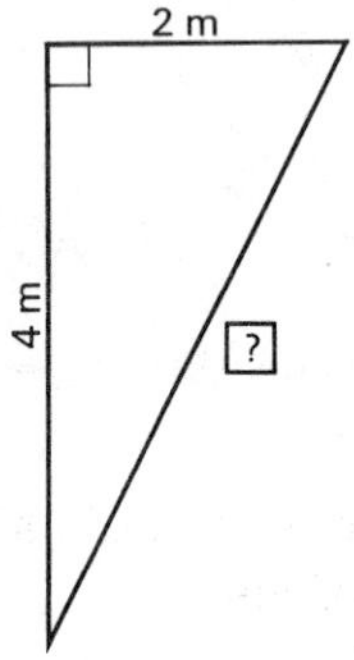

5.

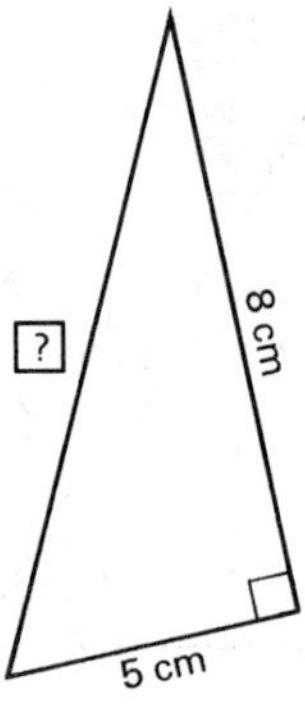

6.

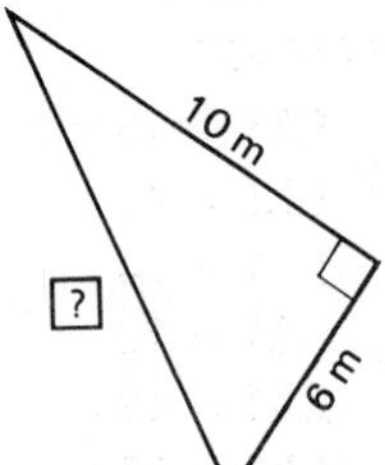

7.

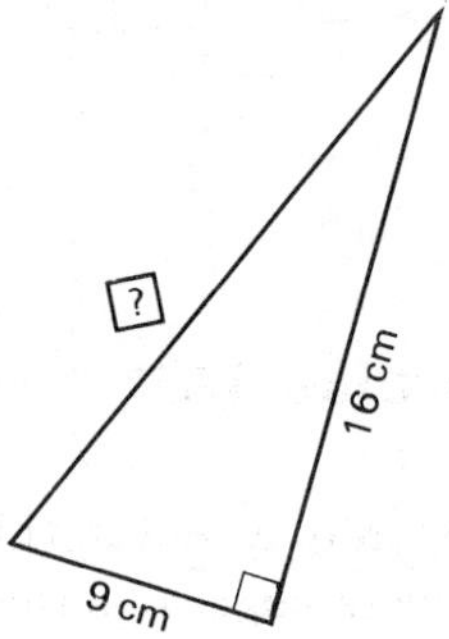

8.

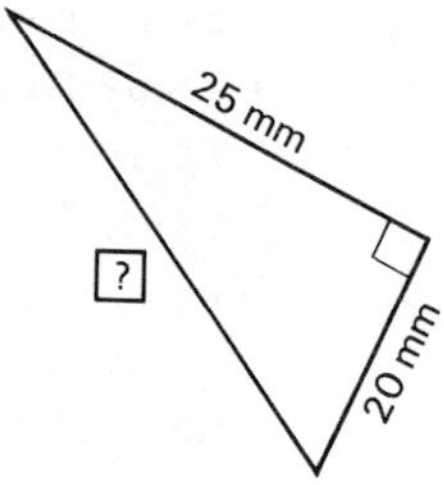

9.

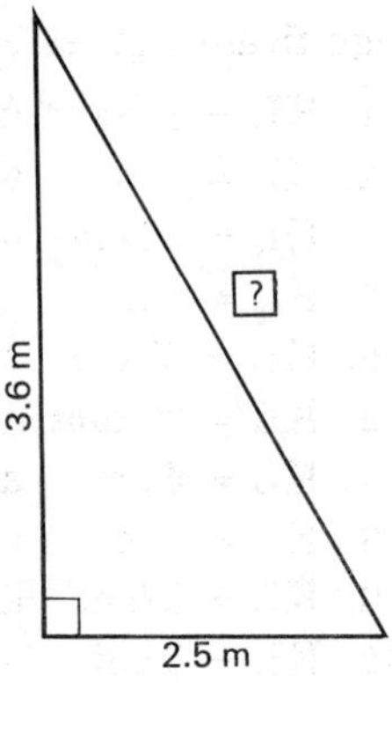

10.

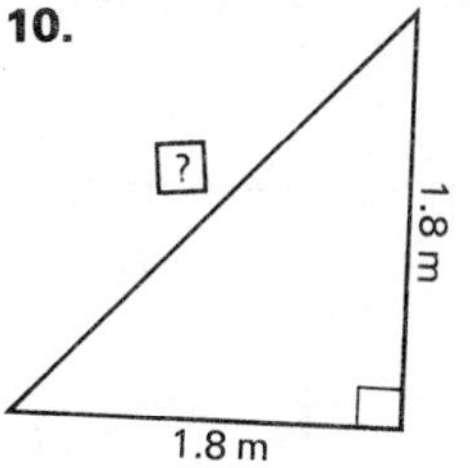

11.

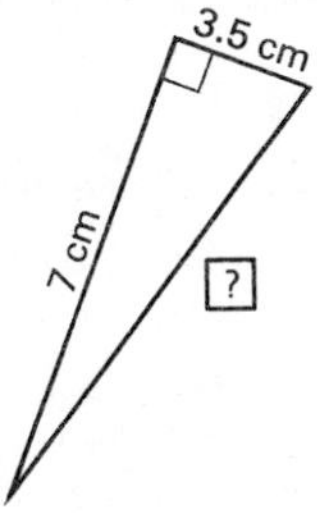

12.

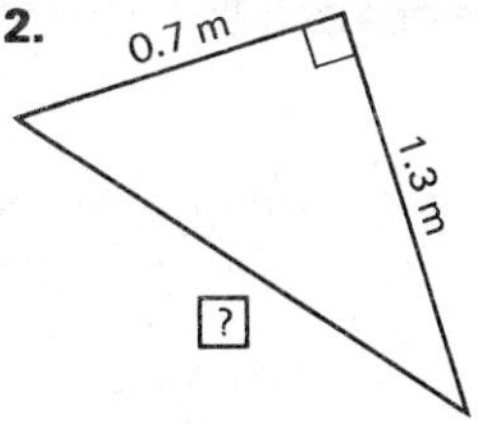

Exercise 11

Each question in this exercise refers to a right-angled triangle KLM where angle L is the right-angle.

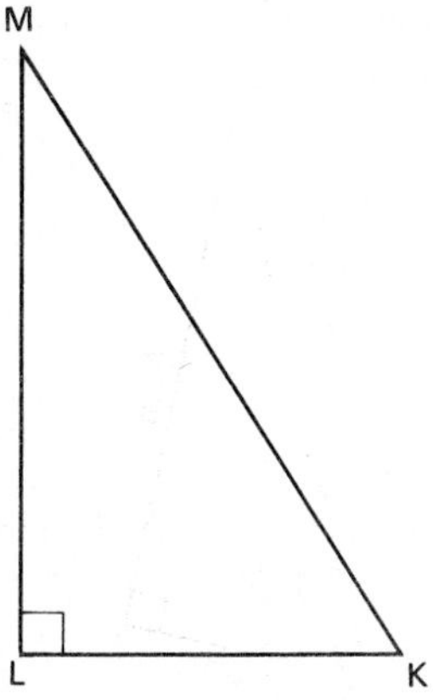

Find the length of hypotenuse KM giving answers correct to three significant figures as necessary:

1. KL = 8 cm and LM = 15 cm
2. KL = 9 m and LM = 40 m
3. KL = 32 cm and LM = 24 cm
4. KL = 3 m and LM = 7.2 m
5. KL = 35 cm and LM = 12 cm
6. KL = 36 mm and LM = 77 mm
7. KL = 4 cm and LM = 9 cm
8. KL = 7 m and LM = 14 m
9. KL = 2.6 m and LM = 5.1 m
10. KL = 5 cm and LM = 5 cm

Exercise 12

Throughout this exercise, where necessary, give answers correct to three significant figures:

1. In Exercise 3, question 1 on p. 274 a scale drawing was made of a rectangular garden of length 24 m and width 10 m.

   By measuring, the length of a diagonal was found.

   Calculate the length of the same diagonal.

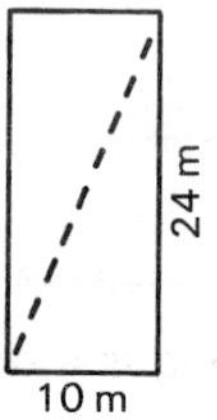

2. After marking the four corner positions to show where a new garage should be erected, both diagonals ought to be measured as a check (see Exercise 3, question 2 on p. 274).

   Calculate the length of the diagonals for a garage measuring 4.5 m by 3 m.

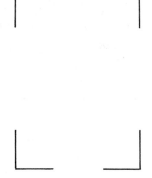

3. How long should diagonals be of garages measuring:
   (*a*) 5 m by 3 m?
   (*b*) 5.6 m by 3 m?
   (*c*) 7.5 m by 3.2 m?
   (*d*) 4.4 m by 2.7 m?

4. A boat in Exercise 5, question 1 on p. 277 sailed 4 km due east then 5 km due south.

   Calculate how far it would have sailed if it had sailed a direct route.

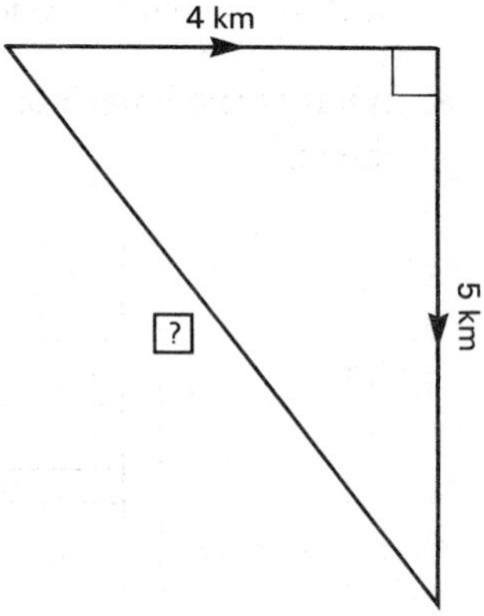

5. If a ship sailed 6 km due north then 9 km due west, calculate how far it would have sailed if it had sailed a direct route.

Exercise 13

Give your answers correct to three significant figures:

1. How long is a diagonal of a rectangle 10 cm by 4 cm?

2. How long is a diagonal of a square of side 6 cm?

3. What length of stay is needed for a drop-leaf table if it is fixed to the wall as shown in the diagram?

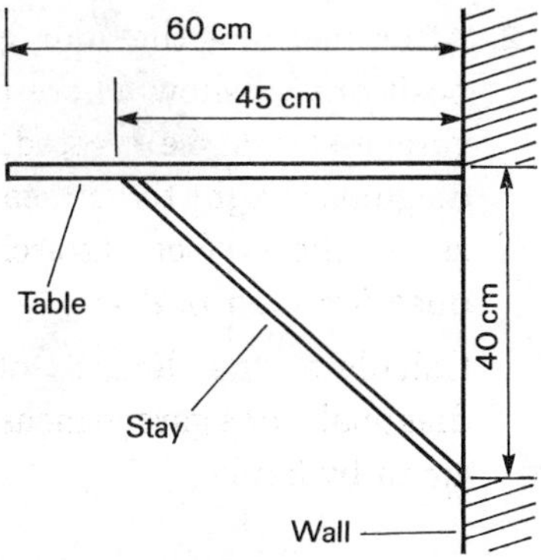

4. A swimming pool is 20 m long and 10 m wide. How far would you swim if you swam diagonally across?

5. A ladder is placed against a wall so that its foot is 2.5 m from the wall. If the ladder reaches 4.33 m up the wall, how long must it be?

6. What is the length of the diagonal piece of wood on the 5-bar gate shown?

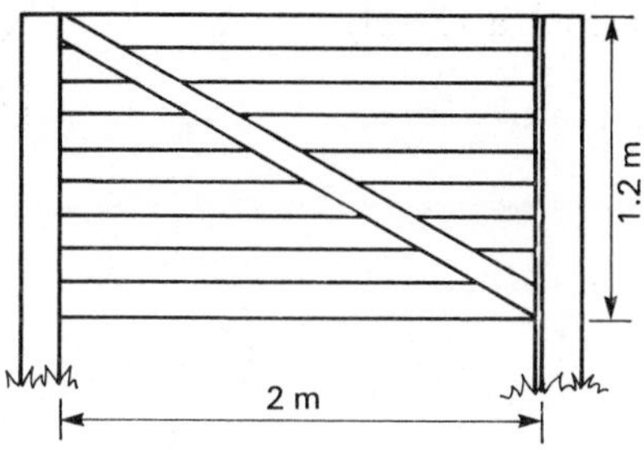

7. The end view of a shed is shown. Using the measurements given, calculate the length of the sloping roof.

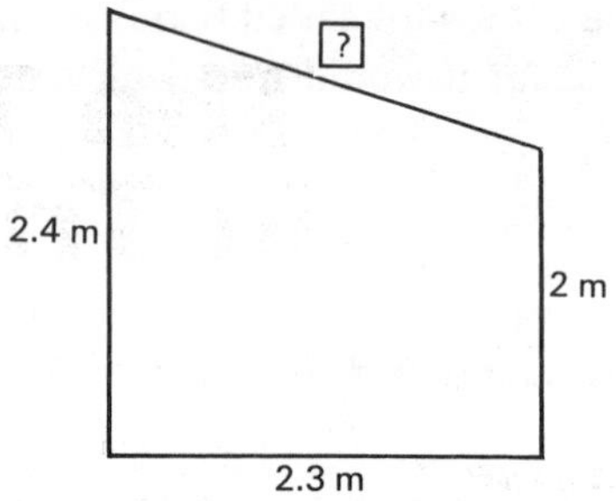

8. A sketch of a coal bunker is shown.

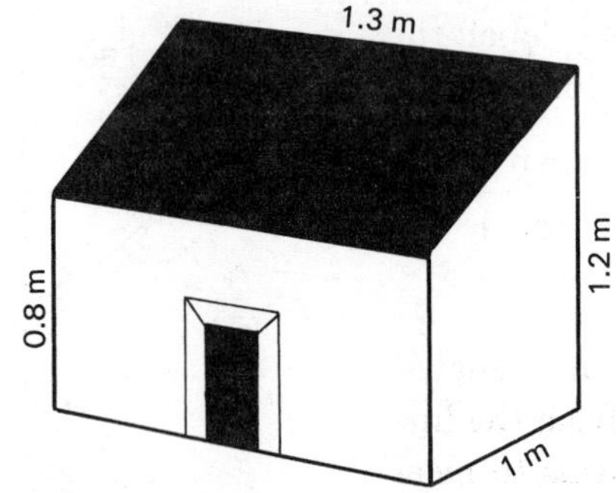

Calculate the area of the sloping roof.

26 The Tangent Ratio in Trigonometry

Exercise 1 M

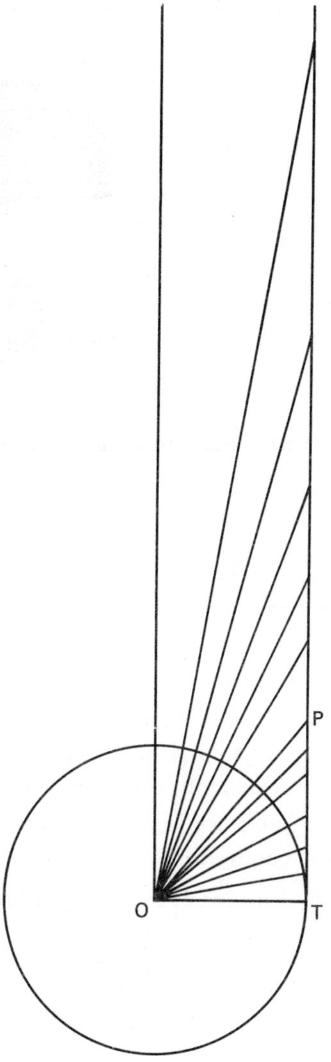

1. Draw a circle of radius 2 cm as shown. Label the centre, O.

2. Draw a radius and label the point at which it touches the circle, T.

3. Draw a tangent to touch the circle at T.

4. Draw the following angles. Measure each one from the line OT. Produce the arms to meet the tangent. The angles should measure 10°, 20°, 30°, 40°, 45°, 50°, 60°, 65°, 70°, 75°, 80° and 90°.

5. Copy the table on p. 300. Copy the first column and complete the second and third columns. Note that the length of each tangent should be measured from T.

   e.g. Angle TOP = 50°
   PT = 2.4 cm
   so PT = 1.2 units
   (by dividing the length of PT by 2 since each unit = 2 cm.)

   Radius OT = 2 cm, but we can say it has a radius of 1 unit (if we call every 2 cm one unit).

Angle θ	Length of tangent measured from T in centimetres	in 2 cm units	tan θ
0°	0	0	
10°			
20°			
30°			
40°			
45°			
50°	2.4	1.2	
60°			1.73
65°			
70°			
75°			
80°			
90°			

6. You need a calculator to complete the last column. The calculator must have a 'tan' key on it. Also, it must be in 'degree mode'. Although we have measured angles in degrees, angles may be measured in radians or in grades (often called gradients or grads in calculator instruction books).

Key in: [AC] [6] [0] [tan]

If the display shows [1.7320508] then the calculator is using degrees.

This means that: $\tan 60° = 1.732\,050\,8$

so $\tan 60° = 1.73$ to 2 d.p.

In the 60° row in your table, enter 1.73 in the tan θ column.

Now complete the last column of your table using the tan key on your calculator. Give each entry in the table correct to two decimal places.

7. Compare the last two columns of your table (that is, compare tan θ with the length of the tangent measured in units). Write what you notice.

You should have discovered that tan θ is the length of a tangent drawn touching a unit circle.

Notice also that as the angle gets bigger in going from 0° to 90°, the tangent gets longer and tan θ gets bigger.

When $\theta = 90°$, the arm of the angle (not OT, but the other one) never meets the tangent. The tangent continues for ever. We say it has *infinite* length. 'Infinite' means 'not finite', that is, 'never finishes'. Trying to find tan 90° on your calculator will probably give an error message.

Exercise 2

Find (correct to four decimal places):

1. tan 35°
2. tan 56°
3. tan 18°
4. tan 62°
5. tan 47°
6. tan 71°
7. tan 9°
8. tan 24°
9. tan 83°
10. tan 79°
11. tan 43.6°
12. tan 14.8°
13. tan 52.3°
14. tan 87.2°
15. tan 31.9°
16. tan 25.4°
17. tan 68.1°
18. tan 39.7°
19. tan 76.3°
20. tan 4.5°

If tan $\theta = 0.787$, then angle θ can be found by keying in:

[AC] [·] [7] [8] [7] [INV] [tan]

(or [AC] [·] [7] [8] [7] [arc] [tan] or perhaps

[AC] [·] [7] [8] [7] [F] [$\tan^{-1}$] on some calculators).

Try it. You should find that $\theta = 38.2°$ correct to one decimal place.

Exercise 3

Find angle θ correct to 1 d.p. if:

1. $\tan\theta = 0.512$
2. $\tan\theta = 0.776$
3. $\tan\theta = 0.356$
4. $\tan\theta = 0.5$
5. $\tan\theta = 1.5$
6. $\tan\theta = 0.869$
7. $\tan\theta = 1.13$
8. $\tan\theta = 2.116$
9. $\tan\theta = 0.66$
10. $\tan\theta = 1.43$
11. $\tan\theta = 5.1$
12. $\tan\theta = 1.658$
13. $\tan\theta = 0.153$
14. $\tan\theta = 0.9$
15. $\tan\theta = 0.9759$
16. $\tan\theta = 7.6996$
17. $\tan\theta = 2.4504$
18. $\tan\theta = 0.3134$
19. $\tan\theta = 3.0961$
20. $\tan\theta = 10.3854$

In right-angled triangle ABC, where angle B is the right-angle, AC is called the *hypotenuse* (the side opposite the right-angle).

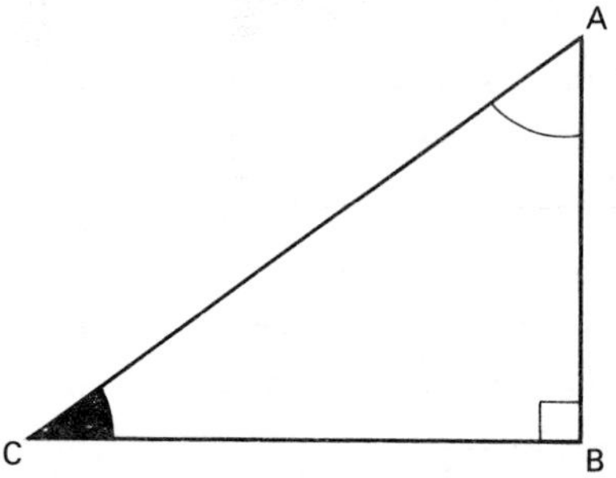

Side AB is opposite angle C and side BC is next to (adjacent to) angle C. So, if we refer to angle C, then AB is the *opposite* side and BC is the *adjacent* side. For angle A, BC is the opposite side and AB is the adjacent side.

Note For any angle other than the right-angle, although there are two sides next to (adjacent to) the angle, only one of them is called the adjacent side. The other side (opposite the right-angle) already has its own special name, the hypotenuse.

Exercise 4

A In each triangle, which side is the hypotenuse?

1.

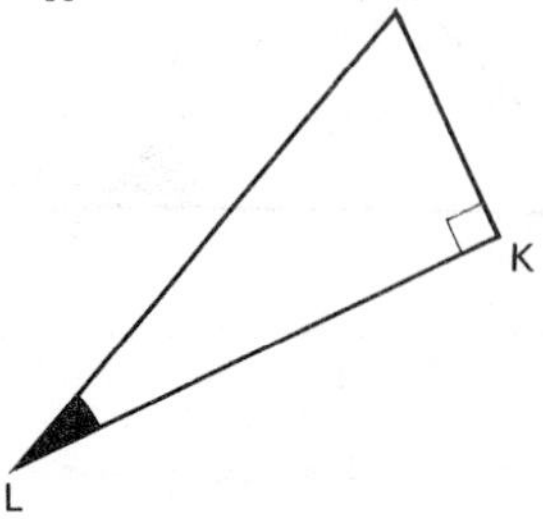

2.

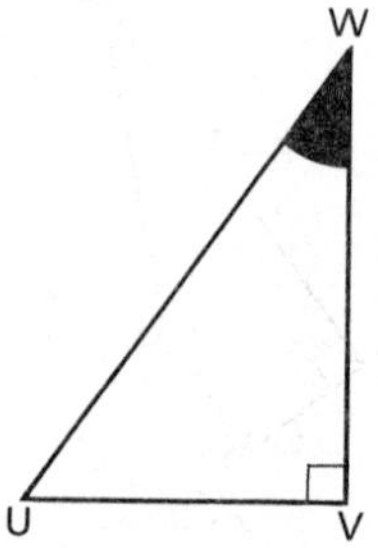

3.

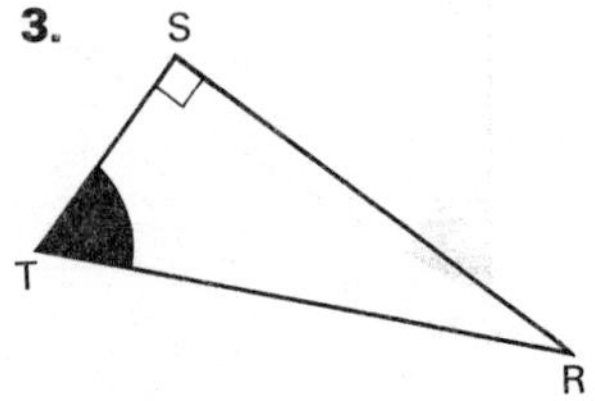

B Which side is opposite the shaded angle?

1.
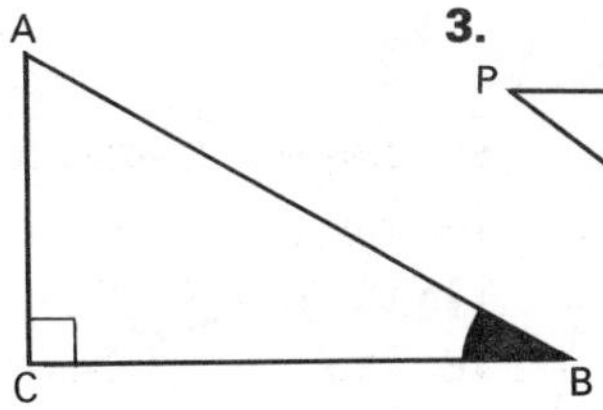

2.
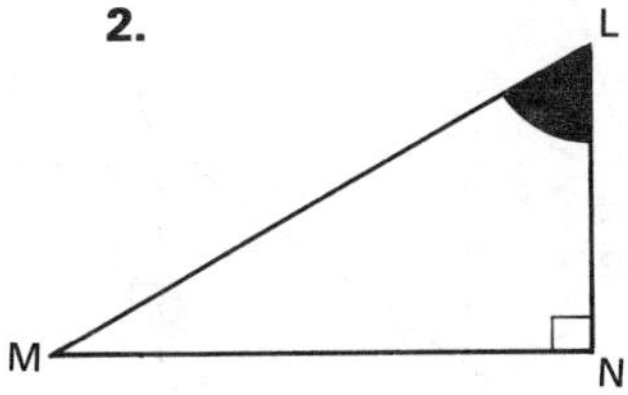

3.
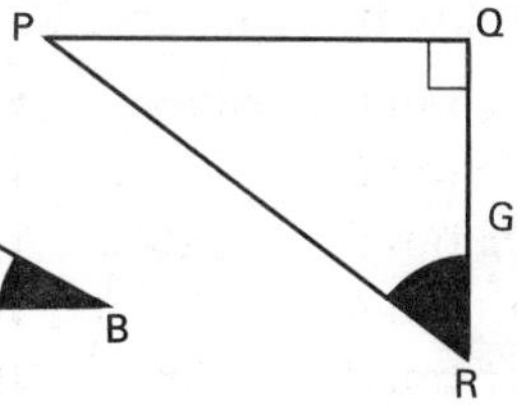

4.
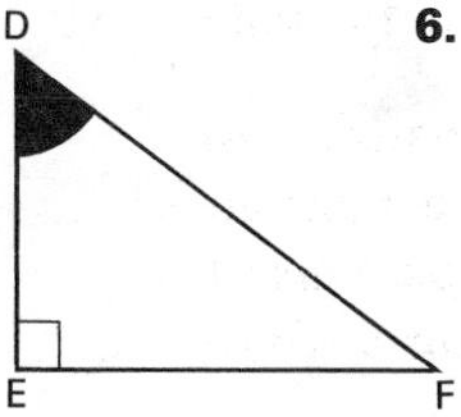

5.
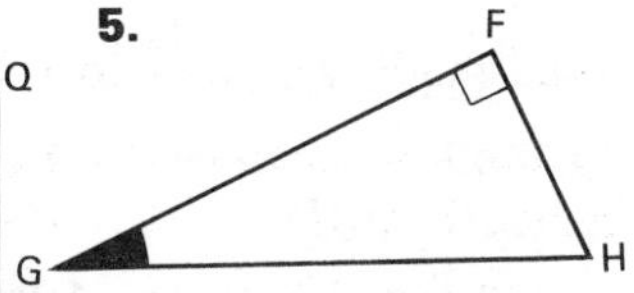

6.
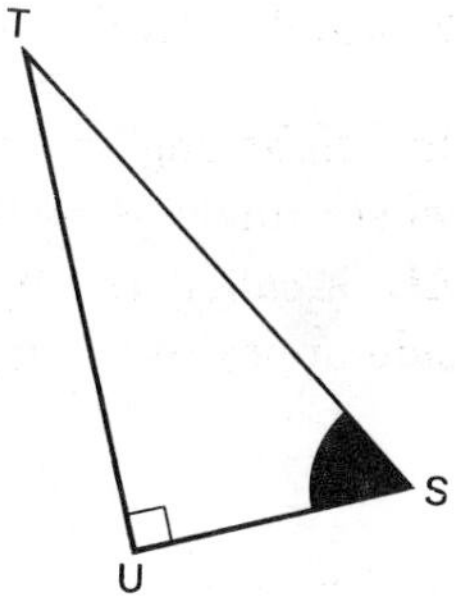

C Considering the shaded angle, which side is the adjacent side?

1.
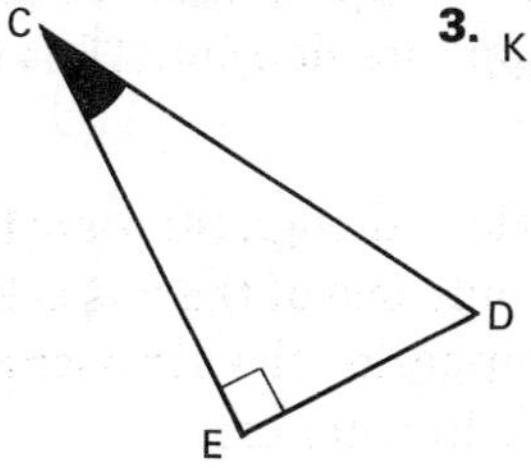

2.
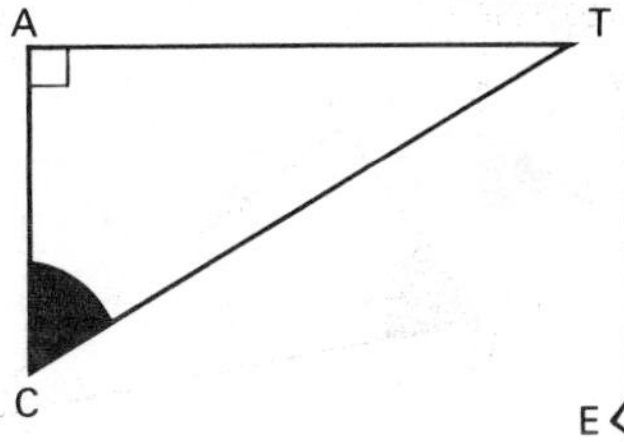

3.
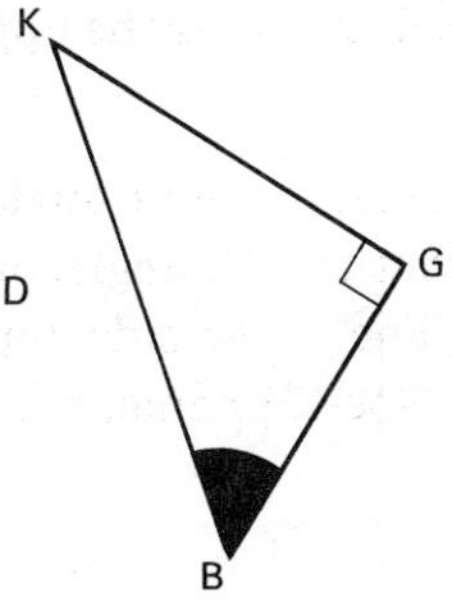

4.
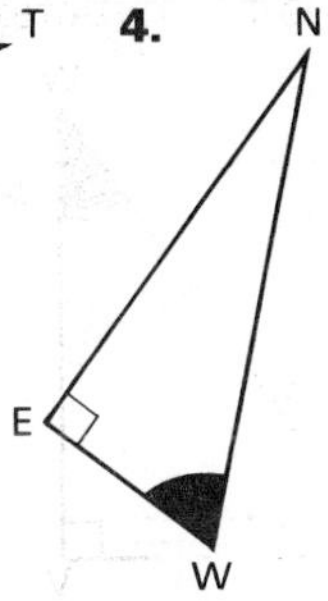

5.
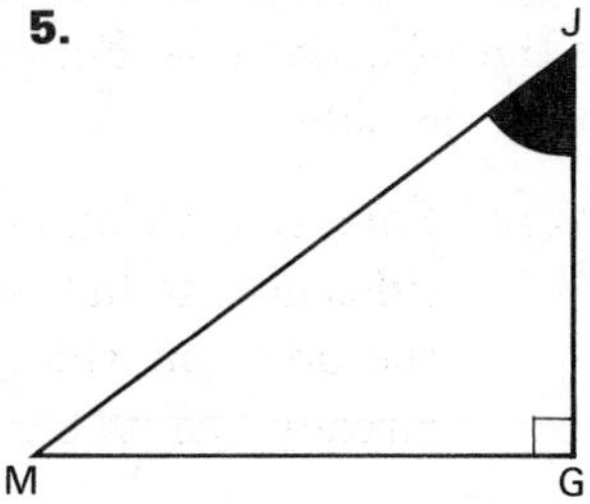

6.
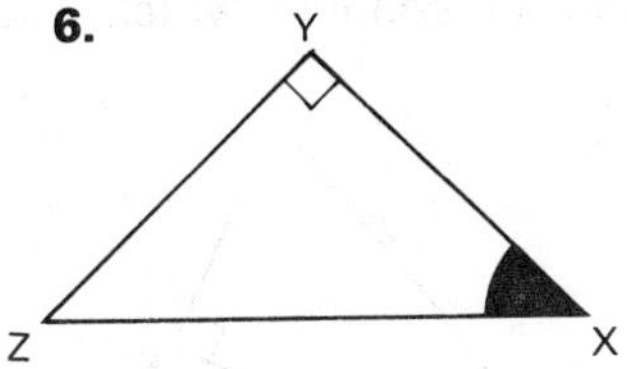

Exercise 5

For each triangle, write whether the side marked with the question mark is the opposite side, adjacent side or hypotenuse in relation to the shaded angle:

1.

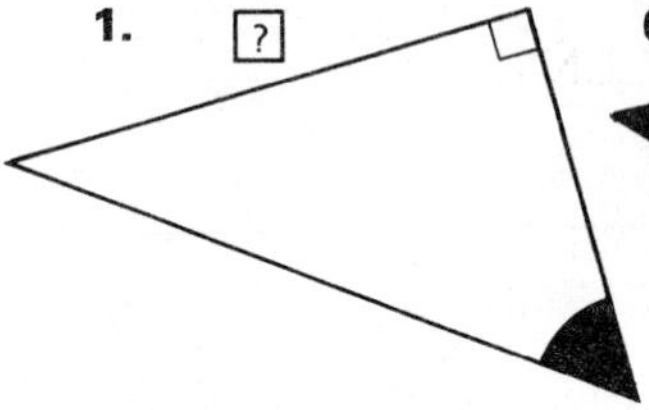

2.

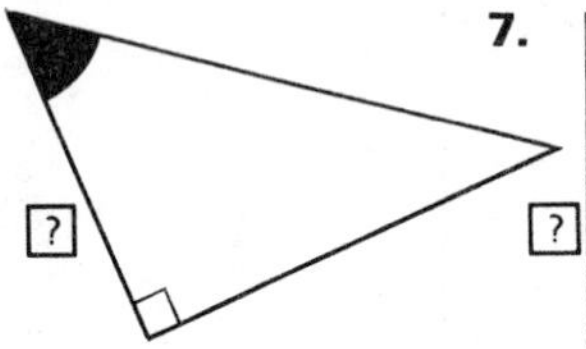

3.

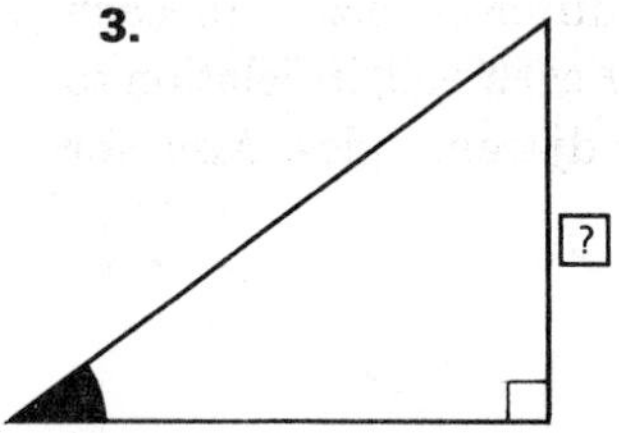

4.

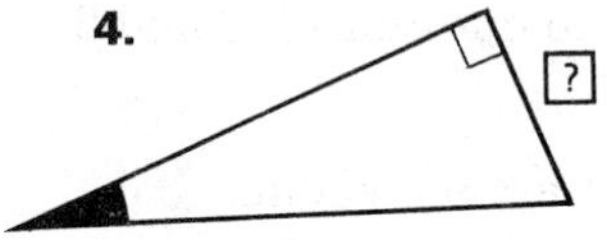

5.

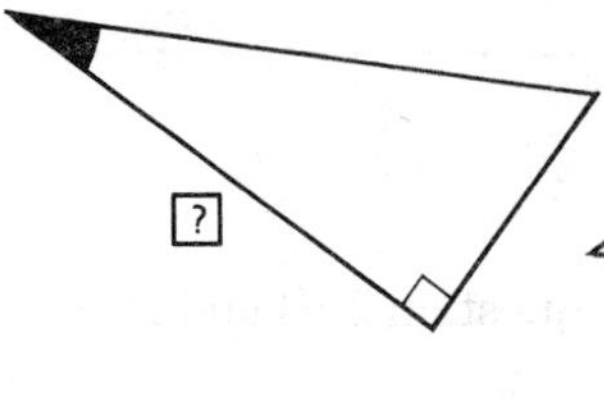

6.

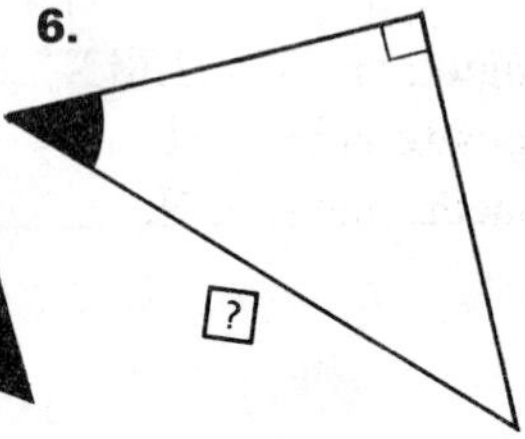

7.

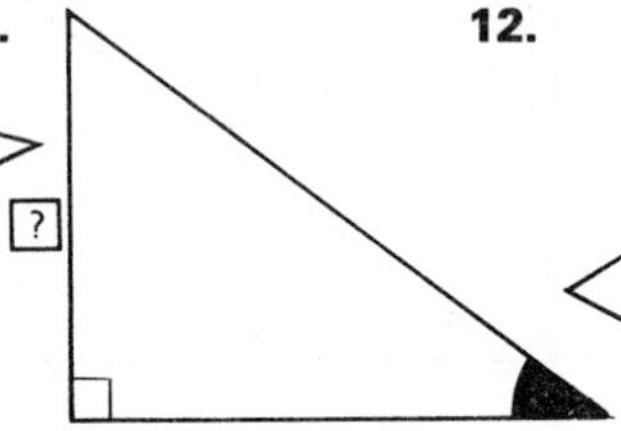

8.

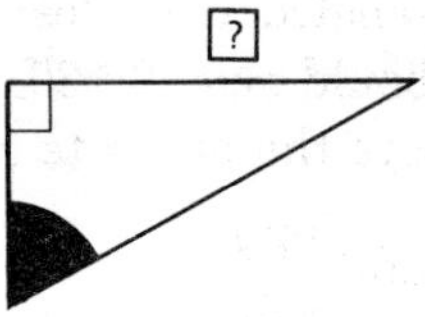

9.

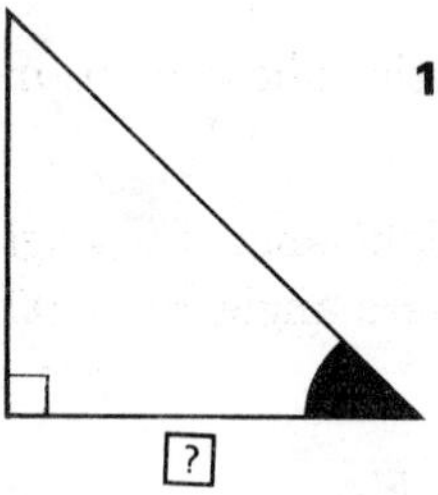

10.

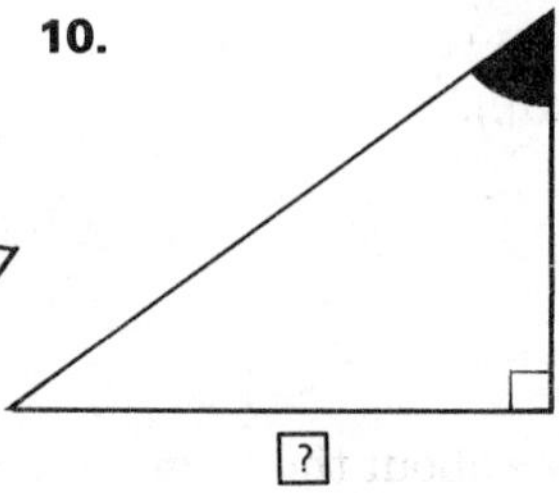

11.

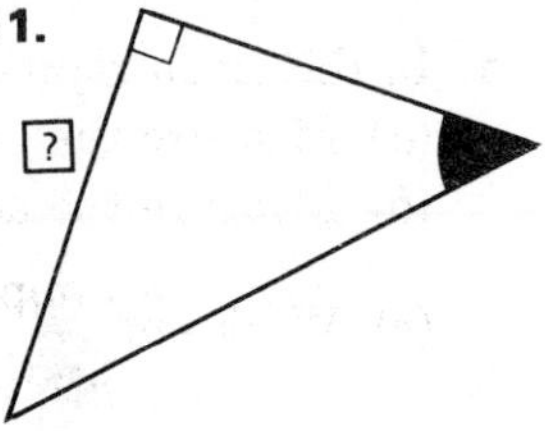

12.

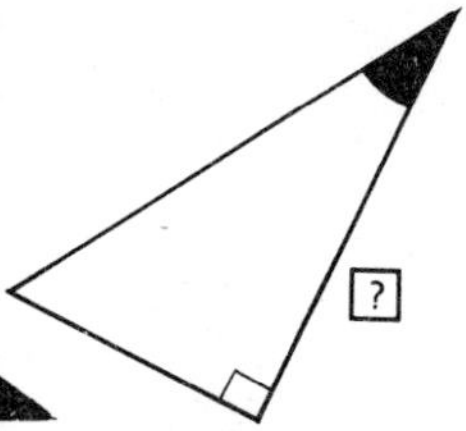

13.

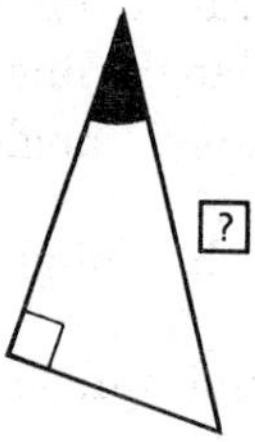

14.

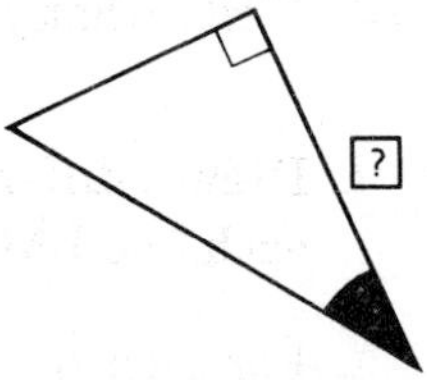

15.

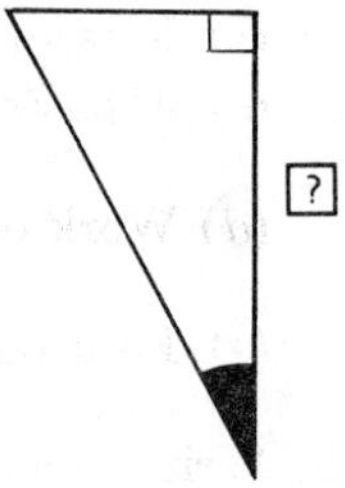

The abbreviation **opp.** is usually used for the opposite side and **adj.** for the adjacent side.

Exercise 6

A 1. In the given right-angled triangle LMN, $L\hat{N}M = 35°$.

(*a*) Measure the opposite side, LM.

(*b*) Measure the adjacent side, MN.

(*c*) Work out $\dfrac{\text{opp.}}{\text{adj.}}$

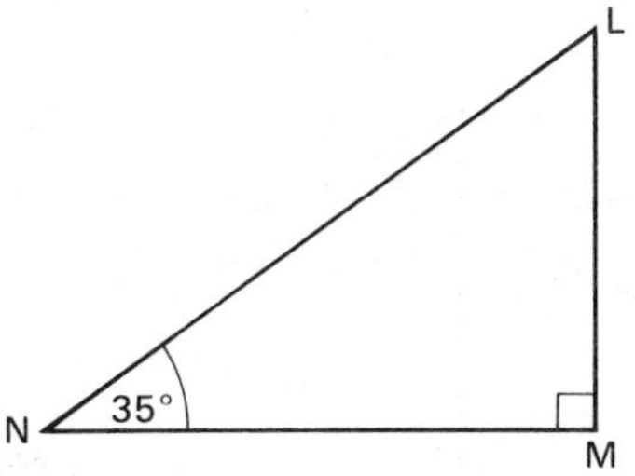

2. Draw 3 more right-angled triangles, all different sizes. In each triangle, one angle should measure 35°. For each one, in relation to the 35° angle, measure the opposite and adjacent sides. Also, for each triangle, work out $\dfrac{\text{opp.}}{\text{adj.}}$.

3. Find $\tan 35°$.

4. Write what you notice about your answers to questions 1, 2 and 3.

B 1. Draw 8 different right-angled triangles that are not similar. Label each one LMN where angle $M = 90°$.

2. For each triangle:

(*a*) Measure angle N.

(*b*) Measure LM (opp.)

(*c*) Measure NM (adj.).

(*d*) Work out $\dfrac{\text{opp.}}{\text{adj.}}$.

(*e*) Find $\tan \hat{N}$.

3. Write what you notice about the answers to question 2(*d*) and 2(*e*).

From Exercise 6, you should have discovered that for any right-angled triangle:

$$\tan\theta = \frac{\text{opp.}}{\text{adj.}}$$

We usually simply write:

$$\tan = \frac{\text{opp.}}{\text{adj.}}$$

Exercise 7

In each right-angled triangle, find the required angle giving each answer in degrees (correct to one decimal place):

e.g. Find angle *R*.

In right-angled $\triangle PQR$:

since $\tan = \dfrac{\text{opp.}}{\text{adj.}}$

$$\tan \hat{R} = \frac{PQ}{QR} = \frac{5}{4} = 1.25$$

since $\tan \hat{R} = 1.25$

$\hat{R} = \underline{\underline{51.3°}}$ (1 d.p.)

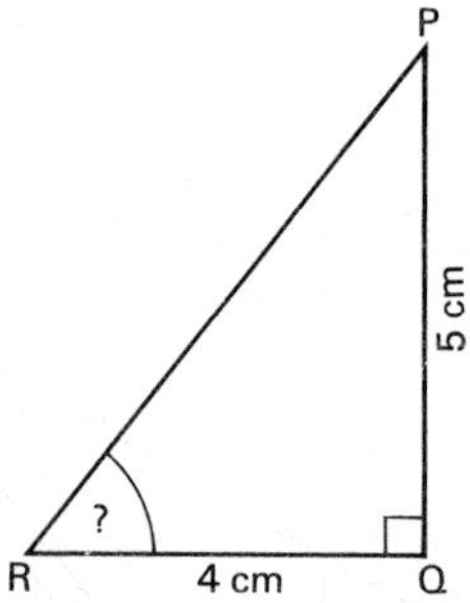

1.

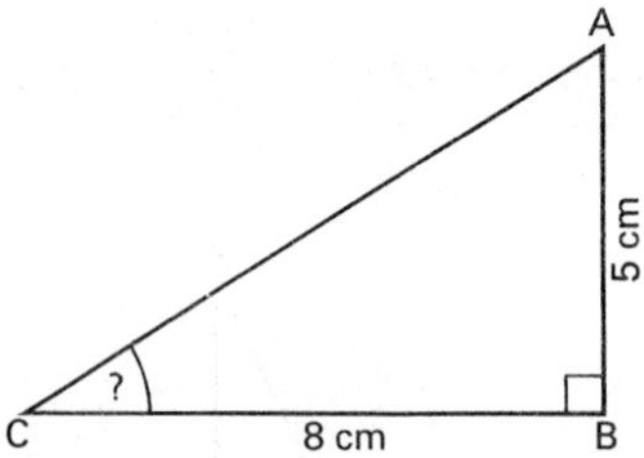

2.

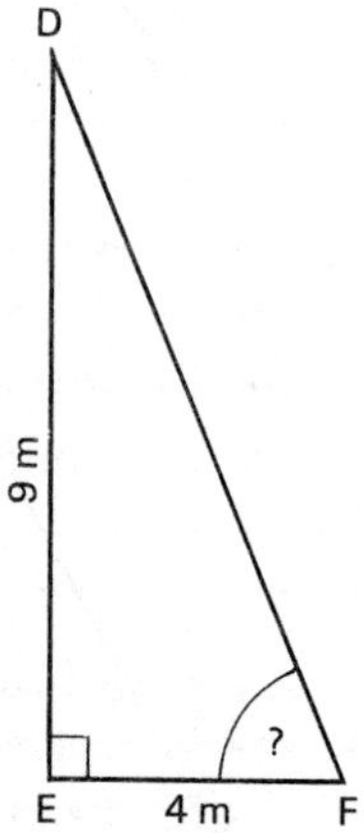

3.

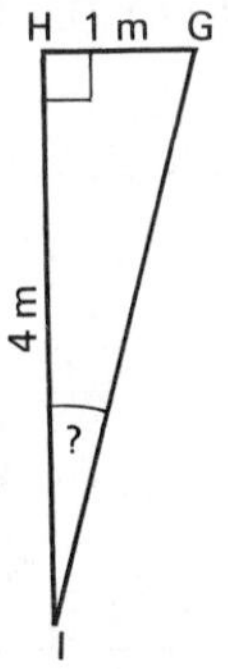
H
1 m
G
4 m
?
I

4.

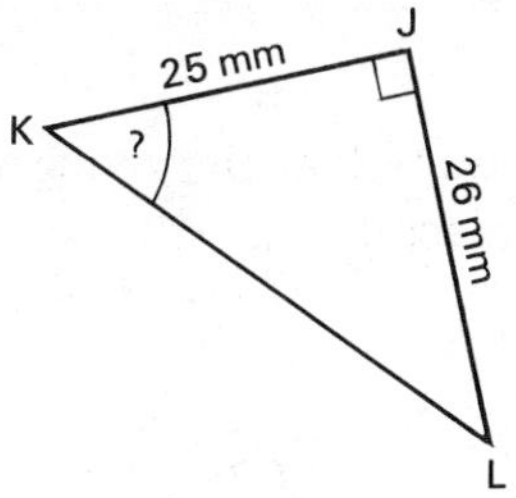
J
25 mm
K
?
26 mm
L

5.

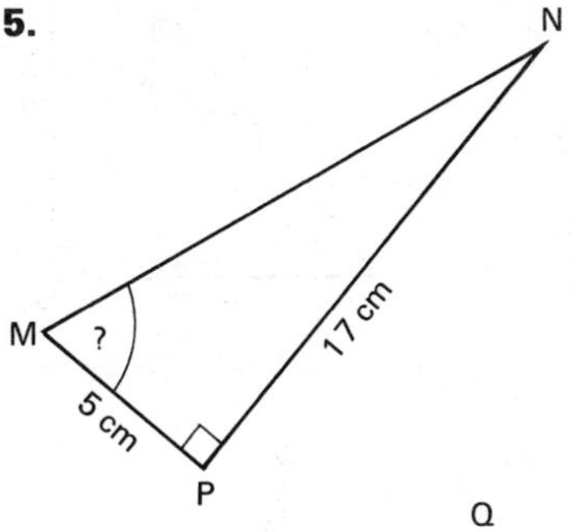
N
M
?
17 cm
5 cm
P

6.

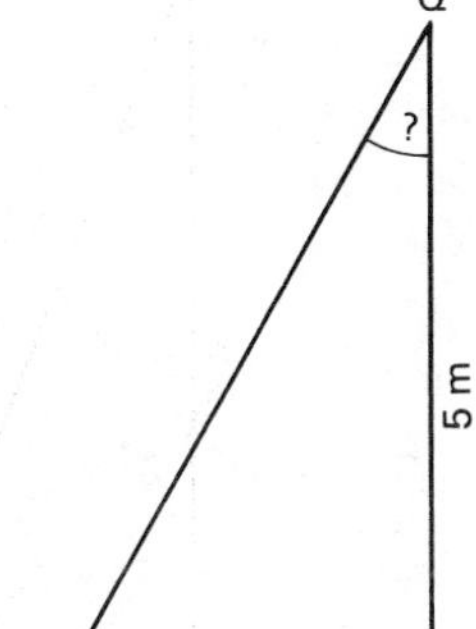
Q
?
5 m
S
1 m
R

7.

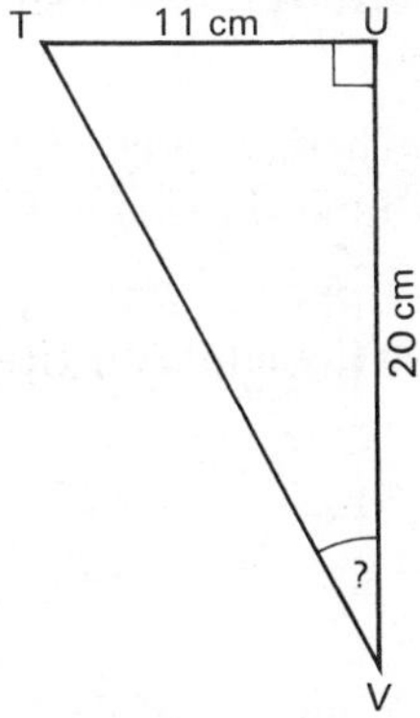
T
11 cm
U
20 cm
?
V

8.

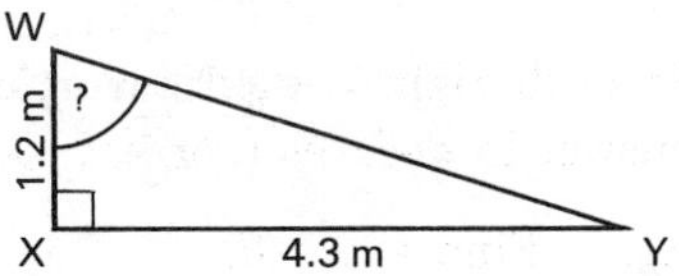
W
?
1.2 m
X
4.3 m
Y

9.

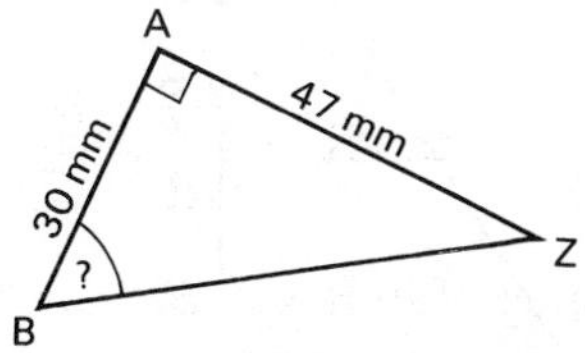
A
47 mm
30 mm
?
Z
B

10.

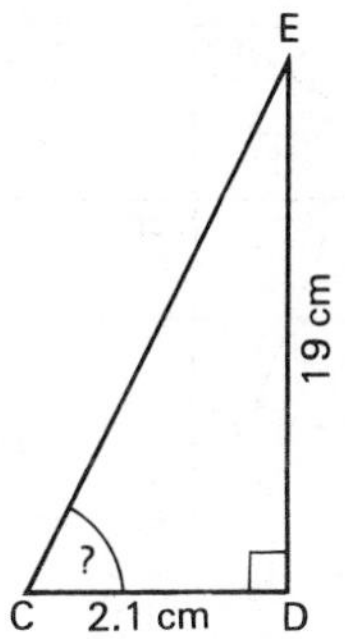
E
19 cm
?
C
2.1 cm
D

Exercise 8

In each right-angled triangle, find the required side giving answers correct to three significant figures:

e.g. Find side BC in the given triangle.
In right-angled $\triangle ABC$,

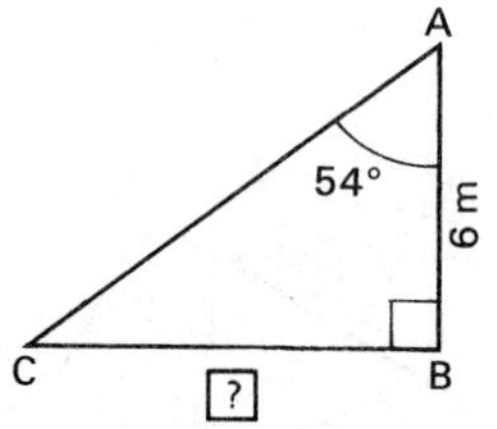

$$\text{since} \quad \tan = \frac{\text{opp.}}{\text{adj.}}$$

$$\tan 54° = \frac{BC}{6}$$

$$\text{so} \quad BC = 6 \tan 54°$$

$$BC = \underline{\underline{8.26\text{ m}}} \quad (3\text{ s.f.})$$

1.

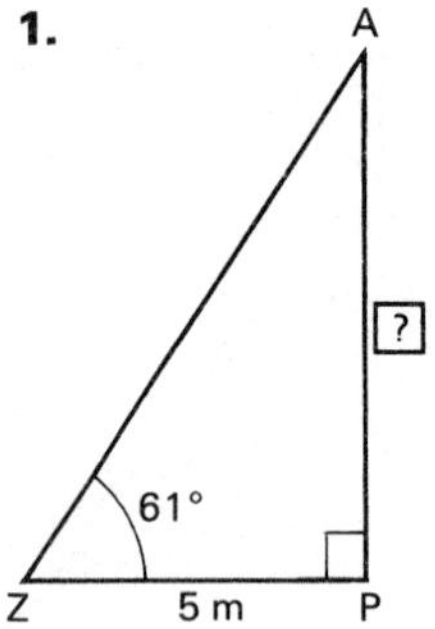

3.

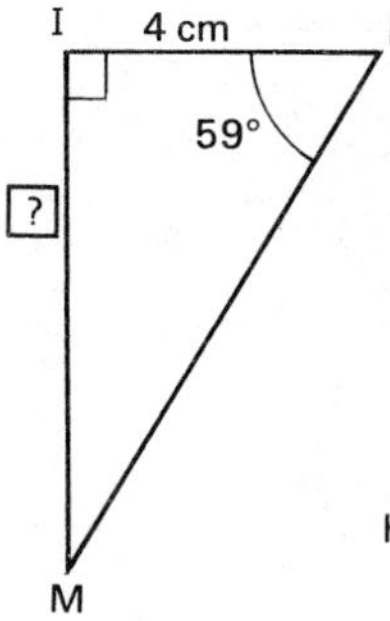

5.

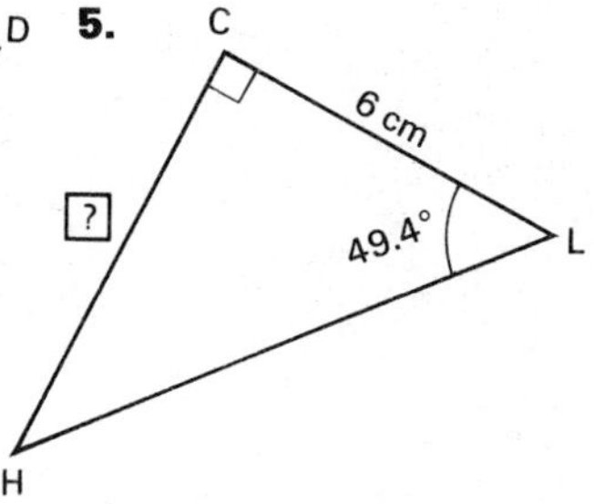

2.

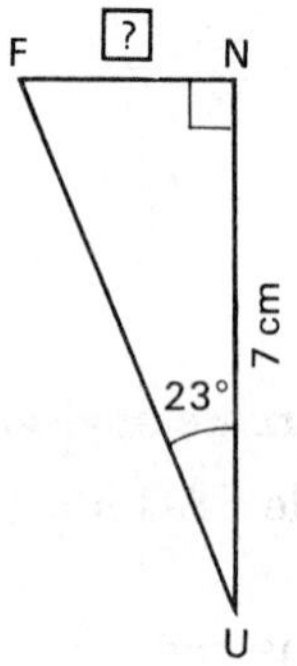

4.

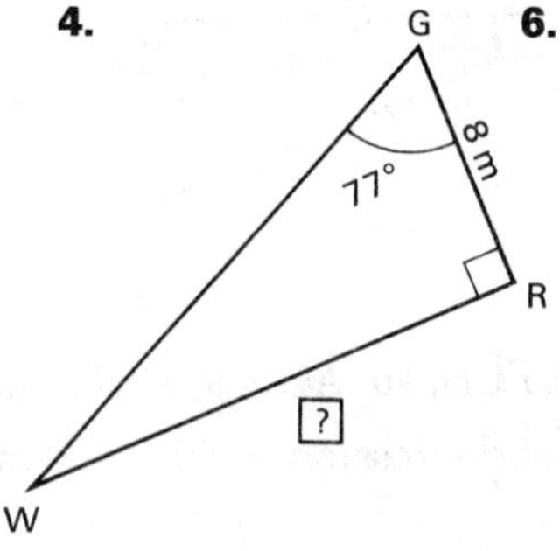

6.

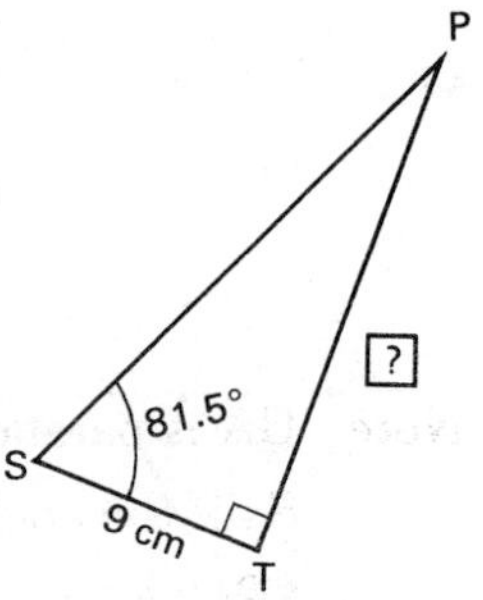

7.

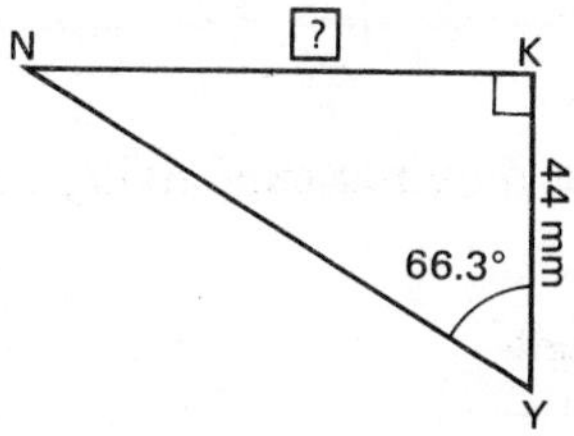

9.

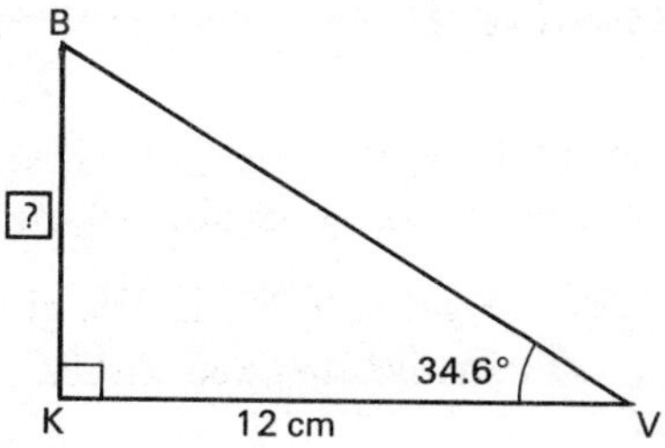

8.

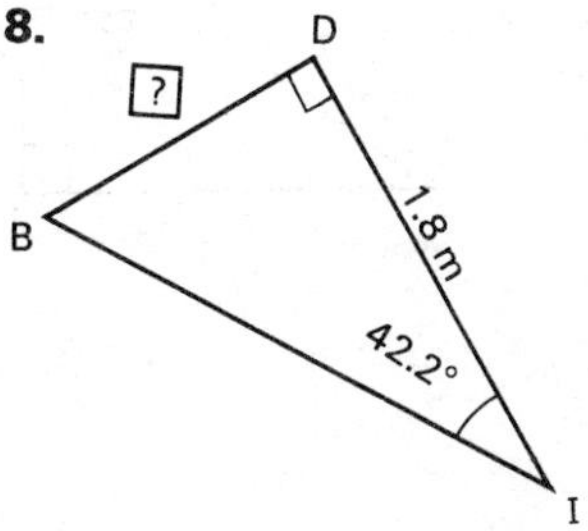

10.

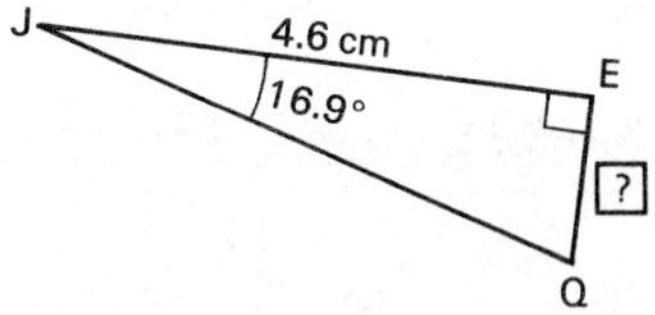

Reminder: The Angle of Depression

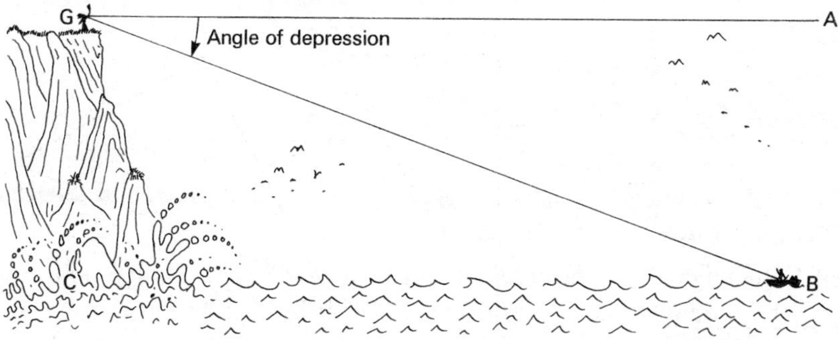

The above can be shown in a small sketch using only straight lines. The sketch is lettered in the same way as the original drawing.

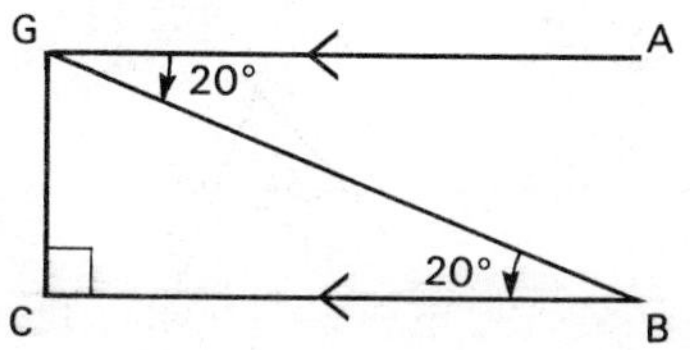

Note GA is parallel to CB, so $A\hat{G}B = C\hat{B}G$ (alternate angles).

So if the angle of depression $= 20°$, the angle CBG must also equal $20°$.

Note also that angle $CGB = 90° - 20° = 70°$.

Exercise 9

Referring to the diagram below find $C\hat{B}G$ and $C\hat{G}B$ if $A\hat{G}B$ is:

1. 14°
2. 27°
3. 19°
4. 61°
5. 75°
6. 6°
7. 15.6°
8. 63.7°
9. 42.3°
10. 8.4°
11. 18.2°
12. 56.8°
13. 80.9°
14. 62.1°
15. 7.5°

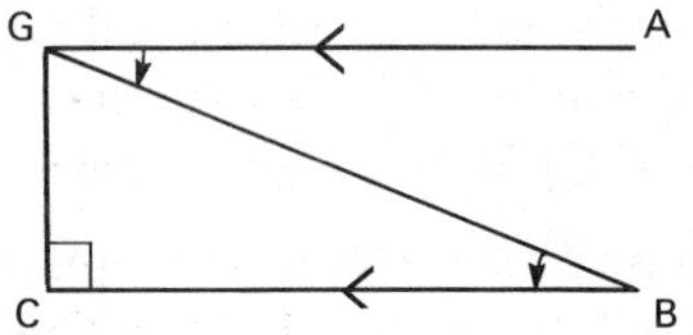

Exercise 10

In this exercise, give angles correct to one decimal place and lengths correct to three significant figures.

1. The angle of elevation of the top of a Douglas Fir from a point on the ground 40 m from the tree, is 31°. Find the height of the tree.

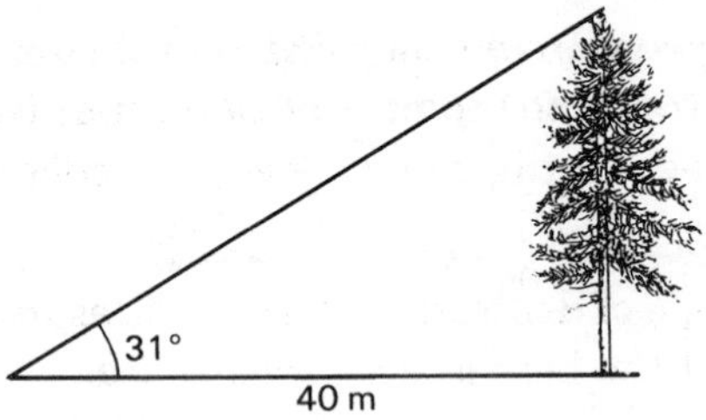

2. A point on level ground is 30 m from a tower. The angle of elevation of the top of the tower from that point is 57°. Calculate the height of the tower.

3. The height of a radio mast built in Rugby in 1925 was 250 m. Calculate the angle of elevation of the top of the mast from a point at ground level that is 125 m from the mast.

4. Using the information given in the diagram, calculate the width of the river.

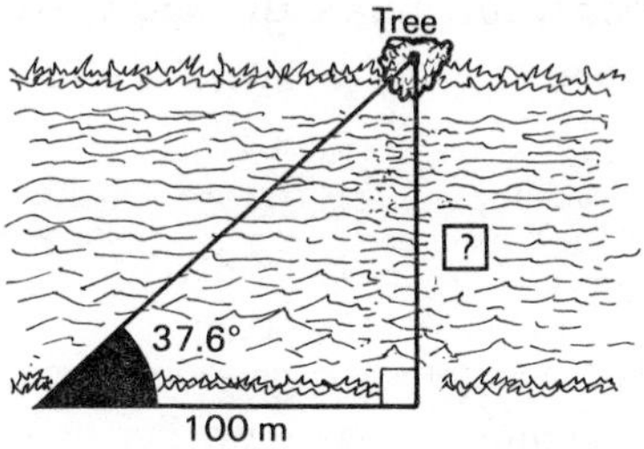

5. A ladder is placed against a vertical wall so that is reaches 4.2 m up the wall. If its foot is on level ground and 2 m from the wall:
(*a*) Find the angle the ladder makes with the ground.
(*b*) Find the length of the ladder (use Pythagoras' theorem).

6. The angle of elevation of the top of a telegraph pole from a point on level ground 2.44 m from the pole is 72.8°. Calculate the height of the pole.

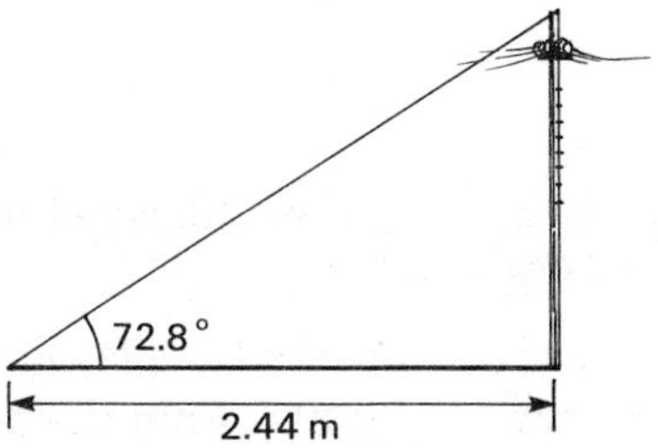

7. The angle of depression of a boat that is 400 m out to sea is 28° when measured from the top edge of the cliff at Great Hangman Hill, near Coombe Martin, North Devon. Calculate the height of the cliff.

8. Calculate the angle of depression of a boat measured from the top of a 145 m cliff if the boat is 300 m out to sea.

9. The angle of elevation of the top of the TV antenna on the Eiffel Tower is 69.8° when measured from a point on the ground that is 118 m from the tower. Calculate the height of the tower to the top of the TV antenna.

10. From the top of a tower, the angle of depression of a point on the ground is 41.7°. If the point is 110 m from the foot of the tower, then calculate the height of the tower.

Making and Using a Clinometer

A clinometer can be used to measure angles of elevation and depression. The instructions for making one are given in Exercise 11.

Exercise 11

You need a piece of stiff card measuring about 18 cm by 10 cm, a straw, a piece of thread, a 'weight' such as a washer or a mint with a hole, Sellotape, a ruler, pencil, protractor and pair of compasses.

1. On the piece of card, draw a straight line 1 cm from a long edge and parallel to that edge.

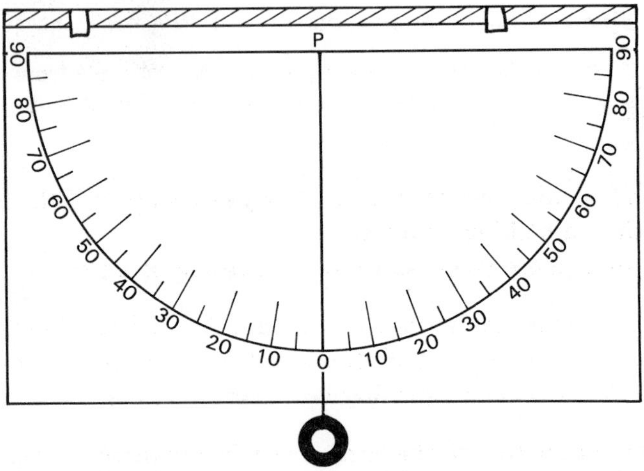

2. Mark the mid-point of that line, P.

3. With that mid-point as centre, draw a semi-circle having a radius of 8 cm.

4. Mark angles on it as shown, marking every 5°.
Note A clinometer is numbered from the centre, unlike a protractor.

5. Make a small hole at P and fasten the piece of thread to the card at P. The weight should be hung on the other end of the thread.

6. With the Sellotape, stick the straw to the edge of the card as shown.

The clinometer is now ready for use.

Exercise 12

A

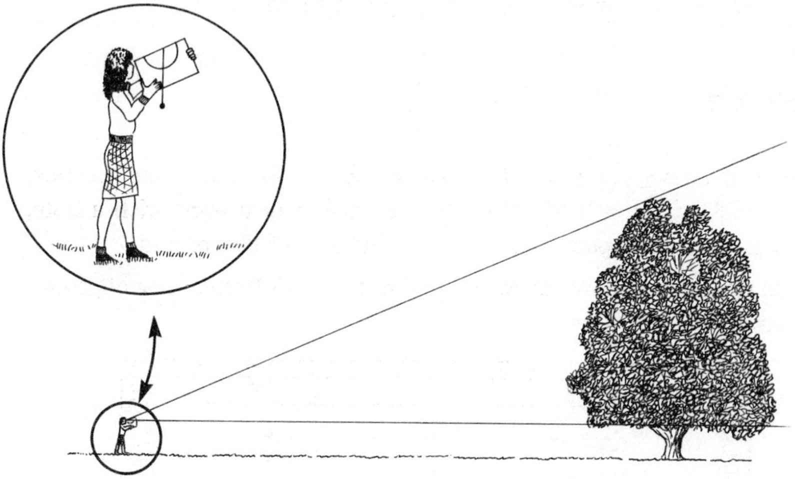

1. Stand at a distance from something you wish to find the height of (such as a building or a tree).
   Let us suppose you wish to find the height of a tree.
2. Hold the clinometer with the straw at the top. Turn the clinometer upwards until you can see the top of the tree through the straw. The thread should hang downwards crossing the scale.
3. Ask someone to read the angle shown by the thread on the scale of the clinometer. This angle is the angle of elevation of the top of the tree.

   Angle a is the angle read on the scale.

   Now $a + b = 90°$

   and $e + b = 90°$

   so angle a = angle e,
   Angle e is the angle of elevation, hence, angle a gives the size of the angle of elevation.

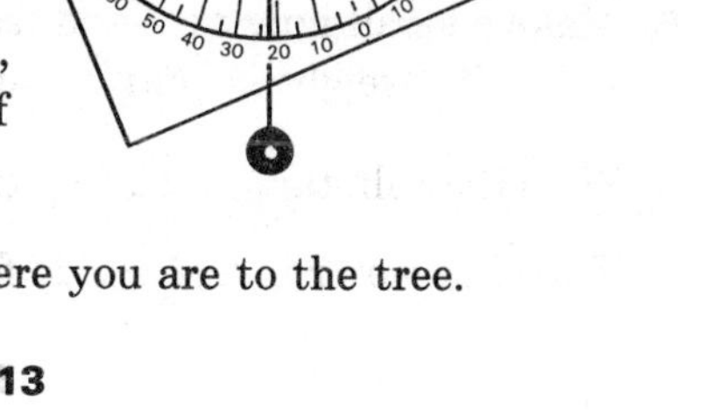

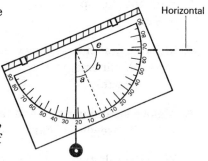

4. Measure the distance from where you are to the tree.

5. Measure the distance from the ground to your eye level.

6. The height of the tree can now be found as in the following example: Suppose the distance from the ground to your eye level is 1.5 m, that the angle of elevation is 35° and that you are 30 m from the tree. In the diagram, UA stands for you and TB stands for the tree. UL and AB are horizontal so ULBA is a rectangle.

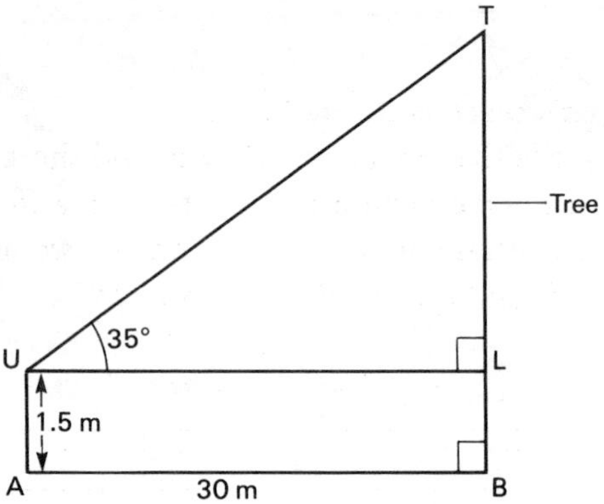

LB = UA = 1.5 m and UL = AB = 30 m

In right-angled △ULT,

since $\tan = \dfrac{\text{opp.}}{\text{adj.}}$

$$\tan 35° = \frac{TL}{30}$$

$$TL = 30 \tan 35°$$

$$TL = 30 \times 0.7002$$

$$TL = 21.00$$

so $TB = 21.00 + 1.5 = 22.50$

The height of the tree = <u>22.5 m</u> (3 s.f.).

B Use your clinometer to help you to find the heights of several buildings and trees.

27 Statistics

Exercise 1

1. A 'A woman's place is in the home.'
B 'If a couple both earn money, they should share the housework.'
C 'Men and women should be paid the same for the same job.'
D 'Washing clothes should still be done by women.'
E 'Cooking should still be done by women.'

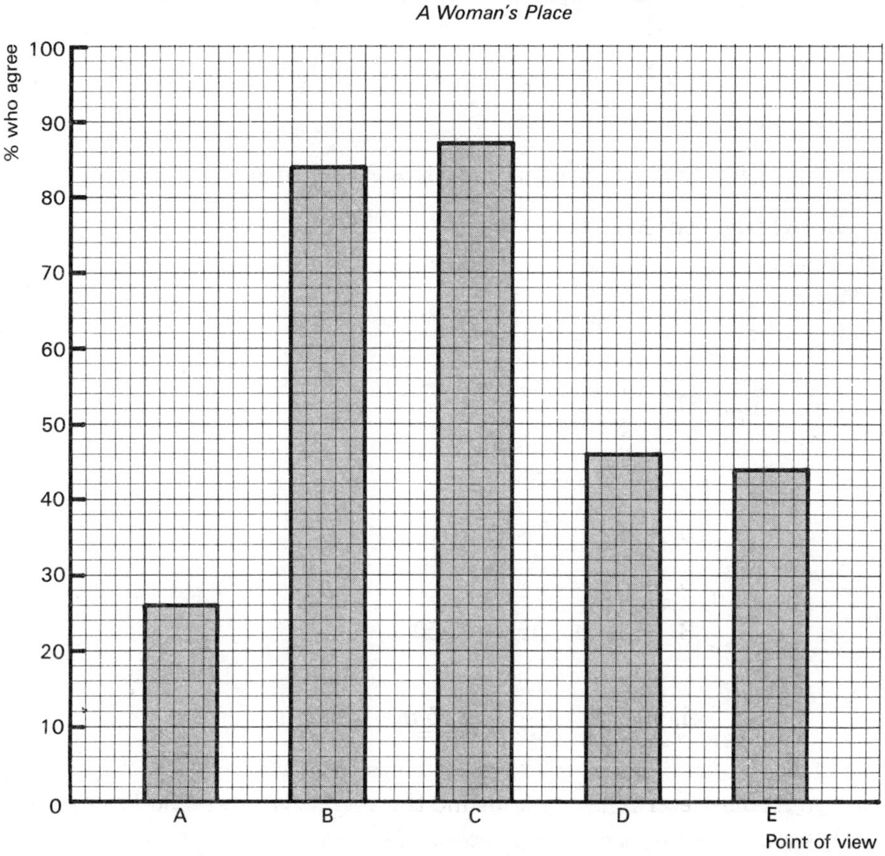

In a survey, the statements on the previous page were made to a number of young people and it was noted whether or not they agreed. The percentage who agreed with each statement was calculated.

The bar chart on the previous page shows the results.

Use the graph to help you with these questions:

(*a*) What percentage think that a woman's place is in the home?

(*b*) What percentage think that men and women should be paid the same for the same job?

(*c*) What percentage think that women should do the cooking?

(*d*) Why do the percentages total to more than 100%?

(*e*) If 500 people gave complete answers in the survey, work out the number who hold each point of view.

2. (*a*) Carry out the same survey, 'A Woman's Place', for the pupils in your class.

(*b*) Draw a bar chart showing the results of the survey on your class.

Exercise 2

A survey was carried out on the reasons for absence or for late arrival at school during a certain week.

Percentages were calculated. Here are some figures:

Overslept	28%
Went to the doctor (or dentist)	9%
Maths test (only admitted by some)	3%
Flu	?
Cough or cold	40%
Broken arm (or neck or heart)	5%
Forgot book 3G (went home for it)	2%

1. What percentage had flu?

2. Draw a bar chart to show the above results.
Make each column 1 cm wide.
For the percentages, use a scale of 2 cm to 5%.

Exercise 3 **R**

A The average heights of several trees are shown in the pictogram.

Average Height of Some Trees

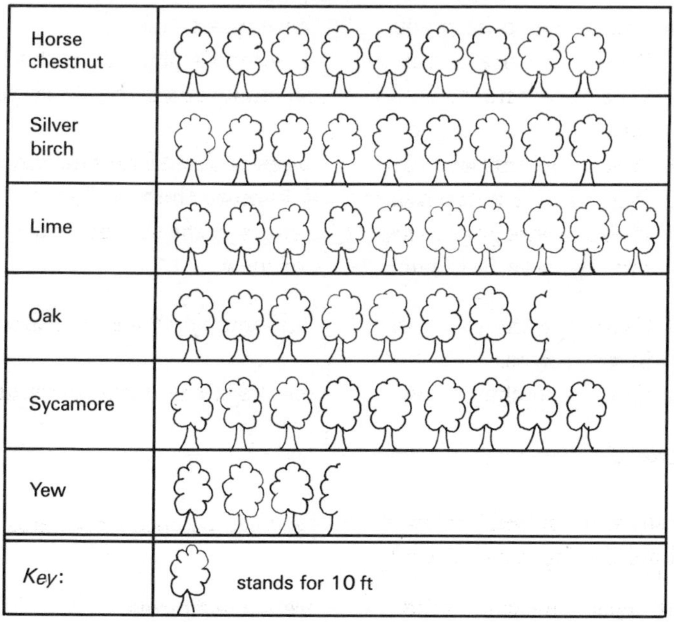

Answer these questions using the above pictogram.

1. Find the height of the sycamore.
2. Find the difference in height between the tallest and smallest trees shown.
3. Which tree has an average height of about 75 ft?
4. To convert feet into metres, multiply the number of feet by 0.3048. Using a calculator, change the height of each of the six trees into metres (to three significant figures).

B 1. Find, to the nearest half hour, how much sleep each member of your class had last night.

2. Show the results on a pictogram. Invent your own symbol to stand for a certain number of people. List the various hours of sleep down the left-hand side of your page.

Exercise 4 R

A The pie chart shows the different hair colourings in a group of 72 people.

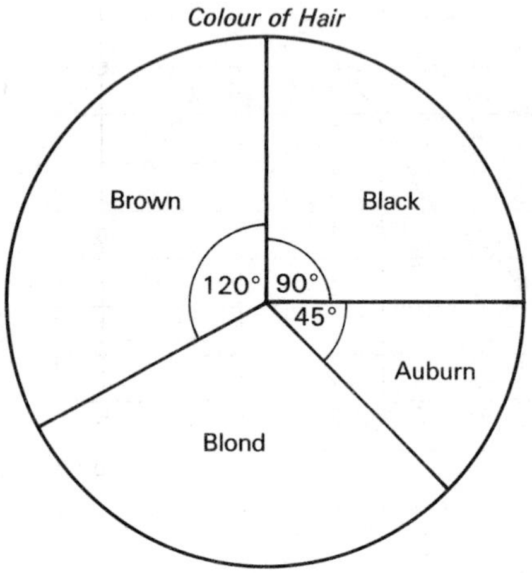

1. How many people have black hair?

2. How many have auburn hair?

3. How many have brown hair?

4. (*a*) What number of degrees should the blond sector have?
   (*b*) How many blonds are there?

B Out of 240 people who ate a school dinner, 90 had beefburgers, 80 had sausages and 70 had fish fingers. Show this on a pie chart.

Exercise 5

1. Jagged-line graphs can be used to compare several lots of information. To do this, the information should be shown on the same diagram.

   The graph opposite compares the monthly temperatures in Lisbon and Manchester.

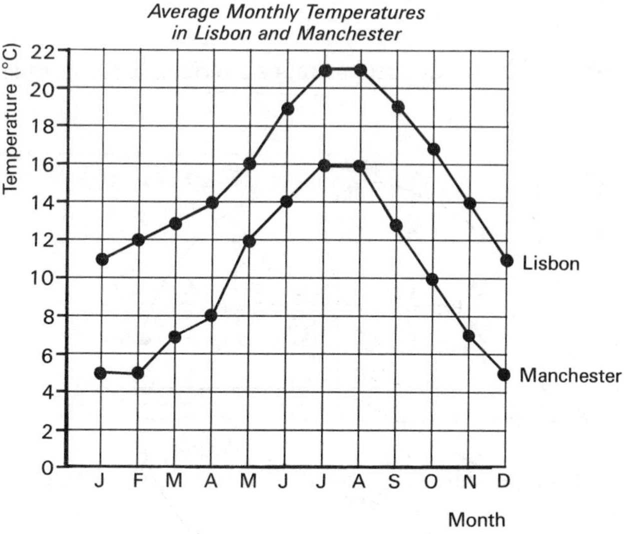

It may help you to answer these questions:

(*a*) Which place is usually warmer?

(*b*) Which are the coldest months in Lisbon?

(*c*) The temparature is 12 °C during two different months in Manchester and Lisbon. Find those two months.

(*d*) What is the difference in temperature between Lisbon and Manchester in September?

(*e*) Find the maximum average temperature in both places.

(*f*) During which month is the temperature in Lisbon exactly twice that in Manchester?

(*g*) During which months is the difference in temperature at these places greatest?

(*h*) During which month is the difference in temperature at these places least?

(*i*) In which country is Lisbon?

2. Here are the average monthly temperatures in Wellington, New Zealand:

Month	Jan	Feb	Mar	Apr	May	June	July	Aug	Sept	Oct	Nov	Dec
Temperature (°C)	17	17	15	13	11	10	9	9	11	12	13	15

Draw, on the same diagram, graphs to compare the average temperatures of Wellington and Manchester.

Frequency Distribution

The number of coins in the pockets or purses of 50 people is given below:

3	2	6	1	5	7	2	3	0	6
4	1	1	5	8	6	1	2	7	2
8	5	0	6	9	7	3	9	2	3
4	8	6	7	1	2	9	1	4	5
7	2	3	6	4	5	5	6	3	5

The data above is called *raw data* because it has not been sorted into any order.

When we sort the data into order by forming a table, we are constructing a *frequency distribution.*

Exercise 6 **M**

1. Construct a frequency distribution from the raw data given above. Use the class intervals 0–1, 2–3, 4–5, 6–7, 8–9. Set out the frequency table as follows.

Number of coins	Tally	Frequency
0–1		
2–3		
4–5		
6–7		
8–9		

2. What is the range of the number of coins?

Histograms*

In a bar chart, the height of each rectangular bar shows the frequency, but in a histogram, the area of each rectangle shows the frequency. This was mentioned in book 2G, Chapter 20, where histograms were drawn.

If for the frequency distribution below, □ stands for 1 coin, then the first 2 columns would be as shown in the diagram on the left.

However, we do not normally draw lots of small blocks but draw rectangular columns instead.

The diagram on the right shows the first two columns of a properly drawn histogram.

Since all the columns have the same width, the histogram looks similar to a bar chart. Further details about histograms are given in the glossary.

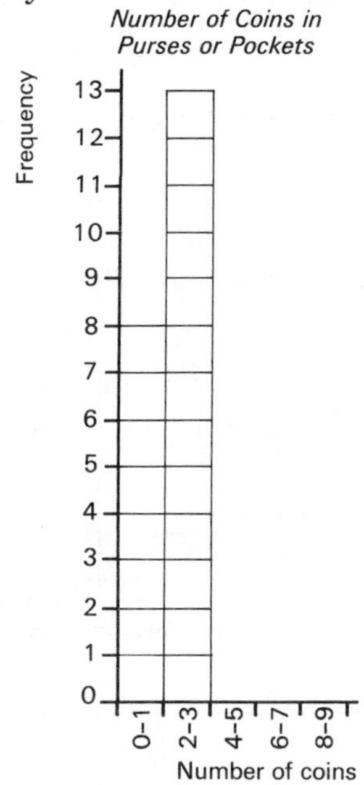

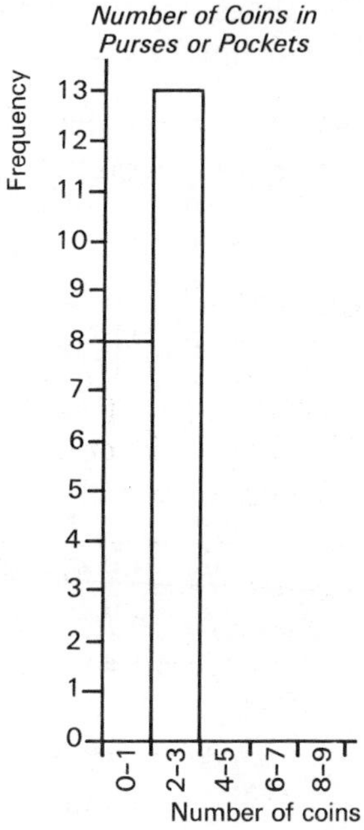

Exercise 7 **R**

1. (*a*) Draw a histogram for the frequency distribution on coins constructed in Exercise 6. Make each column 2 cm wide and for the frequency use 1 cm per unit.
   (*b*) Which is the modal class for this frequency distribution?

* See the glossary, p. 384

2. A survey of the number of children in a family was taken. Here are the results:

2	3	1	2	2	0	5	2	2	4
4	2	4	0	3	3	2	1	3	2
1	2	2	1	2	2	1	3	2	3
0	1	1	2	3	2	3	0	5	0

(*a*) Construct a frequency distribution.
(*b*) Draw a histogram. Each column should be 1 cm wide. For the frequency, use 1 cm per unit.
(*c*) Which is the mode?

3. The times of several runners who ran a marathon were (to the nearest minute):

3 h 24 min	4 h 10 min	2 h 38 min	2 h 46 min	3 h 18 min
4 h 56 min	3 h 45 min	5 h 8 min	3 h 17 min	4 h 19 min
3 h 47 min	3 h 31 min	2 h 19 min	3 h 19 min	5 h 36 min
4 h 39 min	3 h 29 min	3 h 23 min	4 h 50 min	3 h 32 min
3 h 35 min	3 h 10 min	4 h 49 min	2 h 40 min	3 h 56 min
5 h 2 min	4 h 32 min	5 h 15 min	3 h 38 min	4 h 13 min
3 h 19 min	2 h 27 min	3 h 27 min	4 h 33 min	3 h 29 min
3 h 44 min	4 h 3 min	3 h 41 min	3 h 44 min	3 h 11 min
3 h 52 min	4 h 52 min	2 h 55 min	4 h 5 min	4 h 1 min
4 h 6 min	3 h 9 min	3 h 47 min	4 h 12 min	3 h 26 min
5 h 14 min	4 h 25 min	3 h 35 min	4 h 16 min	4 h 22 min
2 h 59 min	5 h 48 min	4 h 39 min	3 h 59 min	4 h 23 min

(*a*) Construct a frequency distribution. Use the class intervals:
2 h–2 h 30 min
2 h 30 min–3 h
3 h–3 h 30 min
3 h 30 min–4 h
4 h–4 h 30 m
4 h 30 min–5 h
5 h–5 h 30 min
5 h 30 min–6 h
(*b*) Draw a histogram. Each column should be 2 cm wide. For the frequency, use 1 cm per unit.
(*c*) Which is the modal class?

4. Carry out a survey of head sizes for pupils in your class (including yourself). Use a tape to measure around each person's head finding the measurements *correct to the nearest centimetre*. Draw a tally chart to collect the data. The headings for the tally chart could be:

Head size (cm)	Tally	Frequency

Draw a histogram of the distribution and find the modal class.

Exercise 8 **R**

Find the mode, median and mean of:

A
1. 2, 2, 4, 5, 7
2. 4, 6, 6, 6, 8
3. 1, 1, 2, 4, 4, 4, 5
4. 1, 4, 4, 6, 7, 8
5. 6, 6, 10, 18
6. 5, 7, 7, 9
7. 1, 2, 3, 2, 4, 2, 3, 3
8. 32, 37, 37, 39, 40
9. 57, 64, 72, 43, 64
10. 92, 98, 96, 92
11. 42, 43, 46, 45, 42, 46
12. 72, 73, 76, 75, 72, 76

B
1. 10 m, 9 m, 5 m, 10 m, 6 m
2. £3, £4, £5, £6, £4, £3, £3
3. 4 km, 4 km, 4 km, 4 km
4. 5 kg, 9 kg, 5 kg, 5 kg
5. 1 gal, 10 gal, 1 gal, 4 gal
6. 51 ℓ, 43 ℓ, 48 ℓ, 44 ℓ, 48 ℓ, 45 ℓ, 43 ℓ
7. 12 cm, 33 cm, 25 cm, 33 cm, 52 cm
8. 910 g, 280 g, 730 g, 450 g, 860 g, 520 g, 730 g

Exercise 9

1. A darts player scored: 60, 20, 1, 6, 19, 40, 20, 18 and 20 with nine darts. Find:
   (*a*) the mode, (*b*) the median, (*c*) the mean.
2. Three pieces of wood measure 1.3 m, 1.4 m and 0.9 m. Find the mean (average) length.

3. A salesman travelled 160 miles on one day and 124 miles on the next. Calculate the mean distance for the two days.

4. The number of hours of television watched last night (to the nearest hour) by 8 people was: 1, 3, 5, 2, 1, 4, 3, 1. Find:
(*a*) the mode, (*b*) the median, (*c*) the mean.

5. A golfer scored: 69, 72, 71, 75, 72 in five rounds of golf. Find:
(*a*) the mode, (*b*) the median, (*c*) the mean.

6. A baby's high chair is tested for safety in several ways. One test is used to find the force needed to make the high chair tip.

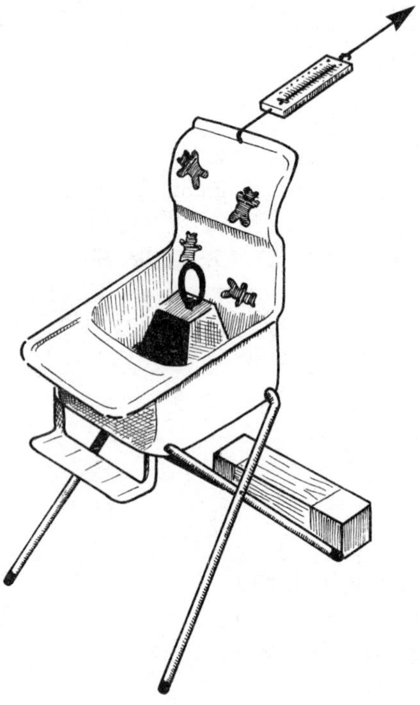

A piece of wood is placed behind two feet to prevent slipping; something having about the same mass as a baby is placed on the chair seat and a newtonmeter is attached as shown. The newtonmeter is pulled horizontally until the chair begins to tip. At that moment a reading is taken and recorded. The experiment is carried out several times (the chair is tested in all four directions and three separate readings are taken in each direction). The median of the three readings is noted for each direction.

Here are the readings (in newtons) for a particular high chair. For each group of three readings, find the median:

	Reading 1	Reading 2	Reading 3	Median
Back	79	76	78	?
Front	60	55	55	?
Right side	59	59	58	?
Left side	58	56	59	?

7. A family used three suitcases to go on holiday. The masses were 19.6 kg, 18.5 kg and 20.3 kg. Calculate the mean mass (correct to three significant figures).

8. A snooker player scored breaks of:

127, 49, 76, 58, 84, 94 and 55.

Find:

(*a*) the median score,

(*b*) the mean score (to the nearest whole number).

9. In a certain exam there were two papers. A candidate had to average 45 to pass. Did Gerald pass if he got 56% on paper 1 and 35% on paper 2?

10. In the Weights and Measures Act it is stated that bread should be baked to a certain mean (average) weight. Bakeries usually weigh some sample pieces of dough (at least 10 every 15 min – by law) rather than weigh the final loaves. In baking an 800 g large white loaf the piece of dough (the doughpiece) needs to be about 100 g heavier, since about 70 g is lost at the baking stage and 30 g while cooling.

Here are the masses of 16 doughpieces (in grams):

912, 912, 916, 912, 906, 900, 897, 903, 898, 894, 904, 905, 902, 898, 903, 903

(*a*) Calculate the mean mass.

(*b*) If the firm's target was 903 g, how many grams higher was their average?

Probability

Exercise 10 R

1. In throwing an ordinary die, what is the probability of getting the following?

(*a*) a 6,
(*b*) a 2,
(*c*) an 8,
(*d*) a 1 or a 2,
(*e*) more than a 4,
(*f*) a factor of 6,
(*g*) a square number,
(*h*) anything other than a 6?

2. A spinner has only the numbers 1, 2, 3, 4 and 5 on it. What is the probability of getting a 3?

3. A spinner has the numbers 1, 2, 2, 2, 2, 4, 4 and 5 on it. What is the probability of getting:

(*a*) a 2?
(*b*) an even number?
(*c*) an odd number?
(*d*) a 3?
(*e*) a number bigger than 2?
(*f*) anything but a 4?

4. One of the hexagonal spinners used on p. 148 (shown again below) has four equals signs on it. What is the probability of obtaining an equals sign?

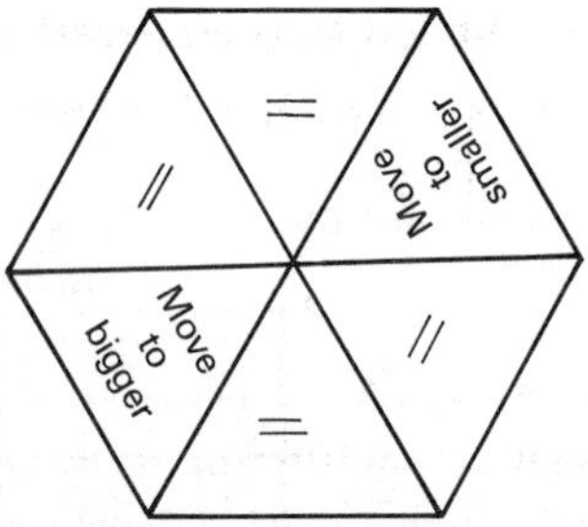

5. Out of 20 girls and 12 boys, one person was chosen at *random* (that is, each person has the same chance of being chosen). What is the probability of:

(*a*) a boy being chosen?
(*b*) a girl being chosen?

6. A box contains two 3-amp, seven 5-amp and nine 13-amp fuses. If one fuse is taken out of the box at random:

(*a*) What is the probability that it is a 13-amp fuse?
(*b*) What is the probability that it is a 5-amp fuse?
(*c*) What is the probability that it is a 3-amp fuse?
(*d*) Which type of fuse are you most likely to have picked out?

7. There are 10 identical batteries in a box. Unfortunately, 4 of them are dead. If you take one of the batteries out of the box, what is the probability that it is a dead one?

8. Out of the set of letters {c, h, e, m, i, s, t, r, y} one letter is selected at random:

(*a*) What is the probability that it is a vowel?
(*b*) What is the probability that it is a consonant?
(*c*) Which type of letter is most likely to be chosen?

9. Out of the set of letters {a, e, i, o, u} one letter is selected at random:

(*a*) What is the probability that it is a vowel?
(*b*) What is the probability that it is a consonant?

10. If the probability of rain is $\frac{2}{7}$, what is the probability that there will be no rain?

11. A pack of 52 ordinary playing cards is cut. It is decided that Roger wins if it is a picture card but Margaret wins if it is a number card. Who is more likely to win?

12. The graph shows the mass of a number of pupils in a certain form. Each mass has been rounded to the nearest kilogram.

A test was given. What is the probability that the person who was top in the test weighed from:

(*a*) 52 to 56 kg?
(*b*) 47 to 51 kg?
(*c*) less than 42 kg?
(*d*) 42 to 46 kg?
(*e*) over 56 kg?
(*f*) less than 51 kg?
(*g*) over 51 kg?
(*h*) between 42 and 56 kg?

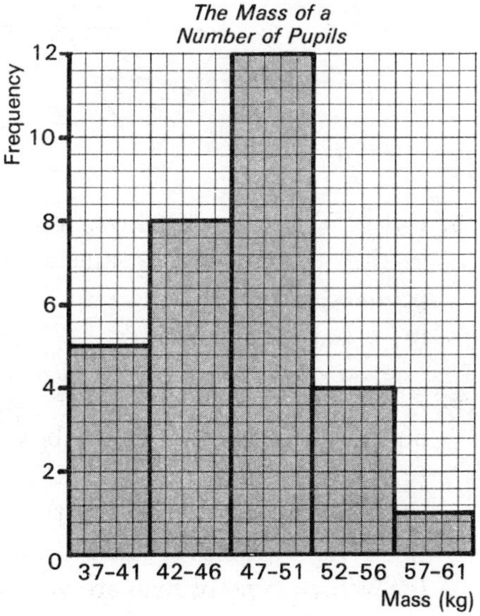

In tossing two coins there were four possible outcomes: {HH, HT, TH, TT}

This was shown in book 2G where a tree diagram was drawn (p. 356). The same set of outcomes could have been shown in a table.

The probability of two heads can be seen to be $\frac{1}{4}$ (since there is only one entry in the table for two heads).

The probability of a head and a tail $= \frac{2}{4} = \frac{1}{2}$ (there are two entries in the table).

		Second coin H	Second coin T
First coin	H	HH	HT
	T	TH	TT

Exercise 11 M

The table shows the totals obtained when two dice are thrown. Copy and complete it.

		Second die 1	2	3	4	5	6
First die	1	2			5		
	2						
	3		5				
	4						10
	5						
	6			9			12

Now use the table to help you to find the following when two dice are tossed:

1. The probability of obtaining a total of nine.

2. The probability of obtaining a total of six.

3. The probability of getting two fours.

4. The probability of getting a two and a six.

5. The total which is most likely.

6. Two totals which have a probability of $\frac{1}{12}$.

28 Vectors

Exercise 1

M

A Copy the map below on to a square grid.

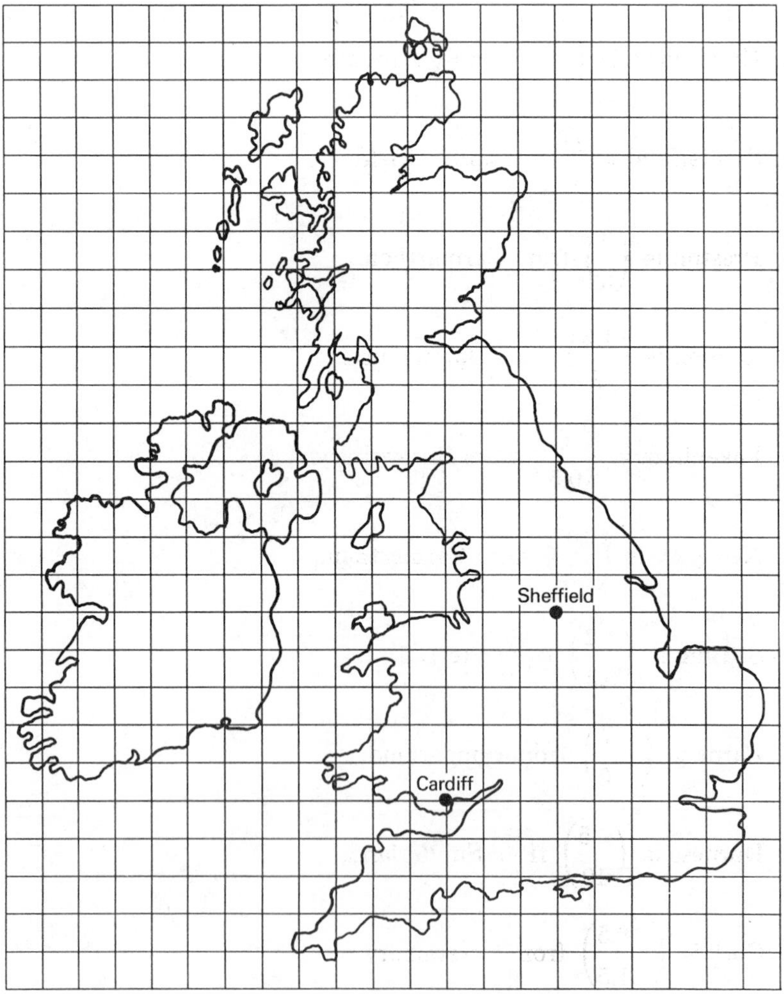

From Cardiff, Sheffield is at the end point of vector $\begin{pmatrix} 3 \\ 5 \end{pmatrix}$. Now mark the following places that are at the end points of the given vectors:

1. Shrewsbury is $\begin{pmatrix} 1 \\ 3 \end{pmatrix}$ from Cardiff.

2. Carmarthen is $\begin{pmatrix} ^{-}2 \\ 1 \end{pmatrix}$ from Cardiff.

3. Portsmouth is $\begin{pmatrix} 4 \\ ^{-}2 \end{pmatrix}$ from Cardiff.

4. Eastbourne is $\begin{pmatrix} 2 \\ 0 \end{pmatrix}$ from Portsmouth.

5. Sunderland is $\begin{pmatrix} 0 \\ 4 \end{pmatrix}$ from Sheffield.

6. Preston is $\begin{pmatrix} 3 \\ 5 \end{pmatrix}$ from Carmarthen.

7. London is $\begin{pmatrix} 1.5 \\ 2 \end{pmatrix}$ from Portsmouth.

8. Fakenham is $\begin{pmatrix} 6 \\ 0.5 \end{pmatrix}$ from Shrewsbury.

9. Newquay is $\begin{pmatrix} ^{-}1 \\ ^{-}4 \end{pmatrix}$ from Carmarthen.

10. Stirling is $\begin{pmatrix} ^{-}2 \\ 6.5 \end{pmatrix}$ from Preston.

11. Larne is $\begin{pmatrix} ^{-}7 \\ 0 \end{pmatrix}$ from Sunderland.

12. Durness is $\begin{pmatrix} ^{-}5 \\ 10 \end{pmatrix}$ from Sunderland.

13. Cork is $\begin{pmatrix} ^{-}9.5 \\ ^{-}1.5 \end{pmatrix}$ from Shrewsbury.

14. Portadown is $\begin{pmatrix} {}^{-}1 \\ {}^{-}1 \end{pmatrix}$ from Larne.

15. Isle of Arran is $\begin{pmatrix} 2 \\ 3 \end{pmatrix}$ from Portadown.

16. Castletown, Isle of Man is $\begin{pmatrix} 3 \\ {}^{-}1 \end{pmatrix}$ from Portadown.

17. Dundee is $\begin{pmatrix} 1.5 \\ 1 \end{pmatrix}$ from Stirling.

18. Castlebay, Barra is $\begin{pmatrix} {}^{-}6.5 \\ 1.5 \end{pmatrix}$ from Dundee.

B If you start at Cardiff and follow the route

$\begin{pmatrix} 1 \\ 2 \end{pmatrix}\begin{pmatrix} 3 \\ 0 \end{pmatrix}\begin{pmatrix} {}^{-}1 \\ 3 \end{pmatrix}\begin{pmatrix} 0 \\ 2 \end{pmatrix}\begin{pmatrix} {}^{-}3 \\ 4 \end{pmatrix}\begin{pmatrix} {}^{-}1 \\ 0 \end{pmatrix}\begin{pmatrix} 0 \\ 1\frac{1}{2} \end{pmatrix}$, where do you arrive?

Exercise 2

A Name each vector and give its length and direction:

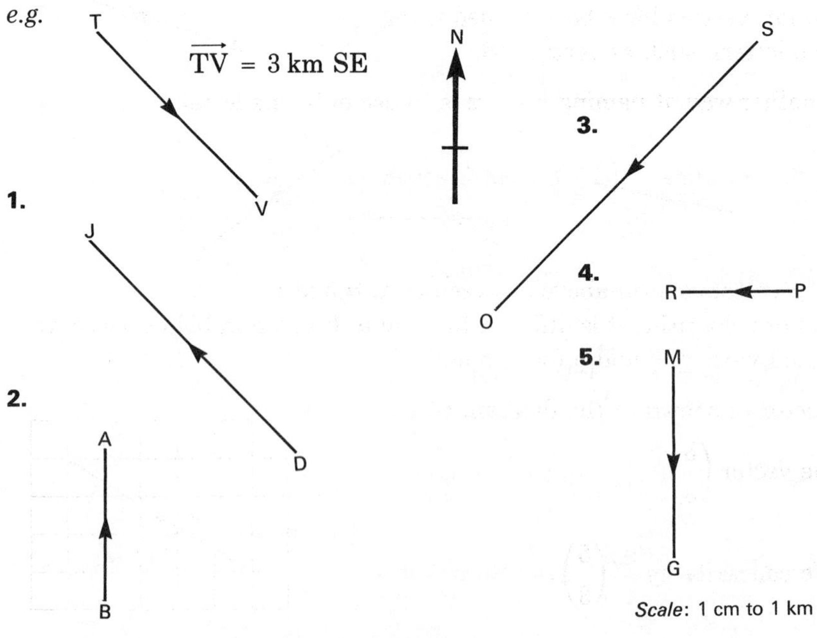

6.

7.

8.

9.

10.

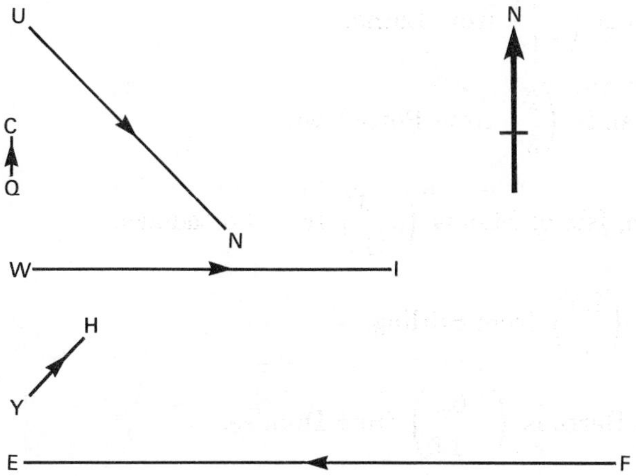

Scale: 1 cm to 1 km

B Draw and label the following vectors. Choose your own scale. (A different scale may be used for each question. Write down which scale you use.)

1. $\overrightarrow{PC}$ is 4 km due W.
2. $\overrightarrow{KT}$ is 8 km due S.
3. $\overrightarrow{AM}$ is 15 m due N.
4. $\overrightarrow{IV}$ is 10 m NE.
5. $\overrightarrow{RE}$ is 12 km SE.
6. $\overrightarrow{US}$ is 20 km NW.
7. $\overrightarrow{BD}$ is 50 m due E.
8. $\overrightarrow{LO}$ is 13 m SW.

So far, vectors have been named using two letters, such as vector $\overrightarrow{AB}$.

Another way of naming vectors is to use only one letter.

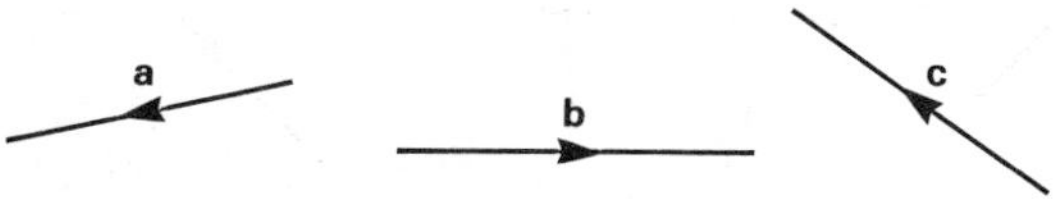

The vectors shown above are vectors **a**, **b** and **c**.
In normal writing it is difficult to write **a**, **b** and **c** in bold type so we would write $\underset{\sim}{a}$, $\underset{\sim}{b}$ and $\underset{\sim}{c}$ (or $\underline{a}$, $\underline{b}$ and $\underline{c}$).

Vector **m** shown in the diagram is

the vector $\begin{pmatrix} 5 \\ 3 \end{pmatrix}$.

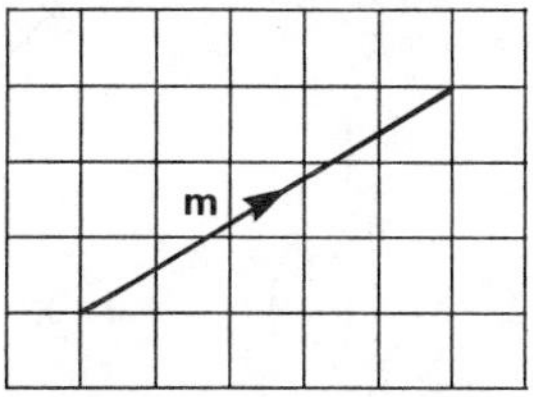

We can write $\underset{\sim}{m} = \begin{pmatrix} 5 \\ 3 \end{pmatrix}$.

Exercise 3

In the diagram below, $\underset{\sim}{a} = \begin{pmatrix} 4 \\ 2 \end{pmatrix}$.

A Write in the same way as above, the vectors:

1. t   **3.** q   **5.** b   **7.** h   **9.** n

2. s   **4.** r   **6.** e   **8.** k   **10.** l

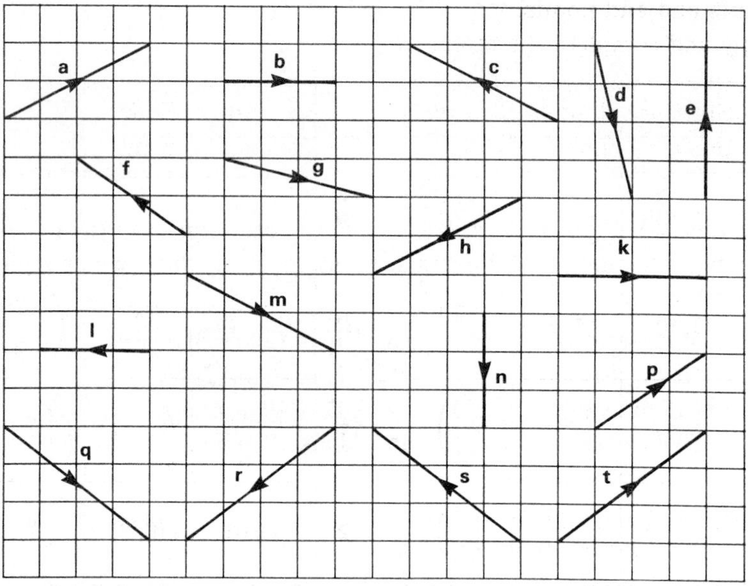

B Write the name of the given vector:

1. $\begin{pmatrix} 4 \\ ^-2 \end{pmatrix}$ **2.** $\begin{pmatrix} 4 \\ ^-1 \end{pmatrix}$ **3.** $\begin{pmatrix} 1 \\ ^-4 \end{pmatrix}$ **4.** $\begin{pmatrix} 3 \\ 2 \end{pmatrix}$ **5.** $\begin{pmatrix} ^-3 \\ 2 \end{pmatrix}$ **6.** $\begin{pmatrix} ^-4 \\ 2 \end{pmatrix}$

Exercise 4 **M**

On squared paper, draw and name the vectors:

1. u = $\begin{pmatrix} 3 \\ 5 \end{pmatrix}$ **3.** w = $\begin{pmatrix} 4 \\ 1 \end{pmatrix}$ **5.** y = $\begin{pmatrix} 0 \\ 2 \end{pmatrix}$ **7.** f = $\begin{pmatrix} ^-1 \\ 3 \end{pmatrix}$

2. v = $\begin{pmatrix} 1 \\ 6 \end{pmatrix}$ **4.** x = $\begin{pmatrix} 2 \\ 0 \end{pmatrix}$ **6.** x = $\begin{pmatrix} 3 \\ 1 \end{pmatrix}$ **8.** g = $\begin{pmatrix} ^-3 \\ 1 \end{pmatrix}$

9. $\mathbf{h} = \begin{pmatrix} 1 \\ 3 \end{pmatrix}$ 11. $\mathbf{l} = \begin{pmatrix} 1 \\ ^-3 \end{pmatrix}$ 13. $\mathbf{n} = \begin{pmatrix} ^-1 \\ ^-3 \end{pmatrix}$ 15. $\mathbf{q} = \begin{pmatrix} ^-3 \\ 7 \end{pmatrix}$

10. $\mathbf{k} = \begin{pmatrix} 3 \\ ^-1 \end{pmatrix}$ 12. $\mathbf{m} = \begin{pmatrix} ^-3 \\ ^-1 \end{pmatrix}$ 14. $\mathbf{p} = \begin{pmatrix} 6 \\ ^-2 \end{pmatrix}$ 16. $\mathbf{i} = \begin{pmatrix} 1 \\ 0 \end{pmatrix}$

Exercise 5 M

A The table gives displacement vectors together with their starting points and end points.
Copy and complete the table:

	Starting point	End point	Vector
1.	(2, 3)	(5, 7)	?
2.	(1, 6)	(4, 4)	?
3.	(3, 4)	?	$\begin{pmatrix} 3 \\ 1 \end{pmatrix}$
4.	($^-2$, 1)	?	$\begin{pmatrix} 3 \\ 3 \end{pmatrix}$
5.	?	(3, 6)	$\begin{pmatrix} 2 \\ 4 \end{pmatrix}$
6.	(2, $^-1$)	(4, 4)	?
7.	(0, 1)	?	$\begin{pmatrix} 1 \\ ^-2 \end{pmatrix}$
8.	?	(5, 4)	$\begin{pmatrix} 5 \\ 2 \end{pmatrix}$

	Starting point	End point	Vector
9.	?	(1, $^-1$)	$\begin{pmatrix} ^-2 \\ ^-3 \end{pmatrix}$
10.	(1, $^-1$)	?	$\begin{pmatrix} ^-2 \\ 3 \end{pmatrix}$
11.	(2, $^-5$)	(0, $^-1$)	?
12.	(0, 0)	(6, 2)	?
13.	(0, 0)	?	$\begin{pmatrix} 3 \\ 5 \end{pmatrix}$
14.	?	(4, 6)	$\begin{pmatrix} 4 \\ 6 \end{pmatrix}$
15.	(0, 0)	?	$\begin{pmatrix} ^-3 \\ 5 \end{pmatrix}$
16.	(0, 0)	(1, $^-6$)	?

B Write what you notice about a vector and its end point when the starting point is (0, 0).

Exercise 6

A Right-angled $\triangle PQR$ has been translated to $P'Q'R'$ by the translation vector $\begin{pmatrix}5\\3\end{pmatrix}$.

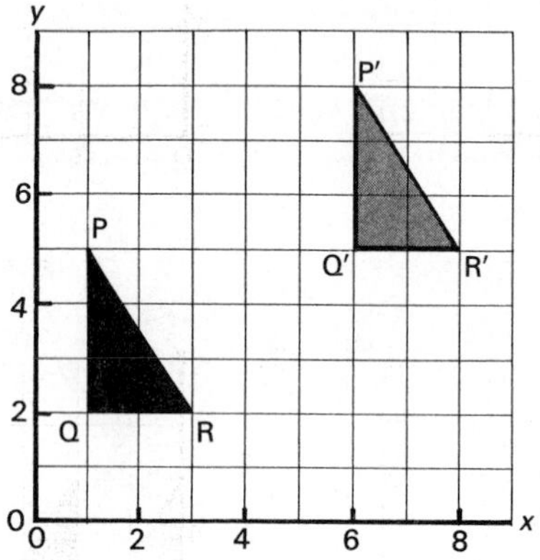

Write the co-ordinates of:

1. P
2. Q
3. R
4. P′
5. Q′
6. R′

B In each question, the black triangle has been translated to a new position. Give the co-ordinates of the vertices of (*a*) the object, (*b*) the image, and write (*c*) the translation vector.

1.

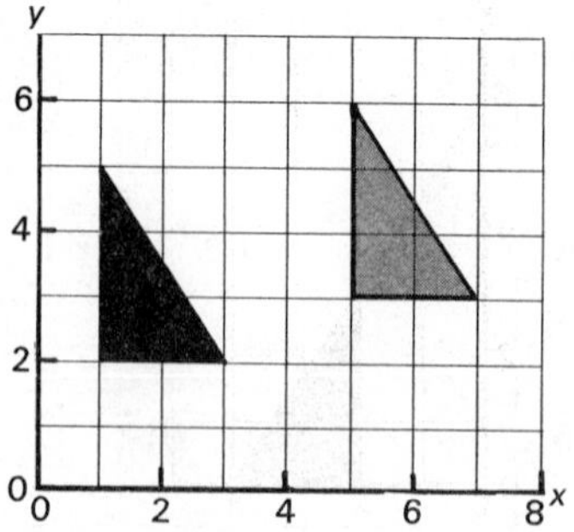

2.

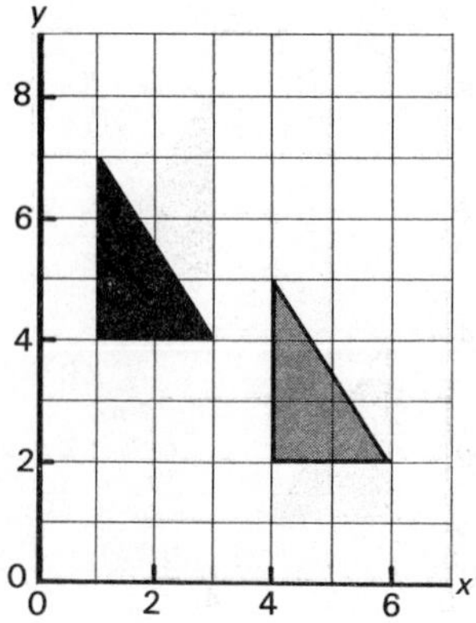

3.

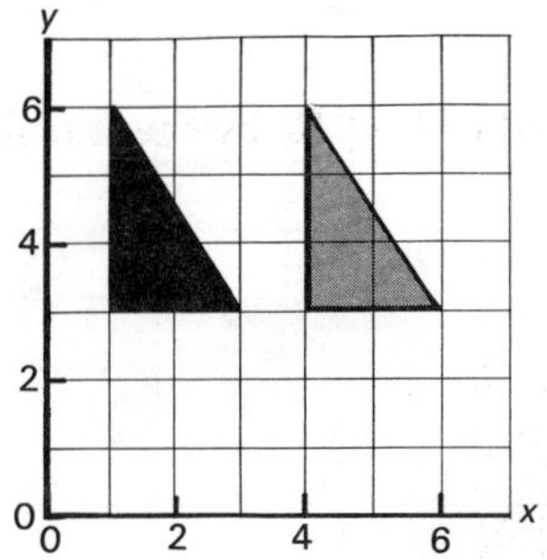

y
6
4
2
0
0
2
4
6
x

6.

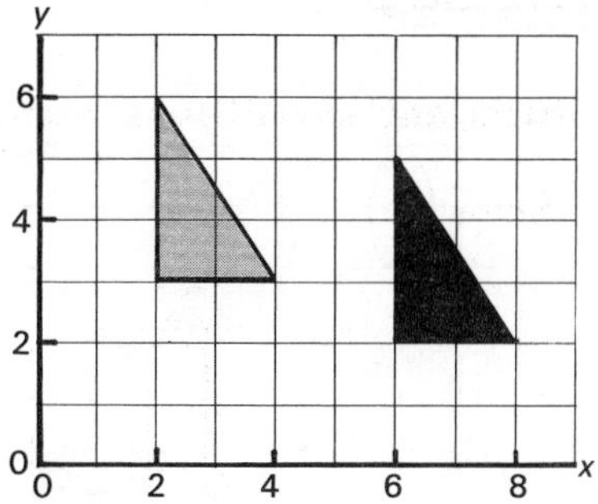

y
6
4
2
0
0
2
4
6
8
x

4.

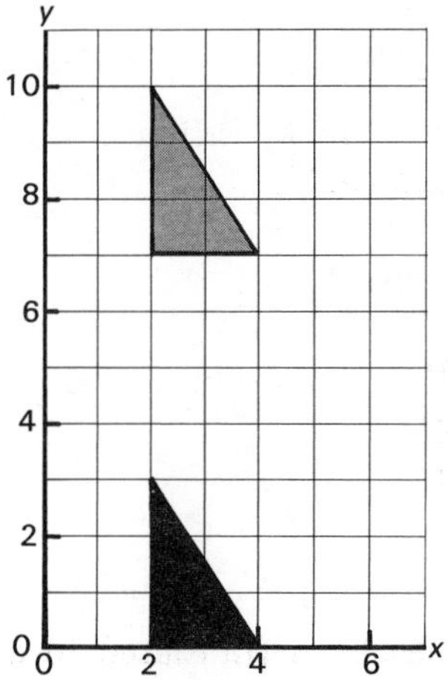

y
10
8
6
4
2
0
0
2
4
6
x

7.

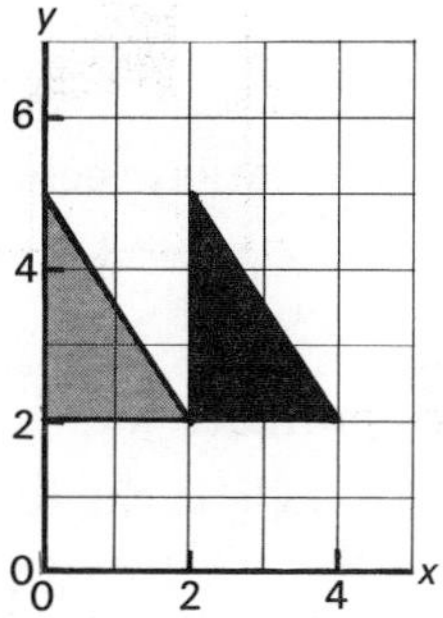

y
6
4
2
0
0
2
4
x

5.

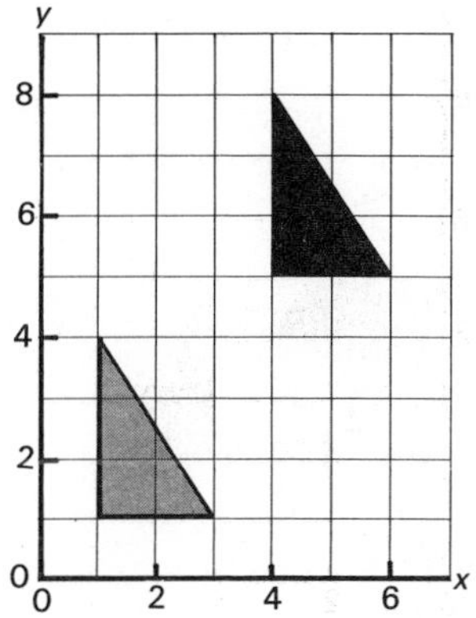

y
8
6
4
2
0
0
2
4
6
x

8.

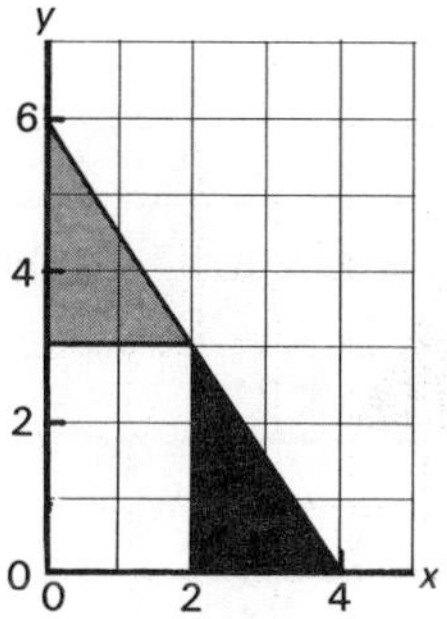

y
6
4
2
0
0
2
4
x

Exercise 7

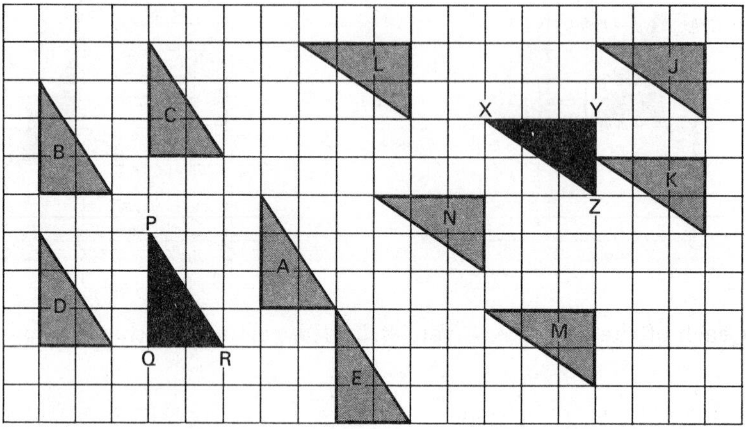

1. Which translation vector moves $\triangle PQR$ to position:
(*a*) A?
(*b*) D?
(*c*) E?

2. Which triangle is the result of translating $\triangle PQR$ using translation vector $\begin{pmatrix} ^-3 \\ 4 \end{pmatrix}$?

3. Which triangle is the result of translating $\triangle XYZ$ using translation vector $\begin{pmatrix} ^-3 \\ ^-2 \end{pmatrix}$?

4. Which translation vector moves $\triangle XYZ$ to position:
(*a*) K?
(*b*) M?
(*c*) L?

5. Which triangle is translated by:

(*a*) $\begin{pmatrix} 3 \\ 1 \end{pmatrix}$ to C?

(*b*) $\begin{pmatrix} ^-2 \\ 3 \end{pmatrix}$ to A?

(*c*) $\begin{pmatrix} 0 \\ ^-4 \end{pmatrix}$ to D?

(*d*) $\begin{pmatrix} ^-8 \\ 0 \end{pmatrix}$ to L?

(*e*) $\begin{pmatrix} 2 \\ ^-4 \end{pmatrix}$ to N?

(*f*) $\begin{pmatrix} ^-3 \\ ^-4 \end{pmatrix}$ to M?

Exercise 8

The diagram shows that:

$$\begin{pmatrix}5\\2\end{pmatrix} + \begin{pmatrix}1\\3\end{pmatrix} = \begin{pmatrix}6\\5\end{pmatrix}$$

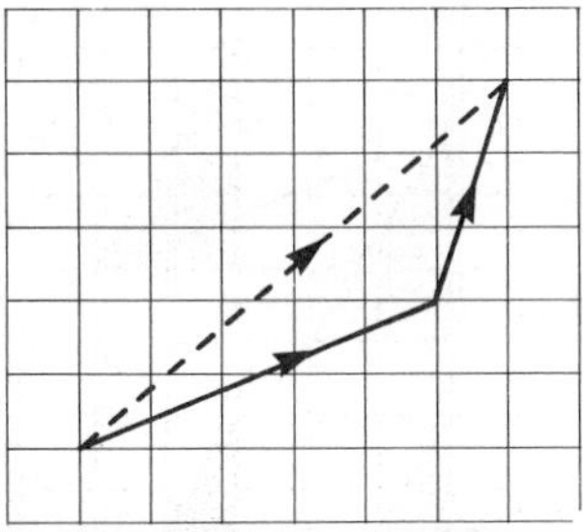

For each of the diagrams given, write the vector sum that is shown:

1.

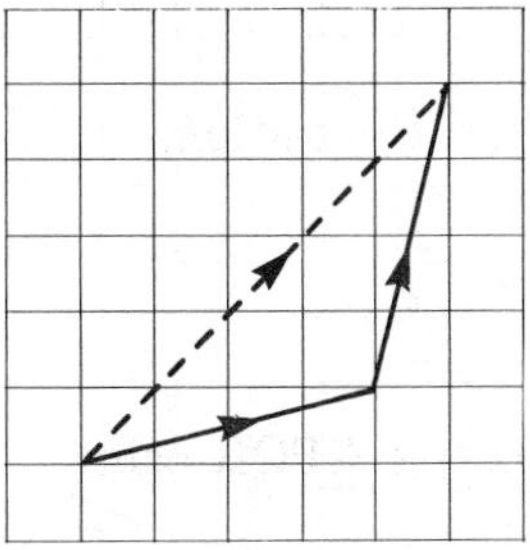

4.

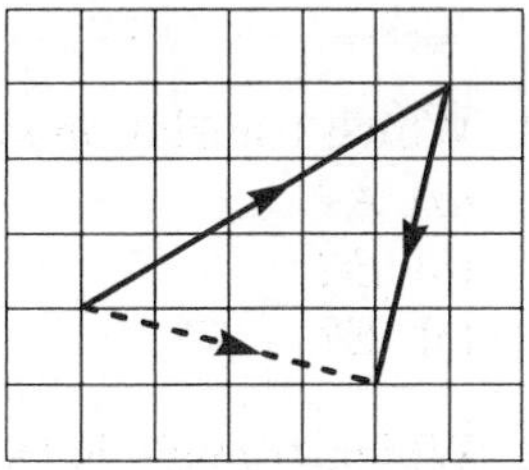

2.

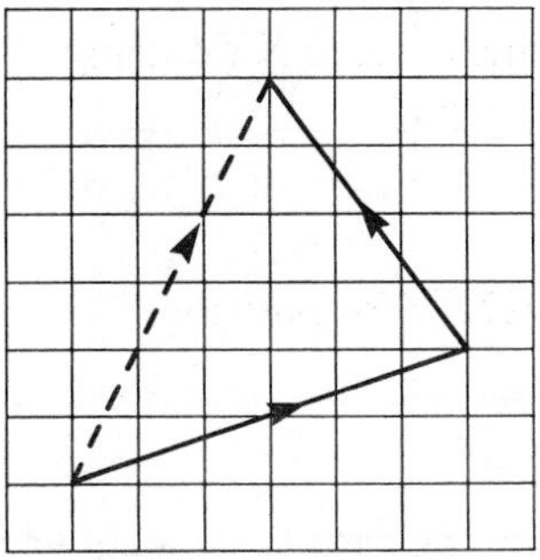

5.

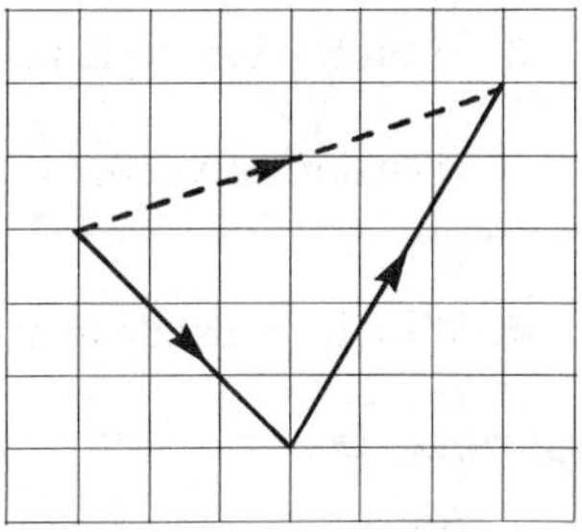

3.

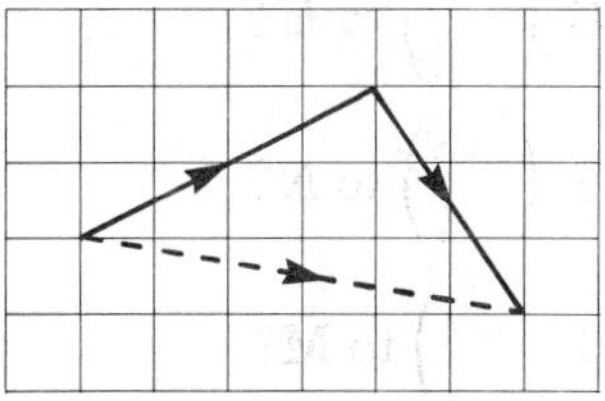

6.

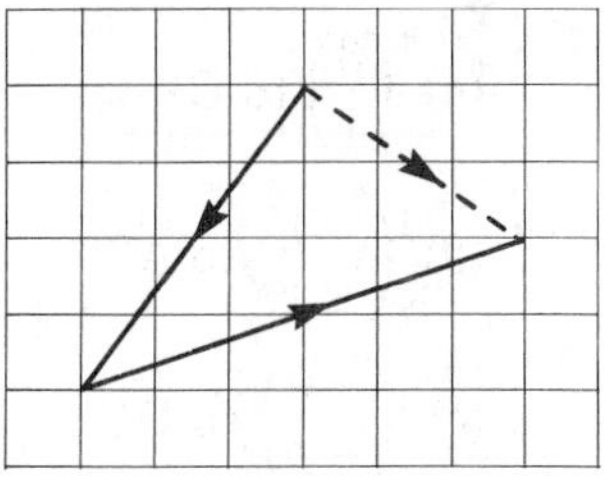

7.

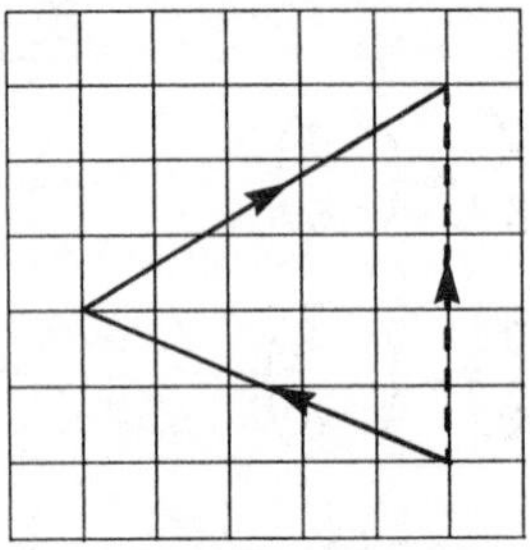

8.

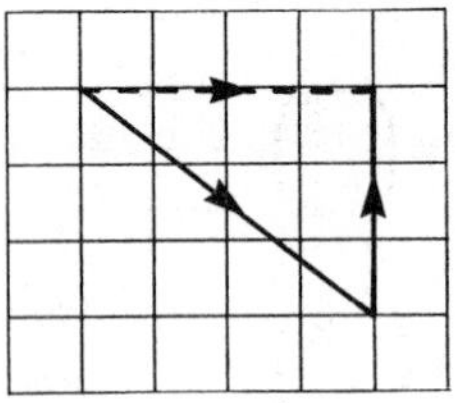

9.

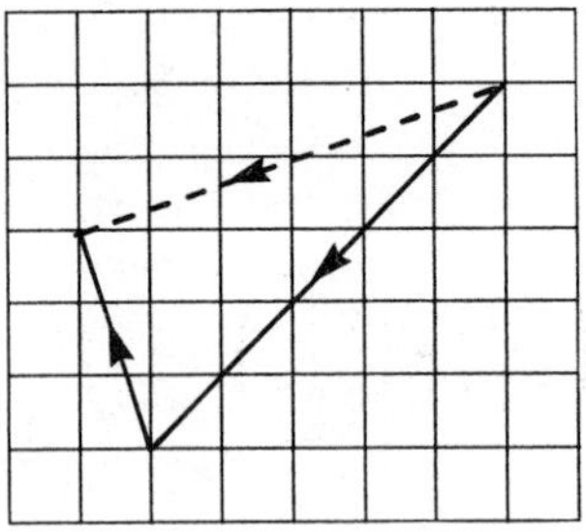

10.

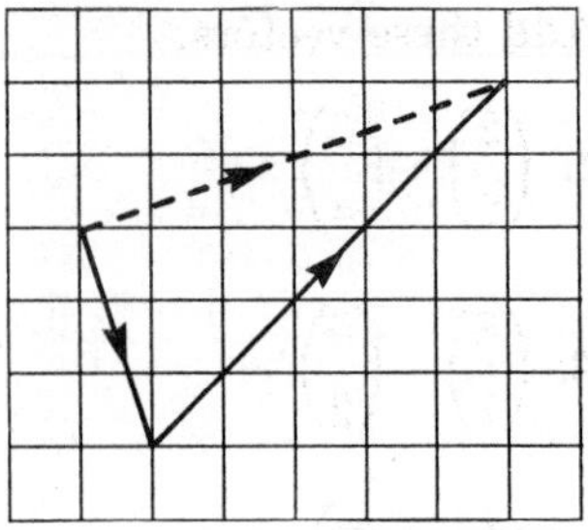

11.

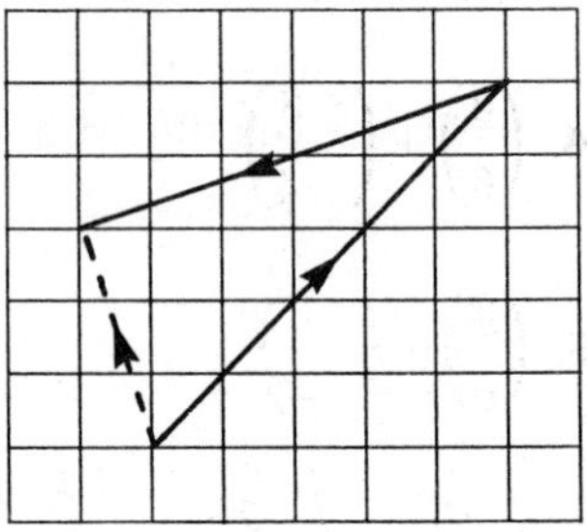

12.

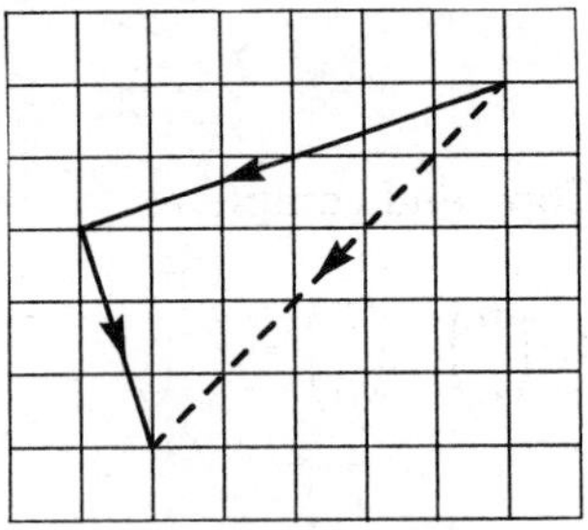

Exercise 9

A Add the given pairs of vectors and draw the results on a square grid:

1. $\begin{pmatrix}3\\1\end{pmatrix}+\begin{pmatrix}4\\4\end{pmatrix}$

2. $\begin{pmatrix}4\\6\end{pmatrix}+\begin{pmatrix}2\\^-1\end{pmatrix}$

3. $\begin{pmatrix}7\\2\end{pmatrix}+\begin{pmatrix}^-2\\6\end{pmatrix}$

4. $\begin{pmatrix}1\\^-5\end{pmatrix}+\begin{pmatrix}^-1\\2\end{pmatrix}$

5. $\begin{pmatrix}4\\^-5\end{pmatrix}+\begin{pmatrix}^-4\\0\end{pmatrix}$

6. $\begin{pmatrix}^-3\\^-6\end{pmatrix}+\begin{pmatrix}^-2\\5\end{pmatrix}$

B Add these vectors:

1. $\begin{pmatrix}2\\2\end{pmatrix}+\begin{pmatrix}5\\4\end{pmatrix}$

2. $\begin{pmatrix}8\\1\end{pmatrix}+\begin{pmatrix}0\\2\end{pmatrix}$

3. $\begin{pmatrix}1\\5\end{pmatrix}+\begin{pmatrix}6\\0\end{pmatrix}$

4. $\begin{pmatrix}3\\6\end{pmatrix}+\begin{pmatrix}^{-}3\\4\end{pmatrix}$

5. $\begin{pmatrix}3\\6\end{pmatrix}+\begin{pmatrix}^{-}3\\^{-}4\end{pmatrix}$

6. $\begin{pmatrix}7\\^{-}3\end{pmatrix}+\begin{pmatrix}^{-}3\\7\end{pmatrix}$

7. $\begin{pmatrix}9\\^{-}5\end{pmatrix}+\begin{pmatrix}^{-}4\\^{-}5\end{pmatrix}$

8. $\begin{pmatrix}^{-}2\\2\end{pmatrix}+\begin{pmatrix}8\\^{-}6\end{pmatrix}$

9. $\begin{pmatrix}0\\3\end{pmatrix}+\begin{pmatrix}^{-}1\\6\end{pmatrix}$

10. $\begin{pmatrix}^{-}5\\2\end{pmatrix}+\begin{pmatrix}^{-}6\\^{-}1\end{pmatrix}$

11. $\begin{pmatrix}^{-}1\\^{-}3\end{pmatrix}+\begin{pmatrix}^{-}2\\0\end{pmatrix}$

12. $\begin{pmatrix}^{-}9\\^{-}7\end{pmatrix}+\begin{pmatrix}^{-}2\\9\end{pmatrix}$

C Copy and complete:

1. $\begin{pmatrix}6\\4\end{pmatrix}+\begin{pmatrix}2\\5\end{pmatrix}=\begin{pmatrix}\boxed{?}\\\boxed{?}\end{pmatrix}$

2. $\begin{pmatrix}5\\1\end{pmatrix}+\begin{pmatrix}\boxed{?}\\6\end{pmatrix}=\begin{pmatrix}7\\\boxed{?}\end{pmatrix}$

3. $\begin{pmatrix}2\\7\end{pmatrix}+\begin{pmatrix}\boxed{?}\\\boxed{?}\end{pmatrix}=\begin{pmatrix}8\\7\end{pmatrix}$

4. $\begin{pmatrix}\boxed{?}\\7\end{pmatrix}+\begin{pmatrix}1\\\boxed{?}\end{pmatrix}=\begin{pmatrix}5\\9\end{pmatrix}$

5. $\begin{pmatrix}\boxed{?}\\\boxed{?}\end{pmatrix}+\begin{pmatrix}2\\^{-}2\end{pmatrix}=\begin{pmatrix}^{-}2\\2\end{pmatrix}$

6. $\begin{pmatrix}3\\^{-}1\end{pmatrix}+\begin{pmatrix}\boxed{?}\\\boxed{?}\end{pmatrix}=\begin{pmatrix}1\\1\end{pmatrix}$

7. $\begin{pmatrix}\boxed{?}\\2\end{pmatrix}+\begin{pmatrix}^{-}8\\\boxed{?}\end{pmatrix}=\begin{pmatrix}^{-}12\\0\end{pmatrix}$

8. $\begin{pmatrix}^{-}3\\^{-}5\end{pmatrix}+\begin{pmatrix}^{-}4\\\boxed{?}\end{pmatrix}=\begin{pmatrix}\boxed{?}\\^{-}6\end{pmatrix}$

9. $\begin{pmatrix}2\\\boxed{?}\end{pmatrix}+\begin{pmatrix}\boxed{?}\\2\end{pmatrix}=\begin{pmatrix}5\\^{-}2\end{pmatrix}$

10. $\begin{pmatrix}\boxed{?}\\\boxed{?}\end{pmatrix}+\begin{pmatrix}^{-}3\\^{-}1\end{pmatrix}=\begin{pmatrix}^{-}4\\3\end{pmatrix}$

Exercise 10

The first diagram shows that if

$\overrightarrow{AB} = \begin{pmatrix}4\\2\end{pmatrix}$ and $\overrightarrow{BC} = \begin{pmatrix}1\\3\end{pmatrix}$, then:

$$\overrightarrow{AC} = \overrightarrow{AB} + \overrightarrow{BC} = \begin{pmatrix}4\\2\end{pmatrix} + \begin{pmatrix}1\\3\end{pmatrix} = \begin{pmatrix}5\\5\end{pmatrix}$$

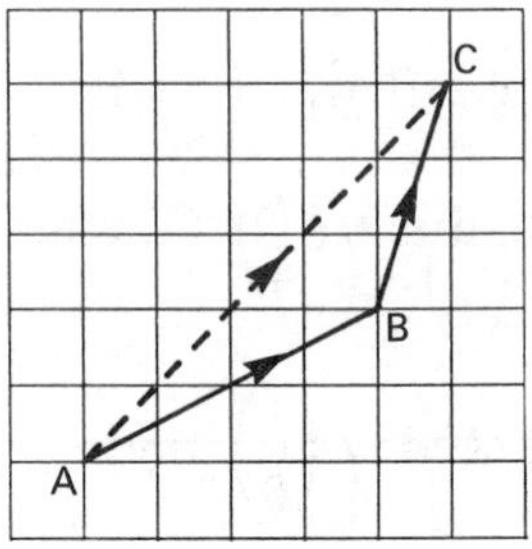

In the diagram on the right $\overrightarrow{AB} = \begin{pmatrix}3\\2\end{pmatrix}$ and $\overrightarrow{BC} = \begin{pmatrix}3\\2\end{pmatrix}$, so:

$$\overrightarrow{AC} = \overrightarrow{AB} + \overrightarrow{BC} = \begin{pmatrix}3\\2\end{pmatrix} + \begin{pmatrix}3\\2\end{pmatrix} = \begin{pmatrix}6\\4\end{pmatrix}$$

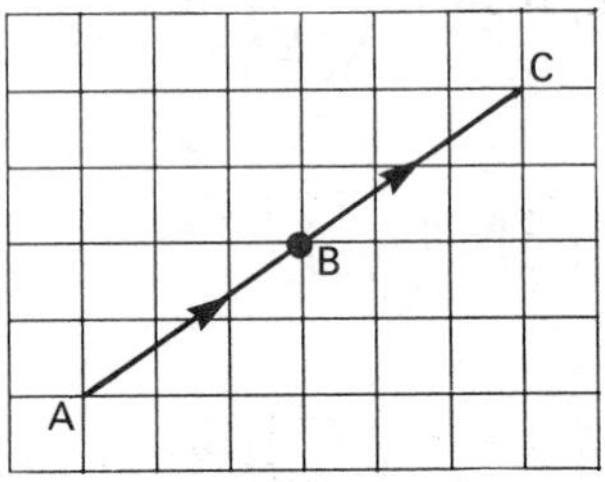

A Draw diagrams to show $\overrightarrow{AB} + \overrightarrow{BC}$ and find $\overrightarrow{AC}$ if:

1. $\overrightarrow{AB} = \begin{pmatrix}2\\4\end{pmatrix}$ and $\overrightarrow{BC} = \begin{pmatrix}2\\4\end{pmatrix}$

2. $\overrightarrow{AB} = \begin{pmatrix}4\\1\end{pmatrix}$ and $\overrightarrow{BC} = \begin{pmatrix}4\\1\end{pmatrix}$

3. $\overrightarrow{AB} = \begin{pmatrix}3\\{}^-4\end{pmatrix}$ and $\overrightarrow{BC} = \begin{pmatrix}3\\{}^-4\end{pmatrix}$

4. $\overrightarrow{AB} = \begin{pmatrix}{}^-6\\1\end{pmatrix}$ and $\overrightarrow{BC} = \begin{pmatrix}{}^-6\\1\end{pmatrix}$

5. $\overrightarrow{AB} = \begin{pmatrix}{}^-2\\5\end{pmatrix}$ and $\overrightarrow{BC} = \begin{pmatrix}{}^-2\\5\end{pmatrix}$

6. $\overrightarrow{AB} = \begin{pmatrix}{}^-5\\{}^-3\end{pmatrix}$ and $\overrightarrow{BC} = \begin{pmatrix}{}^-5\\{}^-3\end{pmatrix}$

B For each question in part A, compare the vector for $\overrightarrow{AC}$ with that for $\overrightarrow{AB}$. Write what you notice.

Exercise 11

A *e.g.* If $\mathbf{a} = \begin{pmatrix} 3 \\ 2 \end{pmatrix}$ then $2\mathbf{a} = \begin{pmatrix} 6 \\ 4 \end{pmatrix}$

1. If $\mathbf{c} = \begin{pmatrix} 3 \\ 4 \end{pmatrix}$ find: (*a*) $2\mathbf{c}$ (*b*) $3\mathbf{c}$ (*c*) $5\mathbf{c}$

2. If $\mathbf{d} = \begin{pmatrix} 1 \\ 6 \end{pmatrix}$ find: (*a*) $2\mathbf{d}$ (*b*) $4\mathbf{d}$ (*c*) $7\mathbf{d}$

3. If $\mathbf{m} = \begin{pmatrix} 4 \\ -2 \end{pmatrix}$ find: (*a*) $2\mathbf{m}$ (*b*) $5\mathbf{m}$ (*c*) $6\mathbf{m}$

4. If $\mathbf{u} = \begin{pmatrix} -1 \\ 4 \end{pmatrix}$ find: (*a*) $3\mathbf{u}$ (*b*) $5\mathbf{u}$ (*c*) $6\mathbf{u}$

5. If $\mathbf{x} = \begin{pmatrix} -2 \\ -3 \end{pmatrix}$ find: (*a*) $4\mathbf{x}$ (*b*) $6\mathbf{x}$ (*c*) $10\mathbf{x}$

6. If $\mathbf{v} = \begin{pmatrix} 3 \\ -6 \end{pmatrix}$ find: (*a*) $2\mathbf{v}$ (*b*) $4\mathbf{v}$ (*c*) $7\mathbf{v}$

7. If $\mathbf{i} = \begin{pmatrix} 1 \\ 0 \end{pmatrix}$ find: (*a*) $2\mathbf{i}$ (*b*) $3\mathbf{i}$ (*c*) $5\mathbf{i}$

8. If $\mathbf{j} = \begin{pmatrix} 0 \\ 1 \end{pmatrix}$ find: (*a*) $2\mathbf{j}$ (*b*) $3\mathbf{j}$ (*c*) $5\mathbf{j}$

B

e.g. $4\begin{pmatrix} 3 \\ 2 \end{pmatrix} = \begin{pmatrix} 12 \\ 8 \end{pmatrix}$

Find:

1. $3\begin{pmatrix} 5 \\ 1 \end{pmatrix}$

2. $6\begin{pmatrix} 2 \\ 7 \end{pmatrix}$

3. $3\begin{pmatrix} 7 \\ 0 \end{pmatrix}$

4. $2\begin{pmatrix} -3 \\ 5 \end{pmatrix}$

5. $4\begin{pmatrix} 7 \\ -2 \end{pmatrix}$

6. $5\begin{pmatrix} -3 \\ -3 \end{pmatrix}$

7. $6\begin{pmatrix} 1 \\ 0 \end{pmatrix}$

8. $7\begin{pmatrix} 0 \\ 1 \end{pmatrix}$

9. $5\begin{pmatrix} ^-8 \\ ^-1 \end{pmatrix}$

10. $8\begin{pmatrix} 0 \\ ^-6 \end{pmatrix}$

11. $4\begin{pmatrix} ^-9 \\ ^-7 \end{pmatrix}$

12. $6\begin{pmatrix} 6 \\ ^-6 \end{pmatrix}$

If I do 3 h swimming and 5 h cycling per week, this can be shown as a vector $\begin{pmatrix} 3 \\ 5 \end{pmatrix}$ where the first component shows the number of hours spent swimming. (Compare, book 2G, p. 413, Exercise 17.) In 2 weeks I do 6 h swimming and 10 h cycling. In vector form, we have:

$$2\begin{pmatrix} 3 \\ 5 \end{pmatrix} = \begin{pmatrix} 6 \\ 10 \end{pmatrix}$$

Exercise 12

For each question, write the given information in the form of a vector (use the order given in the question). Answer each question leaving the answers in vector form.

e.g. If I do 3 h swimming, 4 h cycling and 7 h jogging per week, what do I do in 4 weeks?

$$4\begin{pmatrix} 3 \\ 4 \\ 7 \end{pmatrix} = \begin{pmatrix} 12 \\ 16 \\ 28 \end{pmatrix}$$

1. If I buy 2 jars of honey, 3 jars of marmalade and 1 jar of strawberry jam each month, what do I buy in 6 months?

2. I drink 5 cups of coffee and 3 cups of tea each day. How many do I drink in 7 days?

3. Jackie uses 10 tins of beans, 4 tins of peas and 8 tins of soup in one month. How much does she use in 4 months?

4. Emma does 2 h homework and watches TV for $1\frac{1}{2}$ h each night. How much time is spent on each in 5 nights?

5. Savinder uses 10 fountain-pen cartridges and 3 ballpoint refills in 4 months. What does he use in one year?

29 Matrices

Exercise 1

A During a certain month Carl ate 8 fried eggs, Una ate 5 fried eggs and 3 scrambled eggs and Gary ate 4 poached eggs. Una also had 3 boiled eggs and 1 poached egg while Carl had 2 scrambled eggs and 4 boiled eggs (he didn't have any poached eggs). Gary also ate 3 fried eggs and 5 boiled eggs (he didn't have scrambled eggs).

1. How many scrambled eggs did Carl eat?
2. How many fried eggs did Gary eat?
3. Who ate the most boiled eggs?
4. What sort of egg did Una eat most of?
5. How many poached eggs were eaten altogether?
6. How many fried eggs were eaten?
7. How many eggs did Carl eat?
8. Who ate the most eggs during the month?

B The table below shows the number of each type of egg eaten during another month:

	Boiled	Fried	Poached	Scrambled
Carl	5	6	0	3
Gary	4	7	2	2
Una	2	4	3	5

Now answer the same 8 questions as in part A.

C Was it easier to use the written information as in part A or the table of information as in part B?

D Draw and complete a table to show the information given in part A.

Exercise 2 **M**

Copy and complete the following tables using the given information:

1. Judy owns 6 LP records and 24 singles, while Karen owns 15 LPs and 7 singles.

	LPs	Singles
Judy		
Karen		

2. Mr Andrews' electricity bill came to £86.92 while his gas bill was £67.29. Mrs Gilby's electricity bill was £69.93 and her gas bill came to £103.18.

	Electricity	Gas
Mr Andrews		
Mrs Gilby		

3. A shop sold 47 large tins of beans and 28 small tins, 19 large tins of spaghetti and 25 small tins.

	Large	Small
Beans		
Spaghetti		

4. At a fish and chip shop Mrs Keenan bought 3 fish, 5 portions of chips, 2 cartons of peas and 1 pie while Mr Hogan bought 2 fish, 6 portions of chips, 3 cartons of peas and 4 pies.

	Fish	Chips	Peas	Pies
Mr Hogan				
Mrs Keenan				

5. In the school exams, Nicholas got 74% for maths, 78% for geography and 51% for English; Noel got 45% for maths, 64% for geography and 68% for English; while Nina got 59% for maths, 52% for geography and 66% for English.

	Maths	Geography	English
Nicholas			
Noel			
Nina			

Exercise 3

Draw tables to show the following information.
Label the rows and columns.

1. The number of 60 W and 100 W light bulbs sold at each of two shops is as follows:
Electra sold thirty-two 60 W bulbs and forty-five 100 W bulbs while Dealite sold seventeen 60 W and thirty 100 W bulbs.

2. In a survey it was found that 37 males preferred a ballpoint pen and 14 a fountain pen; 26 females preferred a ballpoint pen while 23 preferred a fountain pen.

3. 100 mℓ of a brand of orange juice contains 38 mg of vitamin C, 10 g of carbohydrates and 35 calories while 100 mℓ of pineapple juice contains 12 mg of vitamin C, 12 g of carbohydrates and 39 calories.

4. The vitamin content of 100 g of each of three different breakfast cereals was as follows:
Cereal A contained 10.6 mg of niacin, 1.06 mg of riboflavin (B_2) and 0.71 mg of thiamin (B_1). Cereal B contained 16.0 mg of niacin, 1.5 mg of B_2 and 1.0 mg of B_1 while cereal C contained 10.0 mg of niacin, 1.0 mg of B_2 and 0.7 mg of B_1.

5. 100 g of breakfast cereal P contains 10.5 g of protein, 12.9 g of dietary fibre, 2 g of fat and 6 mg of iron; while 100 g of cereal Q contains 10.1 g of protein, 15.4 g of dietary fibre, 1.1 g of fat and 40 mg of iron.

Calculations are sometimes carried out on information as given in the tables. To carry out the calculations, headings are not needed. Consider the table given in Exercise 1 part B, p. 345. It can be written as:

$$\begin{pmatrix} 5 & 6 & 0 & 3 \\ 4 & 7 & 2 & 2 \\ 2 & 4 & 3 & 5 \end{pmatrix}$$

This is called a *matrix* (plural *matrices*). Any rectangular array of numbers is called a matrix. The individual numbers given in a matrix are called its *elements* (or components or entries). The matrix $\begin{pmatrix} 4 & 2 & 5 \\ 1 & 3 & 6 \end{pmatrix}$ is called a 2 by 3 matrix (often written 2×3 matrix) since it has 2 rows and 3 columns. $\begin{pmatrix} 3 & ^-1 \\ 5 & 2 \end{pmatrix}$ has 2 rows and 2 columns and so is a 2 by 2 (2×2) matrix. The vectors we have used have 2 rows and 1 column and are special matrices. They are 2 by 1 (2×1) matrices.

Exercise 4

Here are some matrices:

$$\mathbf{A} = \begin{pmatrix} 3 & ^-1 \\ 1 & 5 \end{pmatrix} \qquad \mathbf{F} = \begin{pmatrix} 1 & 4 & 5 & 6 \\ 0 & 4 & ^-1 & 2 \end{pmatrix} \qquad \mathbf{K} = \begin{pmatrix} 5 & 0 \\ ^-2 & 1 \end{pmatrix}$$

$$\mathbf{B} = \begin{pmatrix} 1 & 2 & 4 \\ ^-2 & 6 & 2 \end{pmatrix} \qquad \mathbf{G} = (1 \quad 0) \qquad \mathbf{L} = \begin{pmatrix} 4 & 2 \\ 1 & 0 \\ 6 & 8 \end{pmatrix}$$

$$\mathbf{C} = \begin{pmatrix} 1 & 2 & 0 \\ 0 & 1 & 2 \\ 2 & ^-3 & 1 \end{pmatrix} \qquad \mathbf{H} = \begin{pmatrix} 5 \\ 4 \end{pmatrix} \qquad \mathbf{M} = \begin{pmatrix} 0 & 1 \\ 1 & 0 \end{pmatrix}$$

$$\mathbf{D} = \begin{pmatrix} 4 & 4 \\ 4 & 4 \end{pmatrix} \qquad \mathbf{I} = \begin{pmatrix} 1 & 0 \\ 0 & 1 \end{pmatrix} \qquad \mathbf{N} = \begin{pmatrix} 1 & 0 & 1 & 0 \\ 0 & 1 & 0 & 1 \\ 1 & 0 & 1 & 0 \end{pmatrix}$$

$$\mathbf{E} = \begin{pmatrix} 5 & 2 \\ 1 & ^-3 \\ ^-2 & 0 \end{pmatrix} \qquad \mathbf{J} = (4, \quad ^-2) \qquad \mathbf{P} = \begin{pmatrix} 1 & 0 & ^-1 \\ ^-1 & 2 & 1 \end{pmatrix}$$

$$\mathbf{Q} = \begin{pmatrix} 1 \\ 0 \end{pmatrix} \qquad \mathbf{S} = \begin{pmatrix} 2 & 0 & 1 \\ 2 & 0 & 1 \end{pmatrix} \qquad \mathbf{U} = \begin{pmatrix} ^-1 & 0 \\ 0 & ^-1 \end{pmatrix}$$

$$\mathbf{R} = \begin{pmatrix} ^-2 & 4 \\ ^-1 & 0 \\ ^-5 & ^-3 \end{pmatrix} \qquad \mathbf{T} = \begin{pmatrix} 4 \\ 0 \\ 2 \end{pmatrix}$$

1. Which of the above are 2 by 2 matrices?
2. Which of the above are 3×2 matrices?
3. List the remaining matrices then describe them.

   e.g. C is a 3×3 matrix.

Exercise 5

A Write as matrices, the information given in Exercise 2, p. 346.

B Write as matrices the information given in Exercise 3, p. 347.

C For each question, write the given information as a matrix:

1. 120 people were asked whether they preferred blue ink or black ink. 22 males preferred blue and 37 black. Of the females, 32 preferred blue and 29 black.
2. On a tray in a jeweller's there were 14 gold and 8 silver rings. On another tray there were 9 gold and 12 silver rings.
3. A survey of cat and dog owners was carried out in two streets. It was found that on Oak Avenue there were 8 dogs and 2 cats, while on Ash Lane there were 3 dogs and 4 cats.
4. In a survey of people who watched BBC television last night it was noted that 39 girls watched BBC1 and so did 42 boys, while 26 girls and 19 boys watched BBC2. The number who watched both is not included.
5. In a survey of people who watched only one channel on TV on a particular night it was found that of the girls, 43 watched BBC1, 32 watched BBC2, 30 watched ITV and 15 watched Channel 4; while

of the boys, 31 watched BBC1, 23 watched BBC2, 36 watched ITV and 13 watched Channel 4.

6. While shopping Mrs Iddon spent £14 cash, £26 by cheque and £49 on credit card. Mrs Jarvis spent £19 cash and £75 on credit card. She did not use her cheque book.

7. On Butler Close 5 houses have blinds, 24 have curtains and 2 have shutters, while on George Street 7 houses have blinds, 19 have curtains and only 1 has shutters.
(*a*) Write the information as a 2×3 matrix.
(*b*) Write the information as a 3×2 matrix.

8. 100 people were asked which type of film they preferred to watch. Science fiction was preferred by 23 males and 11 females, 11 males preferred comedy, 9 preferred thrillers and 7 preferred westerns. Comedy was preferred by 14 females, thrillers by 15 and westerns by 10.
(*a*) Write the information as a 2×4 matrix.
(*b*) Write the information as a 4×2 matrix.

Addition of Matrices

In one week, a family ate 4 large loaves of bread and 1 small loaf. This can be shown by the matrix $\begin{pmatrix} 4 \\ 1 \end{pmatrix}$ where the first element stands for the number of large loaves. The following week they ate 3 large loaves and 3 small loaves. This can be shown by $\begin{pmatrix} 3 \\ 3 \end{pmatrix}$ where once again the first element stands for the number of large loaves.

In the 2 weeks, they bought 7 large loaves and 4 small loaves. Using matrices

$$\begin{pmatrix} 4 \\ 1 \end{pmatrix} + \begin{pmatrix} 3 \\ 3 \end{pmatrix} = \begin{pmatrix} 7 \\ 4 \end{pmatrix} \begin{matrix} \leftarrow 7 \text{ large} \\ \leftarrow 4 \text{ small} \end{matrix}$$

$$\begin{matrix} \uparrow & & \uparrow & & \uparrow \\ \text{First week} & + & \text{Second week} & = & \text{Total} \end{matrix}$$

Note This is the same as for adding vectors.

The matrices below show the meals served to 2 different tables by a waitress.
(B = Beef, T = Turkey, H = Hot and C = Cold.)

$$\begin{array}{c} \\ B \\ T \end{array}\begin{array}{c} \quad H \quad C \\ \begin{pmatrix} 2 & 1 \\ 3 & 2 \end{pmatrix} \end{array} + \begin{pmatrix} 3 & 1 \\ 0 & 1 \end{pmatrix} = \begin{pmatrix} 5 & 2 \\ 3 & 3 \end{pmatrix}$$

↑ First table ↑ Second table ↑ Totals

Exercise 6

Add the following matrices:

1. $\begin{pmatrix} 3 \\ 6 \end{pmatrix} + \begin{pmatrix} 2 \\ 3 \end{pmatrix}$

2. $(1 \quad 4) + (3 \quad 3)$

3. $\begin{pmatrix} 2 & 0 \\ 4 & 5 \end{pmatrix} + \begin{pmatrix} 5 & 3 \\ 1 & 4 \end{pmatrix}$

4. $\begin{pmatrix} 6 & 1 \\ 2 & 3 \\ 1 & 3 \end{pmatrix} + \begin{pmatrix} 2 & 5 \\ 1 & 0 \\ 3 & 4 \end{pmatrix}$

5. $(7 \quad 1 \quad 4) + (2 \quad 2 \quad 1)$

6. $\begin{pmatrix} 3 & 6 \\ 1 & 2 \end{pmatrix} + \begin{pmatrix} 4 & 0 \\ 5 & 7 \end{pmatrix}$

7. $\begin{pmatrix} 4 & 1 & 3 \\ 2 & 5 & 5 \end{pmatrix} + \begin{pmatrix} 3 & 2 & 5 \\ 1 & 4 & 0 \end{pmatrix}$

8. $\begin{pmatrix} 1 \\ 0 \\ 2 \end{pmatrix} + \begin{pmatrix} 3 \\ 0 \\ 3 \end{pmatrix}$

9. $\begin{pmatrix} 4 \\ 7 \end{pmatrix} + \begin{pmatrix} ^-2 \\ 0 \end{pmatrix}$

10. $\begin{pmatrix} 4 & ^-2 \\ 0 & 1 \end{pmatrix} + \begin{pmatrix} 3 & 4 \\ 2 & ^-5 \end{pmatrix}$

11. $\begin{pmatrix} 6 & ^-2 & ^-1 \\ ^-2 & 0 & 3 \end{pmatrix} + \begin{pmatrix} ^-1 & ^-4 & 0 \\ 5 & 2 & ^-1 \end{pmatrix}$

12. $(5 \quad ^-3 \quad ^-1) + (^-2 \quad 2 \quad 2)$

13. $\begin{pmatrix} 1 & 0 \\ 0 & 1 \end{pmatrix} + \begin{pmatrix} 1 & 0 \\ 0 & 1 \end{pmatrix}$

14. $\begin{pmatrix} 7 & 3 \\ ^-2 & 0 \\ ^-5 & 4 \end{pmatrix} + \begin{pmatrix} ^-6 & ^-3 \\ 5 & 6 \\ 5 & ^-4 \end{pmatrix}$

15. $\begin{pmatrix} 5 & 8 \\ 3 & ^-2 \end{pmatrix} + \begin{pmatrix} ^-4 & ^-8 \\ 4 & 4 \end{pmatrix}$

Exercise 7

For each question, find the missing matrix:

1. $\begin{pmatrix} 4 & 2 \\ 1 & 6 \end{pmatrix} + \begin{pmatrix} \boxed{?} & \boxed{?} \\ \boxed{?} & \boxed{?} \end{pmatrix} = \begin{pmatrix} 7 & 5 \\ 5 & 7 \end{pmatrix}$

2. $(3 \quad 4) + (\boxed{?} \quad \boxed{?}) = (4 \quad 9)$

3. $\begin{pmatrix} \boxed{?} \\ \boxed{?} \end{pmatrix} + \begin{pmatrix} 3 \\ 2 \end{pmatrix} = \begin{pmatrix} 5 \\ 8 \end{pmatrix}$

4. $\begin{pmatrix} 2 & 0 & 1 \\ 3 & 1 & 4 \end{pmatrix} + \begin{pmatrix} \boxed{?} & \boxed{?} & \boxed{?} \\ \boxed{?} & \boxed{?} & \boxed{?} \end{pmatrix} = \begin{pmatrix} 6 & 1 & 1 \\ 3 & 4 & 4 \end{pmatrix}$

5. $\begin{pmatrix} 2 \\ 4 \\ 1 \end{pmatrix} + \begin{pmatrix} \boxed{?} \\ \boxed{?} \\ \boxed{?} \end{pmatrix} = \begin{pmatrix} 4 \\ 4 \\ 4 \end{pmatrix}$

6. $(\boxed{?} \quad \boxed{?} \quad \boxed{?}) + (1 \quad 5 \quad 2) = (1 \quad 6 \quad 4)$

7. $\begin{pmatrix} 3 & 1 \\ 4 & 5 \end{pmatrix} + \begin{pmatrix} \boxed{?} & \boxed{?} \\ \boxed{?} & \boxed{?} \end{pmatrix} = \begin{pmatrix} 4 & 2 \\ 4 & 6 \end{pmatrix}$

8. $\begin{pmatrix} 3 & ^-2 \\ ^-1 & 0 \end{pmatrix} + \begin{pmatrix} \boxed{?} & \boxed{?} \\ \boxed{?} & \boxed{?} \end{pmatrix} = \begin{pmatrix} 5 & 0 \\ 0 & 5 \end{pmatrix}$

9. $\begin{pmatrix} 4 \\ 2 \\ 5 \end{pmatrix} + \begin{pmatrix} \boxed{?} \\ \boxed{?} \\ \boxed{?} \end{pmatrix} = \begin{pmatrix} 4 \\ 0 \\ 3 \end{pmatrix}$

10. $(\boxed{?} \quad \boxed{?}) + (1 \quad ^-3) = (^-3 \quad ^-1)$

11. $\begin{pmatrix} \boxed{?} & \boxed{?} \\ \boxed{?} & \boxed{?} \end{pmatrix} + \begin{pmatrix} 5 & ^-4 \\ ^-2 & 0 \end{pmatrix} = \begin{pmatrix} 2 & ^-2 \\ 3 & 6 \end{pmatrix}$

12. $\begin{pmatrix} 3 & 1 \\ ^-3 & 4 \\ 0 & ^-2 \end{pmatrix} + \begin{pmatrix} \boxed{?} & \boxed{?} \\ \boxed{?} & \boxed{?} \\ \boxed{?} & \boxed{?} \end{pmatrix} = \begin{pmatrix} ^-1 & 4 \\ ^-4 & 3 \\ ^-2 & ^-5 \end{pmatrix}$

13. $\begin{pmatrix} ^-4 & 3 \\ 1 & ^-2 \end{pmatrix} + \begin{pmatrix} \boxed{?} & \boxed{?} \\ \boxed{?} & \boxed{?} \end{pmatrix} = \begin{pmatrix} 0 & 0 \\ 0 & 0 \end{pmatrix}$

14. $\begin{pmatrix} \boxed{?} \\ \boxed{?} \end{pmatrix} + \begin{pmatrix} ^-1 \\ 1 \end{pmatrix} = \begin{pmatrix} 2 \\ 2 \end{pmatrix}$

15. $\begin{pmatrix} 1 & 0 \\ 0 & ^-1 \\ 1 & 0 \end{pmatrix} + \begin{pmatrix} \boxed{?} & \boxed{?} \\ \boxed{?} & \boxed{?} \\ \boxed{?} & \boxed{?} \end{pmatrix} = \begin{pmatrix} ^-2 & 3 \\ 0 & 1 \\ 2 & ^-3 \end{pmatrix}$

Exercise 8

1. The matrices show the number of people working on the night-shift and the day-shift on two successive days. Write a matrix to show the total number on each shift for the two days.

   Night Day

   $\begin{pmatrix} 18 & 29 \end{pmatrix} + \begin{pmatrix} 13 & 33 \end{pmatrix} = \begin{pmatrix} \boxed{?} & \boxed{?} \end{pmatrix}$

2. The matrices show the number of boys and girls in two different classes. Write a matrix to show the total number of boys and the total number of girls.

   Boys, Girls: $\begin{pmatrix} 17 \\ 14 \end{pmatrix} + \begin{pmatrix} 15 \\ 16 \end{pmatrix} = \begin{pmatrix} \boxed{?} \\ \boxed{?} \end{pmatrix}$

3. The matrices show the number of pupils absent and present on two successive days:

   Absent Present

   Boys, Girls: $\begin{pmatrix} 3 & 11 \\ 1 & 17 \end{pmatrix} + \begin{pmatrix} 2 & 12 \\ 2 & 16 \end{pmatrix} = \begin{pmatrix} \boxed{?} & \boxed{?} \\ \boxed{?} & \boxed{?} \end{pmatrix}$

   Write a matrix to show the totals for the two days.

4. The matrices show, for two shops, the number of slide films and the number of prints that were sold during two weeks. Write a matrix to show the totals.

   Week 1 Week 2

   Slides Prints

   Shop A, Shop B: $\begin{pmatrix} 23 & 39 \\ 45 & 62 \end{pmatrix} + \begin{pmatrix} 29 & 44 \\ 41 & 58 \end{pmatrix} = \begin{pmatrix} \boxed{?} & \boxed{?} \\ \boxed{?} & \boxed{?} \end{pmatrix}$

5. Here are the results of the home and away matches for two football teams (W = Won, D = Drawn, L = Lost).

$$\begin{array}{lccccc}
 & \text{Home} & & \text{Away} & & \\
 & \begin{matrix} \text{W} & \text{D} & \text{L} \end{matrix} & & & & \\
\begin{matrix}\text{City}\\ \\ \text{United}\end{matrix} & \begin{pmatrix} 13 & 4 & 4 \\ \\ 15 & 2 & 4\end{pmatrix} & + & \begin{pmatrix} 10 & 7 & 4 \\ \\ 11 & 5 & 5\end{pmatrix} & = & \begin{pmatrix} \boxed{?} & \boxed{?} & \boxed{?} \\ \\ \boxed{?} & \boxed{?} & \boxed{?}\end{pmatrix}
\end{array}$$

Write a matrix to show the totals.

6. Here is a record of the letters sent from two post offices on two different days. The number sent by ordinary post, by recorded delivery and by registered mail is shown.

$$\begin{array}{lccccc}
 & \begin{matrix} \text{Ord.} & \begin{matrix}\text{Rec.}\\ \text{del.}\end{matrix} & \text{Reg.} \end{matrix} & & & & \\
\begin{matrix}\text{Post office A}\\ \\ \text{Post office B}\end{matrix} & \begin{pmatrix} 67 & 6 & 4 \\ \\ 115 & 19 & 7\end{pmatrix} & + & \begin{pmatrix} 78 & 9 & 3 \\ \\ 157 & 14 & 12\end{pmatrix} & = & \begin{pmatrix} \boxed{?} & \boxed{?} & \boxed{?} \\ \\ \boxed{?} & \boxed{?} & \boxed{?}\end{pmatrix}
\end{array}$$

Write a matrix to show the totals for the two days.

7. The matrices show the drinks served in a café on two days:

$$\begin{array}{lccccc}
 & \text{Monday} & & \text{Tuesday} & & \\
 & \begin{matrix} \text{With} & \text{Without} \\ \text{sugar} & \text{sugar} \end{matrix} & & & & \\
\begin{matrix}\text{Tea}\\ \text{Coffee}\\ \text{Drinking chocolate}\end{matrix} & \begin{pmatrix} 393 & 184 \\ 416 & 97 \\ 37 & 19\end{pmatrix} & + & \begin{pmatrix} 316 & 205 \\ 478 & 91 \\ 52 & 24\end{pmatrix} & = & \begin{pmatrix} \boxed{?} & \boxed{?} \\ \boxed{?} & \boxed{?} \\ \boxed{?} & \boxed{?}\end{pmatrix}
\end{array}$$

Write a matrix to show the totals for the two days.

8. The matrices show the number of bottles of milk, the number of cartons of cream and the number of eggs used by two families over two months:

$$\begin{array}{lccccc}
 & \text{April} & & \text{May} & & \\
 & \begin{matrix} \text{Milk} & \text{Cream} & \text{Eggs} \end{matrix} & & & & \\
\begin{matrix}\text{The Neales}\\ \\ \text{The Phillips}\end{matrix} & \begin{pmatrix} 62 & 4 & 48 \\ \\ 95 & 6 & 60\end{pmatrix} & + & \begin{pmatrix} 65 & 4 & 48 \\ \\ 108 & 4 & 72\end{pmatrix} & = & \begin{pmatrix} \boxed{?} & \boxed{?} & \boxed{?} \\ \\ \boxed{?} & \boxed{?} & \boxed{?}\end{pmatrix}
\end{array}$$

Write a matrix to show the totals for the two months.

Exercise 9

Sometimes two matrices cannot be added together.

A In this part of the exercise, add together the pairs of matrices that can be added, otherwise write 'impossible':

1. $\begin{pmatrix} 4 & 2 \\ 1 & 5 \end{pmatrix} + \begin{pmatrix} 2 & 8 \\ 6 & 0 \end{pmatrix}$

2. $\begin{pmatrix} 3 & 7 \\ 8 & 2 \end{pmatrix} + \begin{pmatrix} 5 & 3 & 1 \\ 4 & 0 & 2 \end{pmatrix}$

3. $\begin{pmatrix} 7 \\ 1 \end{pmatrix} + \begin{pmatrix} 6 \\ 2 \\ 0 \end{pmatrix}$

4. $\begin{pmatrix} 1 & 2 \\ 0 & 3 \end{pmatrix} + \begin{pmatrix} 4 \\ 5 \end{pmatrix}$

5. $\begin{pmatrix} 5 \\ 1 \\ 6 \end{pmatrix} + \begin{pmatrix} 2 \\ 7 \\ 0 \end{pmatrix}$

6. $\begin{pmatrix} 3 & 6 \\ 9 & 10 \end{pmatrix} + \begin{pmatrix} 5 \\ 1 \end{pmatrix}$

7. $\begin{pmatrix} 3 & 6 \\ 9 & 10 \end{pmatrix} + \begin{pmatrix} 5 & 0 \\ 1 & 0 \end{pmatrix}$

8. $\begin{pmatrix} 1 & 2 \\ 5 & 9 \\ 5 & 3 \end{pmatrix} + \begin{pmatrix} 4 & 2 & 1 \\ 2 & 4 & 6 \end{pmatrix}$

9. $\begin{pmatrix} 1 & 5 & 5 \\ 2 & 9 & 3 \end{pmatrix} + \begin{pmatrix} 4 & 2 & 1 \\ 2 & 4 & 6 \end{pmatrix}$

10. $\begin{pmatrix} 4 & 2 \\ 0 & 0 \end{pmatrix} + \begin{pmatrix} 3 & 0 \\ ^-1 & 0 \end{pmatrix}$

11. $\begin{pmatrix} 6 \\ ^-1 \end{pmatrix} + \begin{pmatrix} ^-1 & 6 \end{pmatrix}$

12. $\begin{pmatrix} 1 & 2 \\ 0 & ^-1 \\ 1 & 3 \end{pmatrix} + \begin{pmatrix} ^-1 & ^-2 \\ 0 & 1 \\ ^-1 & ^-3 \end{pmatrix}$

B Explain how to recognise when two matrices can be added.

Multiplying a Matrix by a Scalar*

Mrs O'Leary bought 3 tins of soup and 2 tins of peaches each week while Mr Roberts bought 4 tins of soup and 1 tin of peaches. What they bought in 3 weeks can be shown using matrices:

$$\begin{array}{c} \text{Soup Peaches} \\ 3\begin{pmatrix} 3 & 2 \\ 4 & 1 \end{pmatrix} \\ \uparrow \\ 3 \times \text{one week} \end{array} \begin{array}{c} \\ = \\ \\ = \end{array} \begin{array}{c} \text{Soup Peaches} \\ \begin{pmatrix} 9 & 6 \\ 12 & 3 \end{pmatrix} \\ \uparrow \\ \text{3 weeks} \end{array} \begin{array}{l} \\ \text{Mrs O'Leary} \\ \text{Mr Roberts} \\ \\ \end{array}$$

Note Each element of a matrix is multiplied.

* See the glossary, p. 385.

Exercise 10

Find:

1. $2\begin{pmatrix} 2 & 3 \\ 1 & 2 \end{pmatrix}$
2. $3\begin{pmatrix} 7 \\ 2 \end{pmatrix}$
3. $5\begin{pmatrix} 4 & 6 \end{pmatrix}$
4. $4\begin{pmatrix} 2 & 1 & 4 \end{pmatrix}$
5. $6\begin{pmatrix} 5 \\ 2 \\ 3 \end{pmatrix}$
6. $8\begin{pmatrix} 1 & 5 \\ 6 & 4 \end{pmatrix}$
7. $3\begin{pmatrix} 2 & 3 \\ 4 & 0 \\ 1 & 5 \end{pmatrix}$
8. $7\begin{pmatrix} 6 & 2 \\ 5 & 8 \end{pmatrix}$
9. $2\begin{pmatrix} -4 \\ 3 \end{pmatrix}$
10. $4\begin{pmatrix} 0 & 5 \\ -2 & 3 \end{pmatrix}$
11. $5\begin{pmatrix} 3 & 0 & 4 \\ 5 & 6 & -2 \end{pmatrix}$
12. $9\begin{pmatrix} 8 & -3 \\ 0 & 5 \end{pmatrix}$
13. $6\begin{pmatrix} 1 & 0 \\ 0 & 1 \end{pmatrix}$
14. $10\begin{pmatrix} 5 & 0 & 0 \end{pmatrix}$
15. $3\begin{pmatrix} -1 & 4 \\ 7 & 5 \end{pmatrix}$
16. $7\begin{pmatrix} -2 & 0 & -1 \\ -5 & 6 & 8 \end{pmatrix}$
17. $8\begin{pmatrix} 4 & -2 & 0 \\ 0 & -9 & 6 \end{pmatrix}$
18. $10\begin{pmatrix} 4 \\ 9 \\ 6 \end{pmatrix}$
19. $9\begin{pmatrix} -2 & -3 \\ -1 & 5 \end{pmatrix}$
20. $5\begin{pmatrix} -8 & 0 \\ 4 & -6 \end{pmatrix}$

Exercise 11

1. Alec and Enid attend Judo and Basketball at a sports centre. The matrix shows the cost of each session in pence.

$$\begin{array}{cc} & \begin{matrix} \text{J} & \text{B} \end{matrix} \\ \begin{matrix} \text{Alec} \\ \text{Enid} \end{matrix} & \begin{pmatrix} 110 & 95 \\ 90 & 75 \end{pmatrix} \end{array}$$

Alec pays more since his sessions are longer. Write matrices to show:
(*a*) The costs per session if they were double those shown.
(*b*) The costs for Alec and Enid to attend 6 sessions.

2. A newsagent makes weekly deliveries of 2 magazines as shown in the following matrix:

$$\begin{array}{c} \\ \\ \text{Boys} \\ \text{Girls} \end{array} \begin{array}{cc} \text{Teens} & \text{Computer} \\ \text{time} & \text{crazy} \\ \end{array}$$

$$\begin{array}{r} \text{Boys} \\ \text{Girls} \end{array} \begin{pmatrix} 8 & 16 \\ 12 & 13 \end{pmatrix}$$

Write a matrix to show the number of magazines delivered in 4 weeks.

3. On a daily music broadcast on the radio 2 classical, 9 pop, 4 jazz and 3 folk records are always played. This is shown in the matrix $(2 \;\; 9 \;\; 4 \;\; 3)$. Write a matrix to show what is played in 7 days.

4. The given matrix shows the cost per person, in pounds, of 7-, 10- and 14-day holidays offered by 2 different holiday companies:

$$\begin{array}{r} \\ \text{Company A} \\ \text{Company B} \end{array} \begin{array}{c} \begin{array}{ccc} \text{7-day} & \text{10-day} & \text{14-day} \end{array} \\ \begin{pmatrix} 176 & 215 & 260 \\ 187 & 222 & 271 \end{pmatrix} \end{array}$$

Write a matrix to show the cost of holidays for 3 people.

5. A café sells ice-cream and milk shakes. Vanilla, strawberry and chocolate flavours can be bought in each. The matrix shows the sales on a certain day:

$$\begin{array}{r} \\ \text{Ice-creams} \\ \text{Milk shakes} \end{array} \begin{array}{c} \begin{array}{ccc} \text{V} & \text{S} & \text{C} \end{array} \\ \begin{pmatrix} 24 & 14 & 10 \\ 11 & 19 & 7 \end{pmatrix} \end{array}$$

If the ice-creams and milk shakes cost 40 p each, write a matrix to show the takings.

Revision Exercises XXIII to XXIX

Revision Exercise XXIII

1. Which direction is exactly opposite to:
(*a*) N?

(*b*) W?

(*c*) NE?

(*d*) SE?

2. Through how many degrees do you turn if you point NE then turn clockwise to face E?

3. If you point west then turn anticlockwise through 135°, in which direction would you then face?

4. Use the map opposite to find the straight-line distance in kilometres between:
(*a*) Abergavenny and Wells
(*b*) Taunton and Winchester
(*c*) Newport and Reading
(*d*) Oxford and Cirencester
(*e*) Basingstoke and Trowbridge
(*f*) Southampton and Aylesbury

5. A boat is 120 m from the bottom of a cliff. The angle of depression of the boat from the top of the cliff is 14°. Make a scale drawing using a scale of 1 cm to 10 m and find the height of the cliff.

6. A ship sailed 90 km due west followed by 35 km south-east. Make a scale drawing using a scale of 1 cm to 10 km, then find the distance the ship would have sailed if it had sailed a direct route.

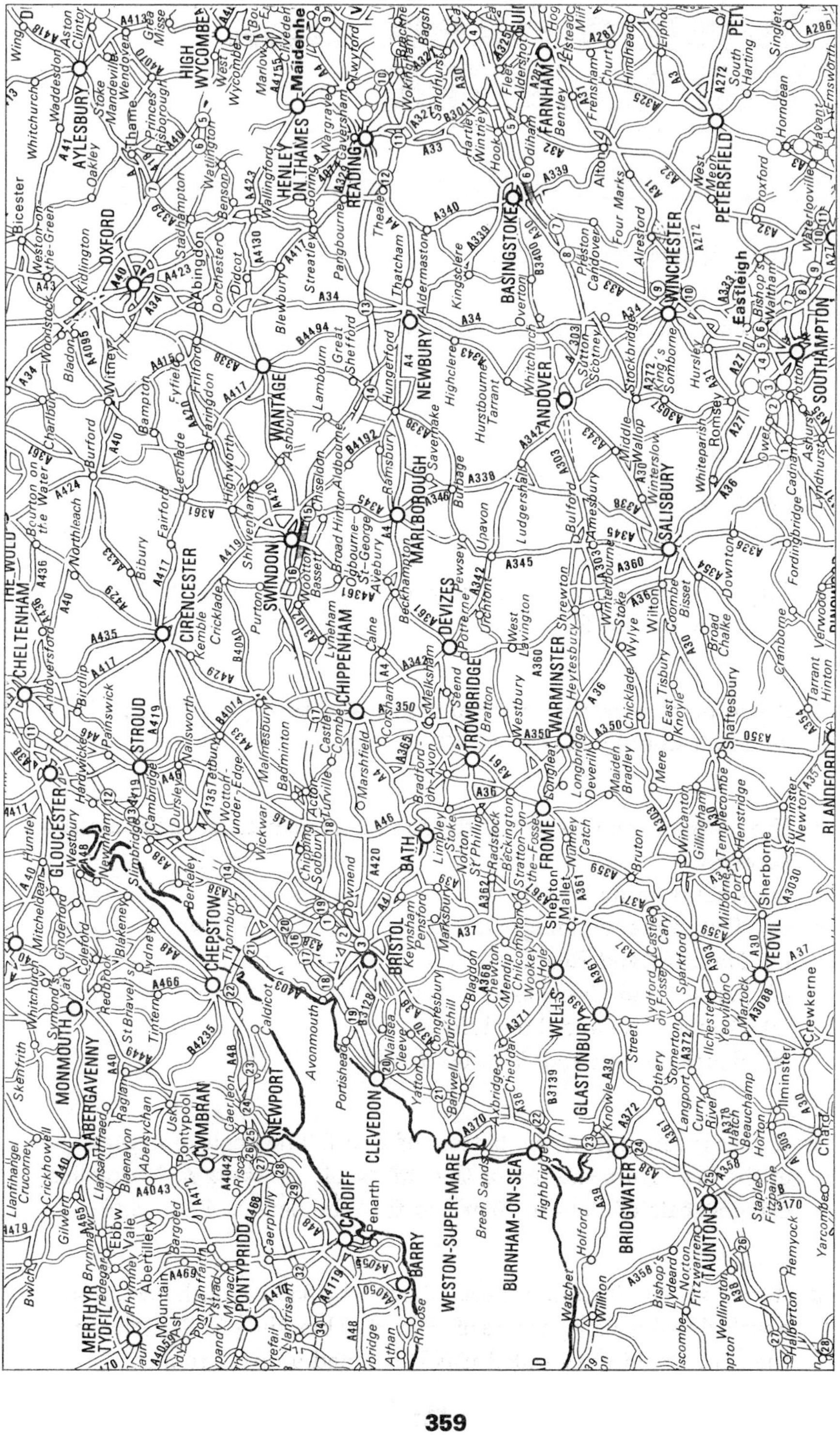

Scale: 1 cm to 10 km

Revision Exercise XXIV

1. Write which two of the three given shapes are similar:

(*a*)

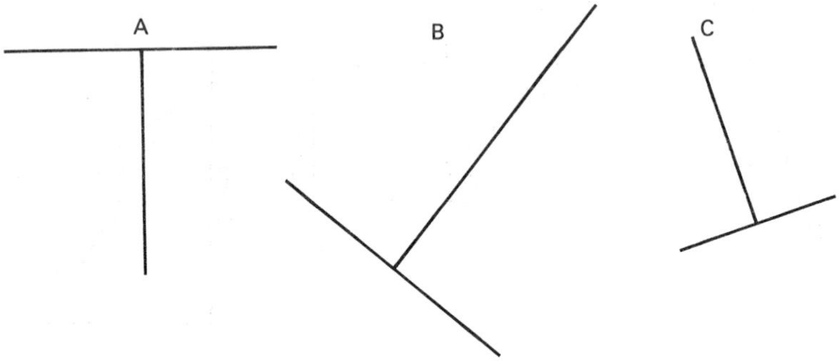

(*b*)

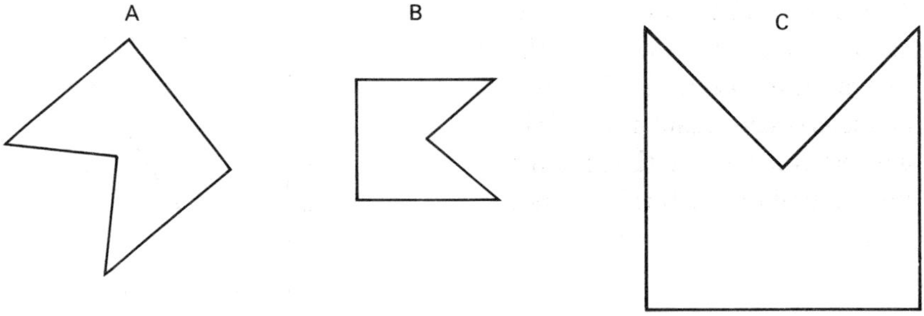

2. (*a*) Draw two triangles, one with sides measuring 3 cm, 4 cm and 5 cm, and the other with sides measuring 6 cm, 8 cm and 10 cm.

(*b*) Are the two triangles drawn in part (*a*) similar?

3. (*a*) Draw two rectangles, one with sides measuring 6 cm and 3 cm, the other with sides measuring 5 cm and 2.5 cm.

(*b*) Are the two rectangles drawn in part (a) similar?

4. If the sides of a square are made three times as long, how many times longer are its diagonals?

5. Are all triangles similar?

6. A model aeroplane is 280 mm long and has a wingspan of 240 mm. The real aeroplane has a wingspan of 60 m. How long is it?

Revision Exercise XXV

1. Calculate the lengths of the missing sides of these right-angled triangles:

(*a*) (*b*) (*c*)

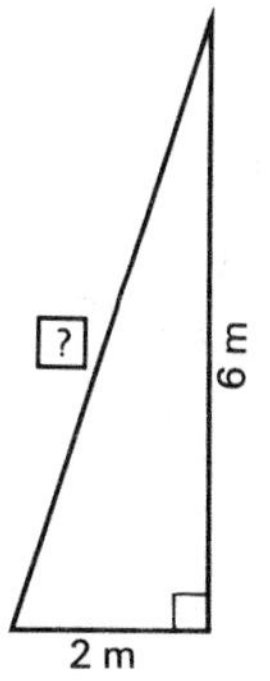

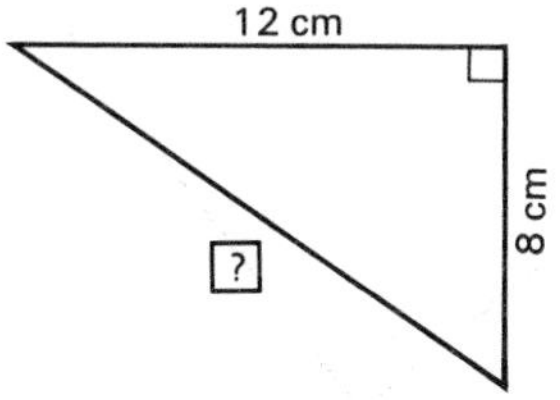

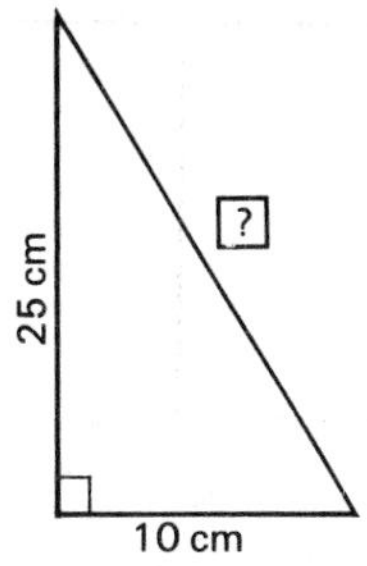

2. A ship sails 15 km due north. It then changes direction and sails 11 km due east. If it now changes course again and sails in a direct line back to the starting port, calculate the total distance sailed.

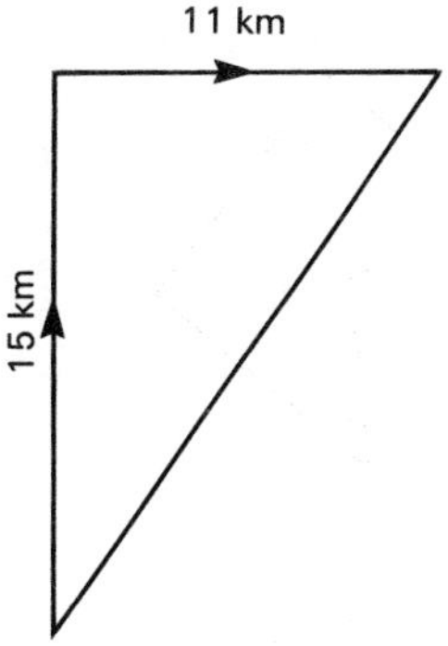

3. Calculate the length of the wire from the pole to the ground.

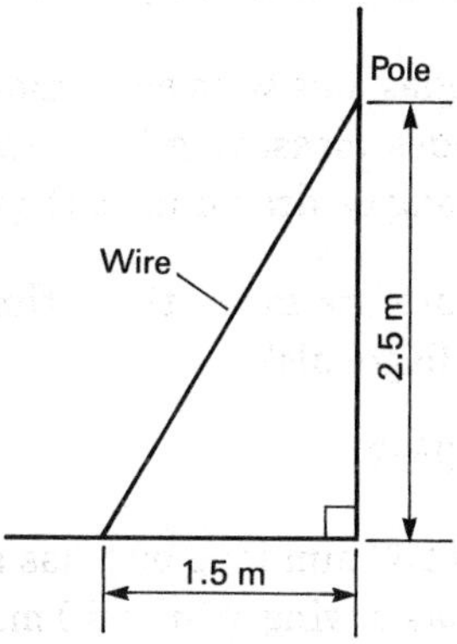

4. The diagonals of a rhombus measure 56 mm and 42 mm. Calculate the lengths of the sides of the rhombus.

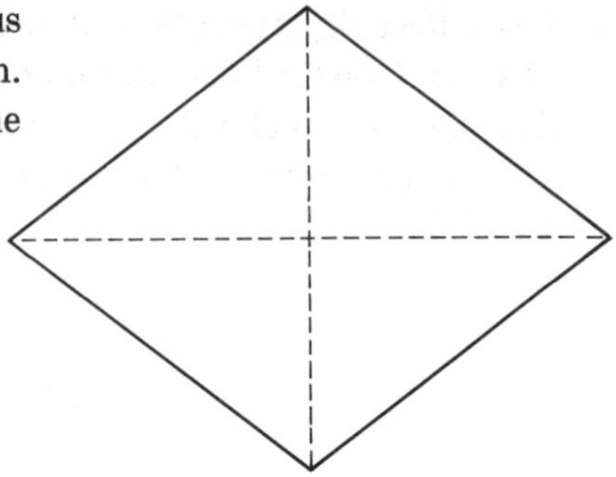

Revision Exercise XXVI

1. Find the required angles giving answers in degrees correct to one decimal place:

(*a*)

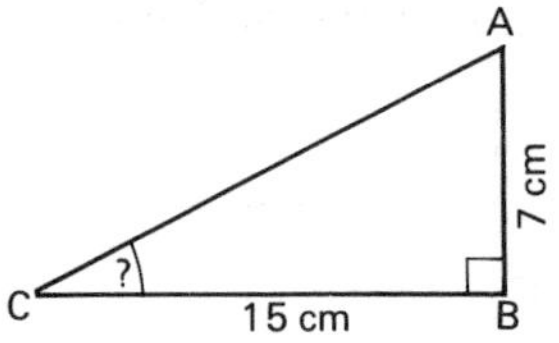

(*b*)

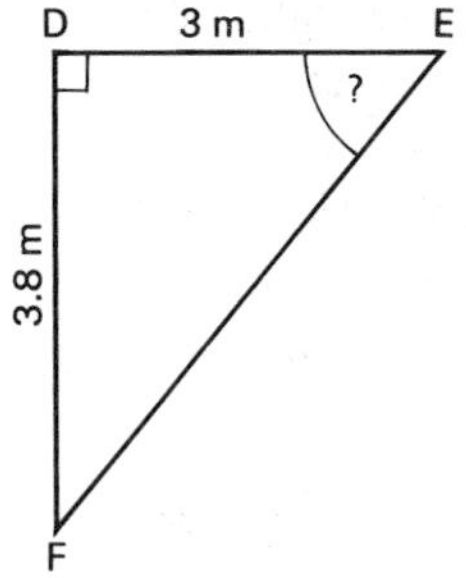

(*c*)

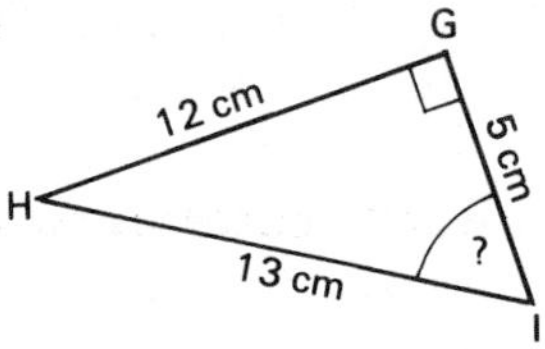

2. Find the required sides giving answers correct to three significant figures:

(*a*)

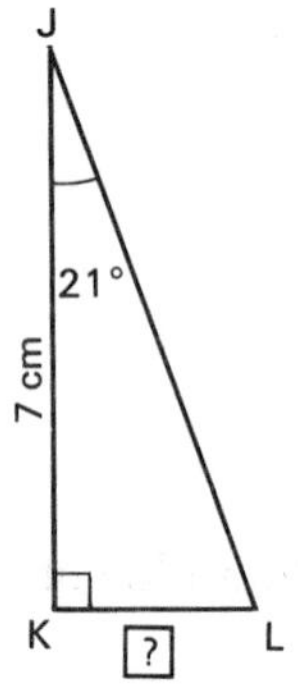

(*b*)

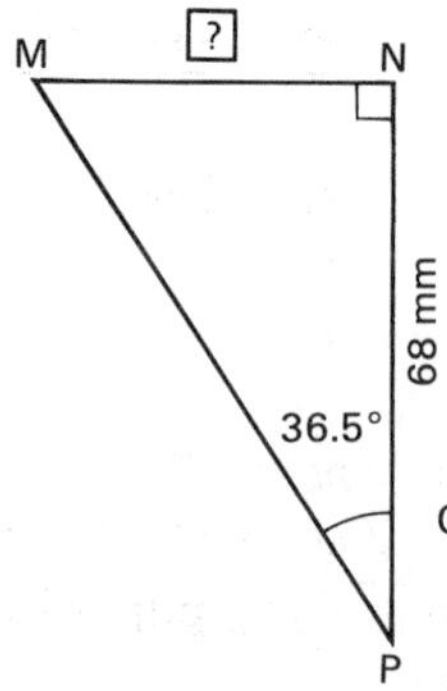

(*c*)

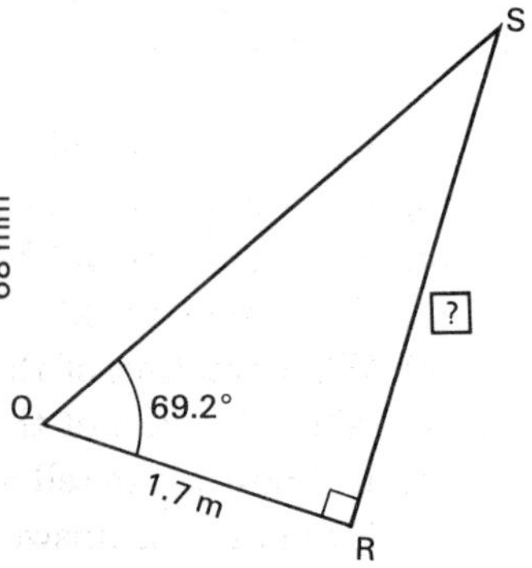

3. The tallest flagstaff in Great Britain is at Kew, Richmond-upon-Thames, Greater London. You can work out its height if you know that the angle of elevation of the top of the pole from a point on the ground, level with the bottom and 42 m from it, is 58.3°. Calculate its height.

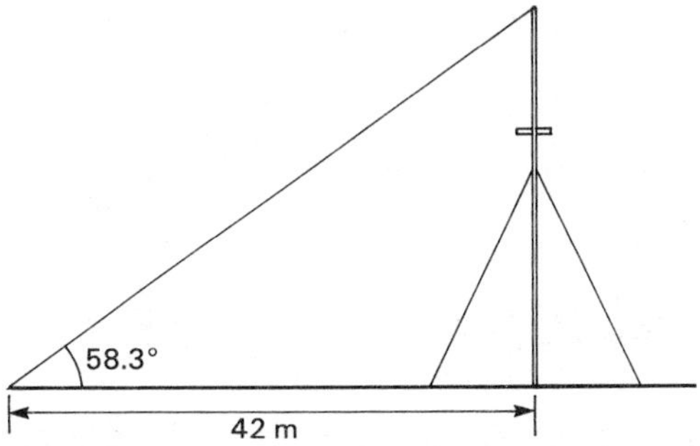

4. From the top of a lighthouse, a boat can be seen. If at an angle of depression of 12.8° the boat is 220 m from the bottom of the lighthouse, calculate the height of the lighthouse above sea level.

Revision Exercise XXVII

1. The pictogram shows how pupils in a certain class travel to school.

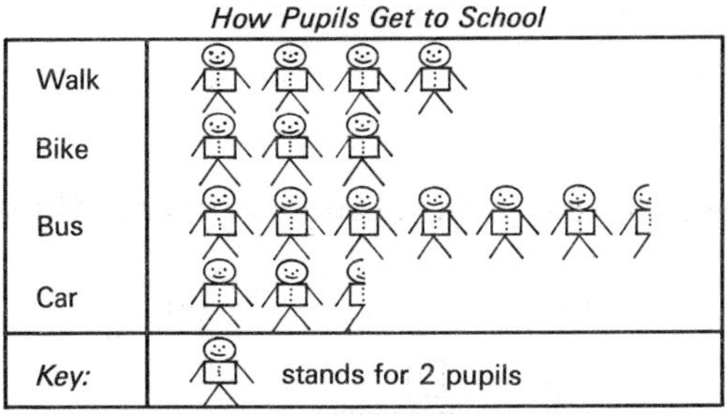

(*a*) How many travel on their bikes?
(*b*) How many travel by car?
(*c*) How many travel by bus?
(*d*) How many walk?
(*e*) What fraction of the class walk to school?
(*f*) What fraction of the class cycle to school?
(*g*) Is it possible to tell how many pupils live within 1 km of school? Explain your answer.

2.

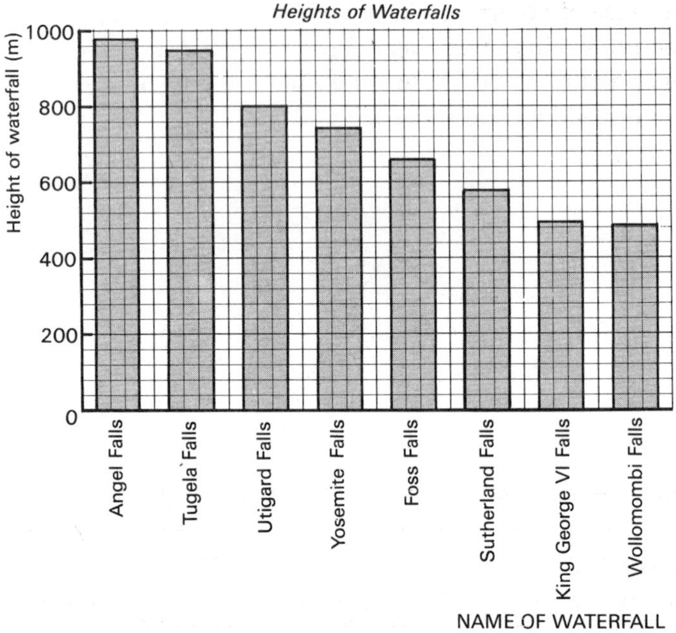

(*a*) Draw a table from the graph above.
You need two columns:

Name of waterfall	Height (m)
Angel Falls	

(*b*) Which is the highest waterfall?
(*c*) Which two waterfalls shown are almost the same height?
(*d*) What is the difference in height between the third and sixth highest waterfalls shown above?
(*e*) Multiplying a height given in metres by 3.28 will change it to feet. Find the height of the Yosemite Falls in feet.
(*f*) Find the height of the second highest waterfall shown above. Give the height in feet.
(*g*) Given that 3 ft = 1 yd, find the height of Wollomombi Falls in yards.
(*h*) Which of the waterfalls above have heights between 500 m and 700 m?
(*i*) Which of the waterfalls above is 488 m high?

3. A spinner has on it the numbers 1 to 8. If all the numbers have an equal chance of occurring, find:

(*a*) The probability of getting a 6.
(*b*) The probability of getting an 8.
(*c*) The probability of getting a 7 or an 8.

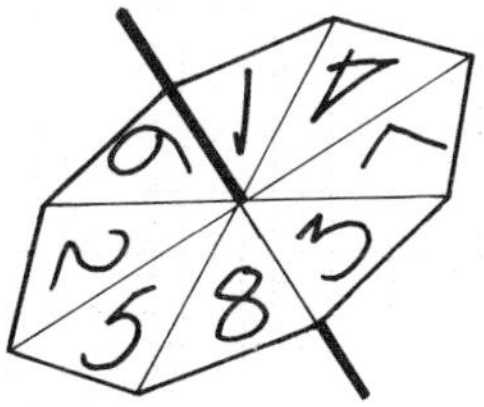

The table below shows the results of using the spinner:

Number on the spinner	Tally	Frequency
1	𝍸 𝍸 |||	
2	𝍸 𝍸		
3	𝍸 𝍸 𝍸		
4	𝍸 |||	
5	𝍸 𝍸 𝍸	
6	𝍸 𝍸 ||	12
7	𝍸 𝍸 ||||	
8	𝍸 𝍸		

(*d*) Which number occurred the least number of times?
(*e*) How many times did 7 occur?
(*f*) How many times did 5 occur?
(*g*) Which numbers occurred the same number of times?
(*h*) How many times altogether was the spinner spun?

(*i*) Draw a histogram of this frequency distribution. Use a scale of 1 cm to 1 unit for the frequency and let 1 cm stand for each number shown on the spinner.

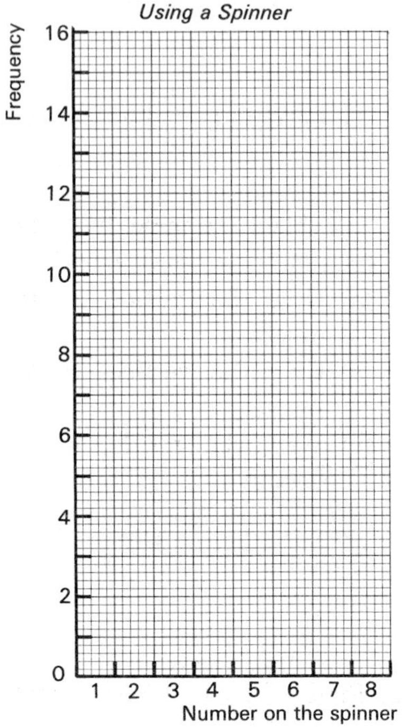

(*j*) Find the mode.

4. The selling prices of a camera from a number of different shops are:

£109, £99, £102, £107, £103, £105, £102, £107, £102

Find:

(*a*) the mode, (*b*) the median, (*c*) the mean.

Revision Exercise XXVIII

1. Write the name of the vector $\begin{pmatrix} 4 \\ -3 \end{pmatrix}$.

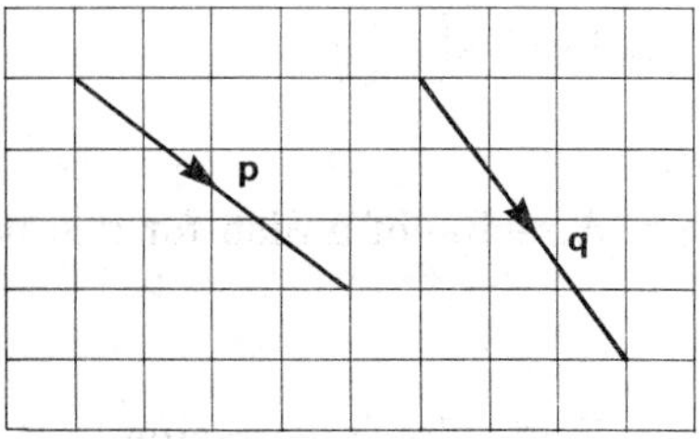

2. On squared paper, draw and name the vector $\mathbf{t} = \begin{pmatrix} ^-2 \\ 5 \end{pmatrix}$.

3. A vector starts at $(2, {}^-3)$. If its end point is $(1, 2)$, give the vector.

4. The vector $\begin{pmatrix} 5 \\ ^-2 \end{pmatrix}$ starts at $(1, 0)$. Give its end point.

5. The black triangle has been translated to a new position.

(*a*) Give the vertices of the object.

(*b*) Give the vertices of the image.

(*c*) Write the translation vector.

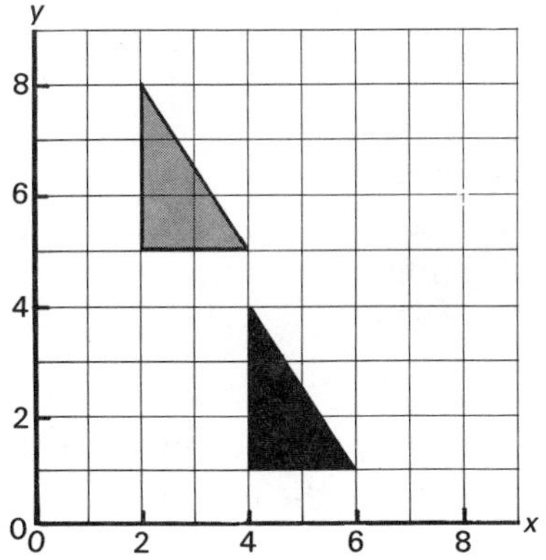

6. Find $\begin{pmatrix} 1 \\ 4 \end{pmatrix} + \begin{pmatrix} 3 \\ 2 \end{pmatrix}$ and draw the results on a diagram.

7. Find $\begin{pmatrix} 6 \\ ^-3 \end{pmatrix} + \begin{pmatrix} ^-2 \\ 4 \end{pmatrix}$.

8. If $\mathbf{w} = \begin{pmatrix} 2 \\ ^-4 \end{pmatrix}$, find:

(*a*) $2\mathbf{w}$ (*b*) $7\mathbf{w}$ (*c*) $9\mathbf{w}$

9. Find $4\begin{pmatrix} ^-3 \\ 5 \end{pmatrix}$.

10. A recipe of a dish for one person is $\begin{pmatrix} 3 \\ 2 \\ 4 \end{pmatrix}$ when written as a vector.

Write the same recipe for 6 people as a vector.

Revision Exercise XXIX

1. A certain washing machine has a special '$\frac{1}{2}$-load' button which allows smaller loads of washing to be washed in less water, thus saving water and electricity costs. For cottons, the maximum full load is 9 lb while the $\frac{1}{2}$ load is 5 lb. For nylon fabrics the maximum full load is 4 lb while the $\frac{1}{2}$ load is 2 lb.

	Maximum full load (lb)	$\frac{1}{2}$ load (lb)
Cotton		
Nylon		

(*a*) Copy and complete the table.
(*b*) Write the information as a 2 by 2 matrix.

2. In the houses on Beech Drive there were 8 coal fires, 10 gas fires and 6 electric fires, while on Elm Street there were 7 coal fires, 12 gas fires and 4 electric fires.
(*a*) Make a table to show this information.
(*b*) Write the information as a 2 × 3 matrix.
(*c*) Write the information as a 3 × 2 matrix.

3. Find $\begin{pmatrix} 4 & 1 \\ 9 & ^-7 \end{pmatrix} + \begin{pmatrix} 2 & 4 \\ ^-3 & 5 \end{pmatrix}$.

4. The matrices show the number of books (fiction and non-fiction) borrowed from a library and sold by a shop on 2 days:

Friday (Fiction, Non-fiction), Saturday, Totals

$$\begin{matrix} \text{Library} \\ \text{Shop} \end{matrix} \begin{pmatrix} 1042 & 874 \\ 58 & 35 \end{pmatrix} + \begin{pmatrix} 269 & 155 \\ 87 & 46 \end{pmatrix} = \begin{pmatrix} \boxed{?} & \boxed{?} \\ \boxed{?} & \boxed{?} \end{pmatrix}$$

Write a matrix to show the totals for the two days.

5. Find: (*a*) $8\begin{pmatrix} 4 & 2 \\ 1 & 7 \end{pmatrix}$ (*b*) $6\begin{pmatrix} 2 & 4 \\ 8 & ^-3 \\ ^-1 & 5 \end{pmatrix}$ (*c*) $9\begin{pmatrix} ^-7 & 3 \\ 0 & 6 \end{pmatrix}$

6. The given matrix shows the number of minutes per week spent on English and history by two classes:

$$\begin{array}{cc} & \begin{array}{cc} \text{H} & \text{E} \end{array} \\ \begin{array}{c} \text{Class 1} \\ \text{Class 2} \end{array} & \begin{pmatrix} 70 & 175 \\ 140 & 210 \end{pmatrix} \end{array}$$

Write a matrix to show the number of minutes spent on English and history in 5 weeks.

Appendix 1 Calculators

Clearing the Display

[C] ([ON/C] or [CE] on some calculators) On many calculators, [C] is used to clear the last number that was keyed in.

[AC] This key usually clears everything from the calculator except for the memory. On certain calculators, [AC] may also clear the memory. Some calculators do not have an [AC] key. On those, pressing [C] (or [CE/C] or [ON/C]) twice normally clears everything from the calculator except the memory.

The Memory Keys

[MR] ([RCL] or [RM]) This key ReCaLls what is in the calculator's Memory and shows it in the display. The number that was in the display is lost, but the number in the memory remains. Some calculators use the key [MRC] or [M^R_C] which work in the same way as the [MR] key when first pressed but usually clear the memory when pressed twice (see [MC]).

[Min] ([STO] or [MS] on some calculators) This key normally STOres in the Memory the number that is shown on the display. Any previous number that was in the memory is lost, but the number in the display stays the same. On some calculators, possibly older models, this key stores the calculation so far.

Key in: [AC] [8] [÷] [2] [Min] [AC] [MR]

If the display shows 2 then [Min] stores the displayed number.
If the display shows 4 then [Min] stores the calculation so far.

(Throughout this series of books, I have let [Min] store the number shown on the display.)
To store the calculation so far,

key in: [AC] [8] [÷] [2] [=] [Min]

↗ This key causes the calculation so far to appear on the display.

[Min] stores this result in the memory.

Keying in [AC] [MR] should now display 4. The sequence [AC] [9] [Min] [AC] [4] [Min] [AC] will store 4 in the memory and leave 0 on the display (9 is lost). Try it. (Depress [MR] afterwards to check that 4 is now in the memory.)

[MC] ([CM] on some calculators) This key clears the memory without clearing the display. Other ways of clearing the memory are: [AC] [Min] or [MRC] [MRC] or [M^R_C] [M^R_C] but these methods affect the display. (Remember, on calculators without an [AC] key, [AC] can probably be replaced by [C] [C] or [ON/C] [ON/C] or [CE/C] [CE/C]).

[M+] ([SUM] on some calculators) This key adds the displayed number to the number already in the memory.
Clear the memory first, then key in:

[AC]	[9]	[M+]	[AC]	[4]	[M+]	[AC]	[MR]
↑	↑	↑	↑	↑	↑	↑	↑
Clears display	Puts 9 in the display	Adds 9 to the memory	Clears display. Leaves 9 in memory	Puts 4 in the display	Adds 4 to the 9 in the memory	Clears display. Leaves memory	Recalls memory

The last key [MR] in the above sequence should cause 13 to appear in the display.
Make certain you know the difference between [Min] and [M+] (that is, [STO] and [SUM] on some calculators).
Note [M+] can be used instead of [Min] as long as you CLEAR THE MEMORY FIRST.
So: [MC] [M+] is the same as [Min]

[M–] This key subtracts the displayed number from the number already in the memory.
Note [MR] [M–] should clear the memory and [MR] [M–] [AC] should clear the memory and the display.
If your calculator does not have the key [M–], but has [M+] and [+/–] then [+/–] [M+] can be used instead of [M–].

Appendix 2 Axes

Axes for oblique projections (pp. 78)

Normally the 3 directions are labelled as shown here. However, pointing the z-axis downwards makes the drawing of a solid clearer.

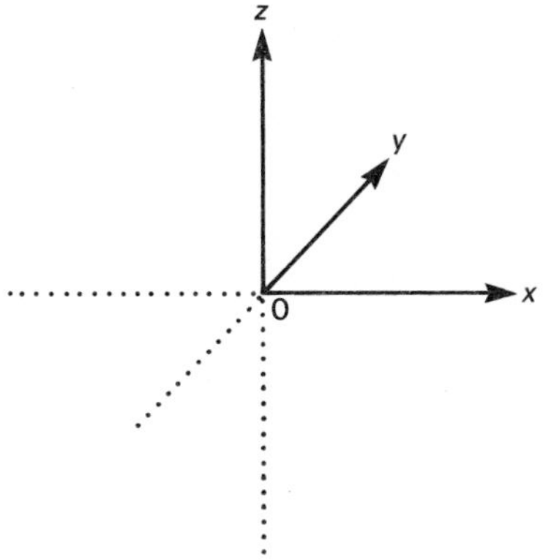

Appendix 3 Pythagoras

Pythagoras (p. 286)

Pythagoras was born on the Greek island of Samos and lived from about 580 BC to 500 BC.

At about 50 years of age he moved to the town of Crotona in southern Italy where he formed a secret society called the Order of Pythagoreans. They had their own badge which was a star pentagram. (*Note* There is a pentagon inside it.)

The Pythagoreans followed very strict rules among which were: they were not to wear wool, they were only to eat meat at religious ceremonies, they were not to tell non-members of the mathematical secrets they discovered (it is believed that the punishment for such a crime was death).

It is not certain what Pythagoras himself discovered, since, whatever was discovered by any members of the society, the credit was always given to Pythagoras, their founder and leader.

Not only did the Pythagoreans discover what is now called Pythagoras's theorem (which is dealt with in Chapter 25), they were the first to discover that the earth was not flat, they discovered the relation between the length of a string and the pitch of its note in early stringed instruments and they discovered the regular solids, the dodecahedron and the icosahedron shown below.

A Dodecahedron

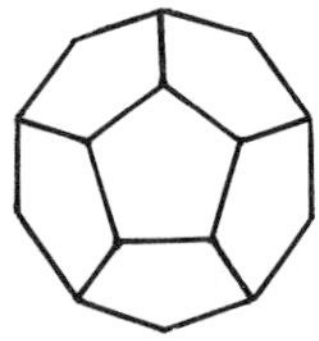

Net of a Dodecahedron

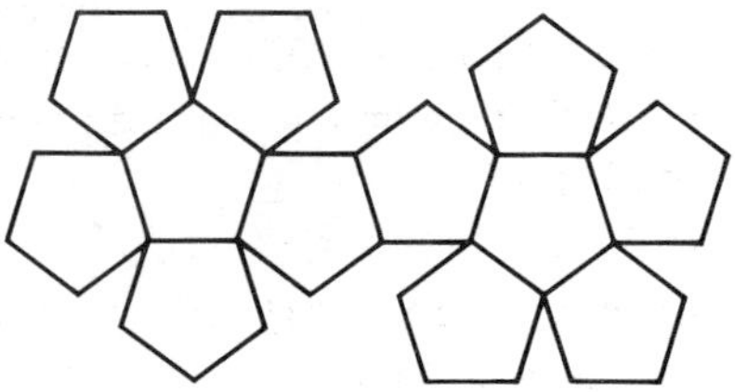

An Icosahedron

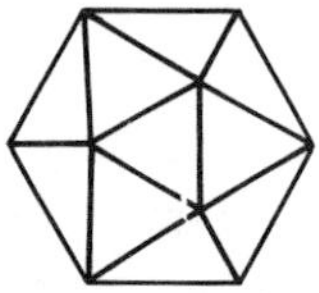

Net of an Icosahedron

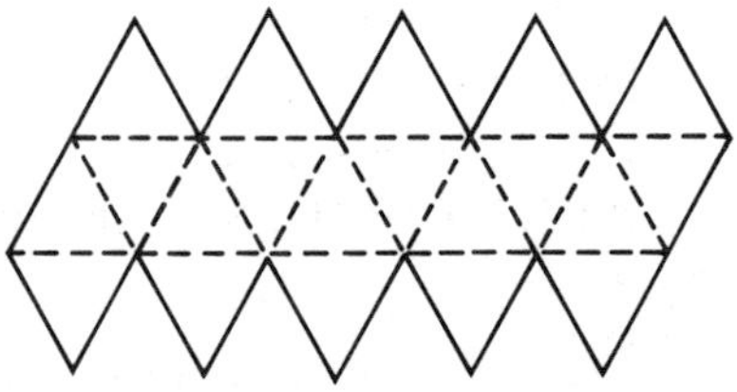

The Egyptians had already discovered the cube (6 faces, all squares), the tetrahedron (4 faces, equilateral triangles) and the octahedron (8 faces, equilateral triangles). These are the only five regular polyhedra*!

The Pythagoreans also gave special meanings to numbers. The odd numbers were divine and were regarded as male. The even numbers were earthly and were female. 1 was regarded as the source of all numbers rather than as a number itself so 3 was the first true odd number and hence the first male number. The first female number was 2.

* See the glossary, p. 385

5 stood for marriage (since 3 + 2 = 5, the combination of the first male and female numbers). The odd numbers were also regarded as lucky and the even numbers as unlucky and this belief was continued even in Shakespeare's day.

The Pythagoreans also used triangular numbers and square numbers. In fact, they called the triangular numbers 'Pythagorean numbers'. They made many other discoveries, particularly about numbers, too numerous to mention here.

Pythagorean triads (p. 287)

A This program lists Pythagorean triads of the form

$$(n, \tfrac{1}{2}(n^2 - 1), \tfrac{1}{2}(n^2 + 1))$$

It should work on most makes of computer using BASIC.

```
1Ø   PRINT "PYTHAGOREAN TRIADS A"
2Ø   PRINT "How many triads do you require?";
3Ø   INPUT M
4Ø   IF M < 1 THEN GOTO 2Ø
5Ø   IF M < > INT (M) THEN GOTO 2Ø
6Ø   LET S = 2*M + 1
7Ø   FOR N = 3 TO S STEP 2
8Ø      LET P = N*N
9Ø      LET Q = (P - 1)/2
1ØØ     LET R = (P + 1)/2
11Ø     PRINT TAB (1); N; TAB (1Ø); Q; TAB (19); R
12Ø  NEXT N
13Ø  END
```

i On some computers line 11Ø must be changed. You may need to type the line without using any brackets:
11Ø PRINT TAB 1; N; TAB 1Ø; Q; TAB 19; R

ii In line 11Ø some computers do not need TAB (1).
Line 11Ø becomes 11Ø PRINT N; TAB (1Ø); Q; TAB (19); R

iii Without using TAB, line 11Ø can be typed in as:
11Ø PRINT N; ","; Q; ","; R

iv If your computer does not accept END then use STOP in line 13Ø.

v In lines 4Ø and 5Ø you may be able to miss out GOTO.

B This program lists Pythagorean triads of the form

$$((l^2 - k^2), 2kl, (l^2 + k^2))$$

You need to input the maximum value of l that you require. (l must be greater than 1.)

```
1Ø   PRINT "PYTHAGOREAN TRIADS B"
2Ø   PRINT "What is the maximum value of l required?";
3Ø   INPUT M
4Ø   IF M < 2 THEN GOTO 2Ø
5Ø   IF M < > INT (M) THEN GOTO 2Ø
6Ø   PRINT TAB (1); "L"; TAB (7); "K"; TAB (13); "F"; TAB (19);
     "S"; TAB (25); "T"
7Ø   FOR L = 2 TO M
8Ø      LET N = M - 1
9Ø      FOR K = 1 TO N
1ØØ        IF K = L THEN GOTO 18Ø
11Ø        LET P = L*L
12Ø        LET Q = K*K
13Ø        LET F = P - Q
14Ø        LET S = 2*K*L
15Ø        LET T = P + Q
16Ø        PRINT TAB (1); L; TAB (7); K; TAB (13); F;
           TAB (19); S; TAB (25); T
17Ø     NEXT K
18Ø  NEXT L
19Ø  END
```

i In lines 6Ø and 16Ø you may need to miss out the brackets.

ii In lines 6Ø and 16Ø you may not need TAB (1).

iii In line 6Ø, instead of F, S and T, you may prefer to use FIRST, SEC and THIRD.

iv In line 19Ø, you may need to use STOP instead of END.

v In lines 4Ø, 5Ø and 1ØØ you may be able to miss out GOTO.

Glossary

ASCII (p. 180)

ASCII stands for American Standard Code for Information Interchange. Each symbol on a key of a computer keyboard (e.g. A to Z, 0 to 9 and others such as + or −) is called a *character*. Each character is changed into a binary code such as ASCII. Although the ASCII code is based on a 7-bit character (a bit is a binary digit), 8 bits are normally used (some computer books will give further information on this).

closed curves and simple closed curves (p. 4)

If you start anywhere on a closed curve and follow the line without breaking off at any point you will arrive at the starting point again. Here are some closed curves:

(*Note.* Straight lines may be used.)

This is not a closed curve:

A simple closed curve is a closed curve that does not cross over itself. Here are some simple closed curves:

Here are some closed curves that are not simple closed curves:

convex polygon (p. 87)

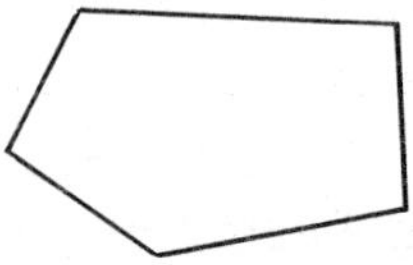

In a convex polygon, each interior angle is less than 180°. By moving along any two adjacent sides towards a vertex you go outwards. The line segment joining *any* two points inside the polygon does not cross any side of the polygon but stays inside.

Polygons that are not convex are called *re-entrant* polygons.

credit card (p. 48)

A credit card is a plastic card that can be used for making payments. The credit-card holder signs the card as soon as he or she receives it.

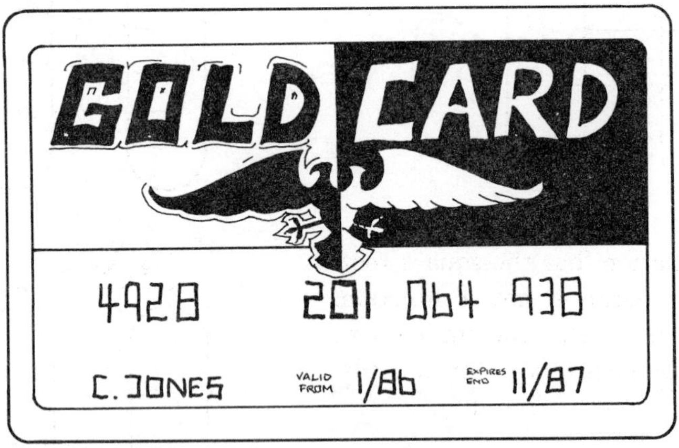

When using the card to pay for something, a slip is signed by the card holder for the amount payable. The credit-card company sends a monthly statement to each card holder listing all such payments. The total amount for the month (or part of it) can then be paid to the credit-card company.

flat rate of interest (p. 159)

There are different ways of stating the rate of interest. The flat rate of interest is a rate per annum based on the amount that was originally loaned. It does not take any repayments into consideration. For example, if £1000 is borrowed at a flat rate of 10% to be repaid over 2 years, the interest *each year* is £100 (10% of £1000). After one year, if £600 has been repaid (that is, £500 + £100 interest) then £500 is still owed from the original loan. Instead of calculating the interest for the second year as 10% of £500 (which is £50) the interest is still 10% of £1000.

function (p. 173)

A function is a relation in which each member of the domain maps on to only one image (a many-one mapping or a one-one mapping). Mapping diagrams such as the two below show *functions*:

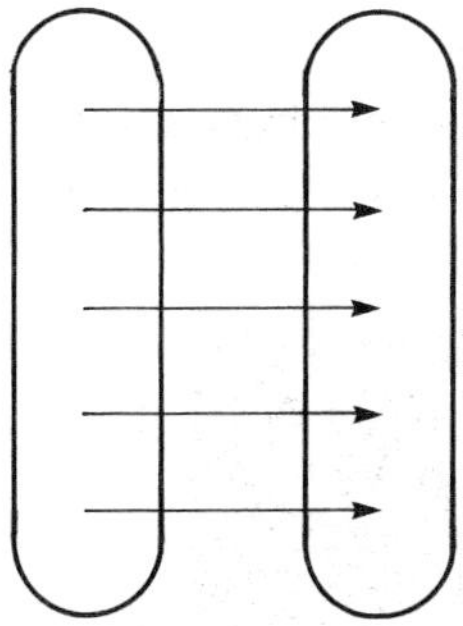

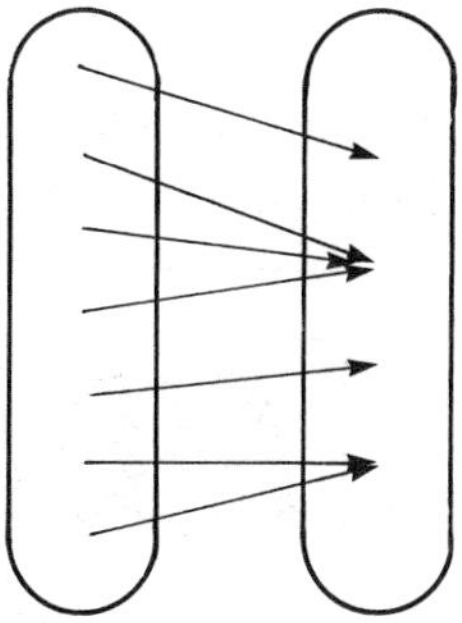

The relation 'has the square root' (shown here) is not a function. Members of the domain map to move than one image (for example, 4 maps to both $^{-}2$ and 2).

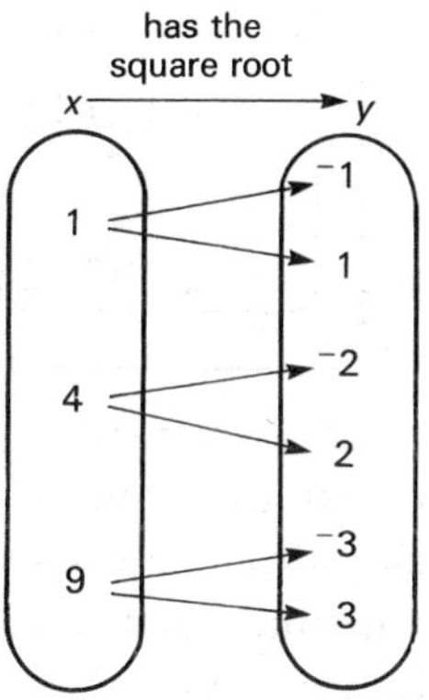

histograms (p. 321)

For a histogram, the area of each rectangle is directly proportional to the frequency.
For the frequency distribution:

Number of coins	0–1	2–3	4–5	6–7	8–9
Frequency	7	11	9	12	6

if ☐ stands for 1 coin, the graph would be as shown.

Each column is 2 units wide since it shows the frequency for 2 coins.

The area of a column is equal to its width × its length.
Since length = frequency,
area of column = width × frequency.

For column 1, area = 2 × 7 = 14
For column 2, area = 2 × 11 = 22
For column 3, area = 2 × 9 = 18
and so on.

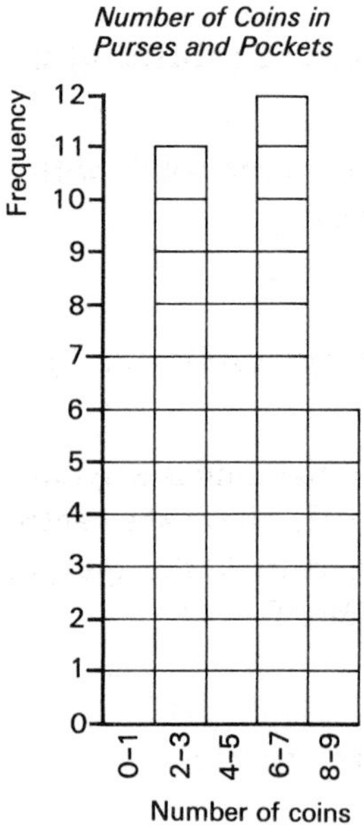

(In this example, the area of each column is always twice the frequency.)

If a frequency of 7 gives a column area of 14 units then a frequency of 1 gives a column area of 2 units and a frequency of 11 gives a column area of 22 units, which illustrates direct proportion and shows that for a histogram, the area of each column is directly proportional to the frequency.

natural numbers (p. 1)

The natural numbers have long been accepted as being the counting numbers {1, 2, 3, 4, 5, . . .}, which do not include zero. More recently, some people have included zero in the set of natural numbers. This is perhaps due to the work of Guiseppe Peano (1857–1932), an Italian, who, in 1891, showed that the properties of the natural numbers can be derived from five axioms. He included zero as a natural number. Throughout this course I have taken the natural numbers to be the set of counting numbers {1, 2, 3, 4, . . .}.
Note that some examining groups include zero and therefore take whole numbers and natural numbers to be one and the same {0, 1, 2, 3, 4, . . .}. Make certain you know which definition you need for your course.

polyhedra (plural of polyhedron) (p. 378)

Polyhedra are solids with plane (flat) faces. The plane faces are all polygons.

right pyramid (p. 77)

A right pyramid is a pyramid in which the apex (the vertex at the top) is directly above the centre of its base. In the square-based pyramid shown on p. 77, the apex, P, is directly above the centre of the square base QRST.

scalar (p. 355)

A scalar has only magnitude (that is size) whereas a vector has both magnitude and direction. Numbers are scalars.

Bibliography

Fibonacci

Jacobs, H. R., *Mathematics: A Human Endeavour*, W. H. Freeman & Co., 1970, pp. 72–6.

Land, F, *The Language of Mathematics*, John Murray, 1964, pp. 215–25.

Mottershead, L., *Sources of Mathematical Discovery*, Basil Blackwell, 1978, pp. 63–73.

Northrop, E. P., *Riddles in Mathematics*, Penguin (Pelican) Books, 1978, pp. 53–60.